IRREDUCIBLE TENSORIAL SETS

PURE AND APPLIED PHYSICS

A SERIES OF MONOGRAPHS AND TEXTBOOKS

CONSULTING EDITOR

H. S. W. MASSEY

University College, London, England

Volume 1. F. H. Field and J. L. Franklin, Electron Impact Phenomena and the Properties of Gaseous Ions. 1957

Volume 2. H. Kopfermann, Nuclear Moments. English Version Prepared from the Second German Edition by E. E. Schneider. 1958

Volume 3. Walter E. Thirring, Principles of Quantum Electrodynamics. Translated from the German by J. Bernstein. With Additions and Corrections by Walter E. Thirring. 1958

Volume 4. U. Fano and G. Racah, Irreducible Tensorial Sets. 1959

IN PREPARATION

J. Irving and N. Mullineux, **Mathematics in Physics and Engineering**

K. F. Herzfeld and T. A. Litovitz, **Absorption and Dispersion of Ultrasonic Waves**

E. P. Wigner, Group Theory and its Application to the Quantum Mechanics of Atomic Spectra. With Additions and Corrections by E. P. Wigner. Translated from the German by J. J. Griffin

Fay Ajzenberg-Selove (ed.). Nuclear Spectroscopy

ACADEMIC PRESS INC • PUBLISHERS • NEW YORK

IRREDUCIBLE TENSORIAL SETS

U. FANO
National Bureau of Standards
Washington, D. C.

G. RACAH
Hebrew University, Jerusalem, Israel

1959

ACADEMIC PRESS INC., PUBLISHERS • NEW YORK

ACADEMIC PRESS INC.
111 FIFTH AVENUE
NEW YORK 3, N. Y.

Library of Congress Catalog Card Number: 58-12760

PRINTED IN THE UNITED STATES OF AMERICA

PREFACE

This book presents mathematical methods which originate from the theory of coupling and recoupling of angular momenta in atomic physics and constitute an extension of vector and tensor algebra. These methods have been developed by numerous authors, for different purposes, and by different approaches, such as group theory, algebra, and quantum mechanical transformation theory. We have endeavored in this book to develop a unified treatment with a compact system of notations, explaining the connections between different points of view and the reasons that have guided us in the various choices of notations and normalizations.

Because of the slow and continuing nature of our endeavor, it seemed desirable to present the material available at this time, accepting the necessity of compromises. Some material we would have liked to elaborate further, other material we left out because it seemed insufficiently developed. The treatment of applications was also limited and no extensive collections of formulas or numerical applications are given. Therefore the book has the character of an essay, rather than of a treatise.

In order to preserve continuity of the main development of concepts and techniques, material of specialized character has been separated out in numerous appendices.

Many authors have contributed to this book, often only through informal communications. Notable is an unpublished manuscript by E. P. Wigner who developed most of the mathematical theory as early as 1937. We wish to thank Prof. Wigner and many other colleagues for their friendly communications and discussions.

U. Fano
G. Racah

Washington, D. C.
August, 1958

CONTENTS

1

Introduction

Vector and tensor algebras serve to treat physical problems where space directions are relevant. They afford a concise formulation of equations among velocities, forces, moments of inertia, polarizabilities, etc.

Atomic mechanics deals with numerous and complex relationships which involve the orientation of orbital and spin motions and the distribution of particles, currents, and radiations. The developments of quantum theory akin to tensor algebra have taken new forms and have also progressed further, as required by the complexity of atomic problems. Some of these developments, like the vector addition technique of angular momenta, have been familiar to physicists for many years (Wigner, 1931; Condon and Shortley, 1935). Other methods have been developed beginning about 1940 (Racah, 1942, 1943) and have been applied over an increasing range of problems and with increasing effectiveness in recent years.

The new methods have served, thus far, primarily to simplify calculations laid out according to standard procedures. The results obtained in this manner were often so simple that they stimulated an effort to rederive them by new, more direct, and transparent procedures. The occurrence of the W coefficients and of related functions in problems of apparently different nature also encouraged the search for a more comprehensive formalism, which is the subject of this book.

The elements of the algebra presented in this book are called "irreducible tensorial sets." The term "tensorial sets" comprehends different sets of quantities, such as tensor components and states of atomic systems, which have common transformation properties and therefore will be treated on an equal footing. The term "irreducible" indicates sets that cannot be resolved into subsets with separate linear transformations. Equations among tensorial sets take their simplest form when the sets are irreducible. The use of a single symbol to indicate a whole irreducible set combines the advantages of vector algebra, where components no longer appear explicitly in the equations, with the wider scope of tensor algebra.

The fundamental algebraic operation with tensorial sets is the construction of irreducible products which is a generalization of the ordinary vector product and of the addition of angular momenta in atomic physics.

The newer development concerns the relationships among products constructed in different manners. These relationships are algebraic identities called recoupling transformations and somewhat analogous to the vector equation $(\mathbf{a} \times \mathbf{b}) \times \mathbf{c} = (\mathbf{a} \cdot \mathbf{c})\mathbf{b} - (\mathbf{b} \cdot \mathbf{c})\mathbf{a}$.

The physical applications reviewed in the second part of this book are drawn from different branches of atomic and nuclear physics, and are classified according to the type of theoretical problem and to the technique utilized in its solution. Most of the techniques are variants of a single general procedure for treating matrices of tensorial operators, their products and their transformations from one scheme to another.

Racah's development of the algebra of tensor operators was primarily algebraic in language and technique. On the other hand, Wigner's parallel development was formulated in terms of the theory of group representations and traces its origin to the investigations of Frobenius and Schur (1906). In this book we have minimized the use of group theory language even though the main concepts of the methods of Frobenius-Schur and of Wigner are in the background of the whole treatment. Instead we have developed the algebra by the methods of quantum mechanics, with emphasis on the classification of the eigenvectors of operators and on the transformations between eigenvectors of different operators.

PART I

ALGEBRA

The objective of the algebra is to construct products, which are generalizations of the vector products and of which there are many types, and to formulate the relationships between different types of products. As a preliminary, various steps will be taken, namely: (a) to generalize the concept of tensor to the concept of tensorial set and to indicate the relevant properties of tensorial sets; (b) to discuss the concept of irreducibility; (c) to show why and how the main operations of the algebra can be kept real even though one starts from a complex formalism; (d) to adopt additional conventions for standardizing the formalism.

2

Tensorial Sets

Various types of quantities encountered in mathematical physics are defined with reference to a system of space coordinates and experience a linear transformation when this system rotates. For example the components V_x, V_y, V_z of a vector $\mathbf{V}$ are transformed into new components

$$\begin{aligned} V_\xi &= D_{\xi x} V_x + D_{\xi y} V_y + D_{\xi z} V_z \\ V_\eta &= D_{\eta x} V_x + D_{\eta y} V_y + D_{\eta z} V_z \\ V_\zeta &= D_{\zeta x} V_x + D_{\zeta y} V_y + D_{\zeta z} V_z \end{aligned} \tag{2.1}$$

when initial coordinate axes (x, y, z) are replaced with new axes (ξ, η, ζ).

A set of vector components is often called itself a vector, especially by analysts. In physics, however, a vector is usually understood to be a quantity characterized by a magnitude and by a direction of the physical space. A set of components identifies the vector in relation to a system of cartesian coordinate axes. To represent a vector in terms of a set of components one must also introduce a set of unit vectors $\mathbf{i}$, $\mathbf{j}$, and $\mathbf{k}$ directed along the coordinate axes, and one writes

$$\mathbf{V} = \mathbf{i} V_x + \mathbf{j} V_y + \mathbf{k} V_z. \tag{2.2}$$

A rotation of the coordinate axes brings about a transformation (2.1) of the components and a related transformation of the set of vectors $\mathbf{i}$, $\mathbf{j}$, $\mathbf{k}$, but $\mathbf{V}$ itself, being associated with a fixed direction of space, is *invariant* under coordinate rotations. On the other hand, one may consider rotations of the vector itself, i.e., changes of its direction. Such a rotation would bring about a transformation of the components alone, of the type (2.1), if the coordinate axes are kept fixed, or a transformation of the unit vectors $\mathbf{i}$, $\mathbf{j}$, $\mathbf{k}$ alone if the axes rotate rigidly with the vector.

In ordinary tensor algebra, a tensor T of degree n has components labeled with n indices, and each index relates to one cartesian axis (x, y, or z). For example, T_{xyy} indicates a component of a tensor of third degree. A rotation of coordinates replaces T_{xyy}, by a transformation analogous to (2.1), with a new component $T_{\xi\eta\eta}$ which is a linear combination of the 27 old components T_{xxx}, T_{xxy} ... T_{zzz}. We regard the tensor T itself as a geometrical entity represented in terms of its components and of a set of unit tensors by an equation analogous to (2.2). The unit tensors may be regarded as combinations of n unit vectors; for example the nine unit tensors of second degree may be indicated as "dyadics" **ii**, **ij**, **ik**, . . . , **kk**. A tensor T is itself invariant under coordinate rotations whereas its components and the unit tensors depend on the orientation of the coordinate axes.

In quantum mechanics, an atomic system with angular momentum quantum number j has eigenstates $u^{(j)}{}_m$ with magnetic quantum numbers m. A generic state a of this system can be described as a superposition of eigenstates with different m by the formula

$$\psi_a = \Sigma_m u^{(j)}{}_m a^{(j)}{}_m, \tag{2.3}$$

which is analogous to (2.2). The quantum number m refers to an axis of quantization, that is, to a system of coordinates. A rotation of this system induces a linear transformation of the coefficients $a^{(j)}{}_m$, which generates a new set of coefficients

$$a^{(j)}{}_\mu = \Sigma_m D^{(j)}{}_{\mu m} a^{(j)}{}_m. \tag{2.4}$$

A rotation of the axis of quantization also induces a related transformation of the set of eigenstates $u^{(j)}{}_m$. When the system itself rotates, e.g., under the influence of a magnetic field, the change of ψ_a is described in the Schroedinger representation by a transformation of the type (2.4) which leaves the states $u^{(j)}{}_m$ fixed, or in the Heisenberg representation by a transformation of the base states $u^{(j)}{}_m$ which leaves the coefficients $a^{(j)}{}_m$ fixed.

Because of the analogy between the transformations (2.4) and (2.1) induced by coordinate rotations, the name "tensor" has been applied occasionally to eigenstates $u^{(j)}{}_m$ or to coefficients $a^{(j)}{}_m$. In fact, among the states of a p-electron in an atom one can choose three basic ones which are called p_x, p_y, and p_z, and have the same transformation laws as the unit vectors **i**, **j**, and **k**. Nevertheless these states cannot be identified with the unit vectors **i**, **j**, **k** or with multiples thereof and cannot properly be called vectors.

The algebra developed in this book deals equally with sets of tensor components and with sets of unit tensors, with sets of coefficients $a^{(j)}{}_m$, and with sets of eigenstates. To treat all these kinds of quantities equally we shall call *tensorial set of order n* any set of n quantities which are defined in connection with a system of space coordinates and which experience a linear transformation when this system rotates. To preserve the advantage of vector algebra, which deals with a vector as a unit, we shall regard as an element of our algebra a whole set rather than its individual elements. It is emphasized that, although in tensor analysis the word "tensor" often indicates the set of components, the definition of tensorial sets given here is more general because it considers as one entity not only a set of components but also a set of unit vectors or tensors.

Our subject is frequently approached from the standpoint of group theory which focuses the attention on the transformations, rather than on the quantities to be transformed. We shall focus, instead, on the quantities themselves in order to adhere more closely to a physical picture.

The elementary algebraic operations on tensorial sets are addition, product, and linear transformation.

Addition. Given two tensorial sets of quantities a_i and b_k of the same order, of the same physical dimensions, and experiencing the same transformations induced by coordinate rotations, the sums of the pairs of corresponding elements of the set, $a_i + b_i$ constitute a new tensorial set, the sum of the initial sets.

Product. Given two tensorial sets, one of n quantities a_i and one of m quantities b_k, the $n \cdot m$ pairs of quantities $a_i b_k$ constitute a new tensorial set because they also experience a linear transformation whenever the a_i and b_k are so transformed. This set is called the *direct product* of the initial sets. The transformation properties of the product are the subject of Sections 6ff.

Here we want to point out that the word "product" includes various manners of combination of the elements of the pair, depending on the nature of the quantities a_i and b_k. Thus if a_i and b_k are the components of two tensors or the components $a^{(j)}{}_m$, $b^{(j')}{}_{m'}$, of two quantum mechanical state functions, the symbol $a_i b_k$ indicates the ordinary algebraic product of a_i and b_k. On the other hand, if the two sets consist of eigenstates of two atomic systems with specified quantum numbers, their product is symbolic; $u^{(j)}{}_m v^{(j')}{}_{m'}$ represents a joint state of the two systems in which one system is in the state $u^{(j)}{}_m$ and the other in the state $v^{(j')}{}_{m'}$. Still different is the combination of a tensorial operator and of a quantum mechanical state $u^{(j)}{}_m$, where the "product" $T_i u^{(j)}{}_m$ implies operation on the state by the operator. The product of two unit base vectors, e.g., **ik**, is a symbol which represents a unit tensor of second degree, called a dyadic.

Linear transformations. Given a tensorial set of n quantities a_i, and a matrix T of n rows and columns, the set of quantities

$$b_k = \Sigma_i T_{ki} a_i \tag{2.5}$$

is clearly also a tensorial set. The transformations of the set a_i induced by rotations of the coordinate system are special cases of (2.5). To prevent confusion we shall refer to the transformations induced by rotations as r-transformations.

If the elements a_i of a tensorial set are visualized as the components of a vector in a representative space, the transformation (2.5) may be regarded as establishing a correspondence between this vector and another one, in the same or in a different space. Alternately the transformation may be regarded as a change of the components due to a change of coordinates of the representative space (including, if necessary, a change in the unit of measure of coordinates). From this standpoint the representative vector is unaffected by the transformation and it is only the form of its representation which is changed from a_i to b_k. This latter point of view implies that the transformation is invertible and, therefore, applies only when the determinant of the matrix is not zero.

We consider here what becomes of (2.5), as regarded from the first point of view, when both sets a_i and b_k are replaced by the sets

$$a'_r = \Sigma_i A_{ri} a_i \tag{2.6a}$$

$$b'_s = \Sigma_k B_{sk} b_k \tag{2.6b}$$

and these substitutions are regarded from the second point of view. The set b'_s is linearly related to a'_r owing to (2.6) and (2.5). The relationship is worked out by entering (2.5) into (2.6b) and then expressing a_i in terms of a'_r by inversion of (2.6a). The result is

$$b'_s = \Sigma_r T'_{sr} a'_r \tag{2.7}$$

where T'_{sr} is given in matrix notation by

$$T' = BTA^{-1} \tag{2.8}$$

The roles of the pairs of transformations A, B, and T, T', may also be interchanged (provided all four matrices are invertible), regarding A and B from the first point of view, and T and T' from the second. The pertinent form of the connection between the transformations is then

$$B = T'AT^{-1} \tag{2.9}$$

which is equivalent to (2.8).

If the sets a_i and b_k are regarded as vectors of the same representative space, they experience identical substitutions, $B = A$, and (2.8) becomes

$$T' = ATA^{-1} \tag{2.10}$$

The transformations T and T' are then called *equivalent*, because they represent the same transformation in different coordinate systems of the representative space.

The r-transformations D are properly regarded as relationships among vectors of the same representative space. Therefore any change of coordinates in this space changes D into an equivalent

$$D' = ADA^{-1} \tag{2.11}$$

Contragredient r-transformations and contragredient sets. The state a of an atomic system is, of course, independent of the choice of the coordinate system used in its description. Thus the state function ψ_a given by (2.3) in terms of eigenstates $u^{(j)}{}_m$ must be equal to the representation of the same state in terms of eigenstates pertaining to a different axis of quantization, i.e., equal to

$$\psi_a = \Sigma_\mu u^{(j)}{}_\mu a^{(j)}{}_\mu \tag{2.12}$$

Equality of (2.3) and (2.12) requires that, when the change of axis of quantization transforms the tensorial set of coefficients $a^{(j)}{}_m$ through the matrix D of (2.4), it transforms the set of eigenstates $u^{(j)}{}_m$ through the reciprocal matrix D^{-1},

$$u^{(j)}{}_\mu = \Sigma_m u^{(j)}{}_m D^{-1}{}_{m\mu} = \Sigma_m \widetilde{D}^{-1}{}_{\mu m} u^{(j)}{}_m \tag{2.13}$$

Here the tilde sign indicates, as usual, transposition of the matrix. The r-transformation (2.13) is called *contragredient* to (2.4) and the set of $u^{(j)}{}_m$ is contragredient to the set of $a^{(j)}{}_m$. Contragredience is reciprocal in that the transformation (2.4) is also contragredient to (2.13), since $\widetilde{(\widetilde{D}^{-1})^{-1}} = D$, and the set of $a^{(j)}{}_m$ is contragredient to the set of $u^{(j)}{}_m$.

Similarly, when a vector $\mathbf{V}$ is represented, as in (2.2), by $\mathbf{V} = \mathbf{i}V_x + \mathbf{j}V_y + \mathbf{k}V_z$, it is itself independent of the orientation of the Cartesian axes, because the base vectors $\mathbf{i}$, $\mathbf{j}$, $\mathbf{k}$, constitute a set contragredient to the set of vector components.

The r-transformations of the ordinary vector components are real and orthogonal and coincide with the contragredient r-transformations of the base vectors (because in this case $\widetilde{D}^{-1} = D$). However, if j is half-integral, the r-transformations of $u^{(j)}{}_m$ and $a^{(j)}{}_m$ are not real orthogonal and cannot even be transformed into orthogonal ones by an equivalence transformation (2.11). Complex non-orthogonal r-transformations occur anyhow when the elements of a set are classified according to the magnetic quantum number m which is usual in quantum mechanics and will be adopted as standard in this book (see Section 5). Therefore contragredience is nontrivial for our purpose‡.

Unitary transformations. The transformation matrices of quantum mechanics, of which D in (2.4) is a special case, are *unitary*. This means that the matrix D^{-1} in (2.13) coincides with $\tilde{D}^* = D^\dagger$, the complex conjugate transposed (hermitian conjugate) of D, and that $\tilde{D}^{-1}$ coincides with D^*.

Thus, for example, the set of quantum mechanical coefficients $a^{(j)}{}_m{}^*$, complex conjugate to the $a^{(j)}{}_m$, has an r-transformation matrix D^* instead of D; since $\tilde{D}^* = D^{-1}$ this set is contragredient to the set of $a^{(j)}{}_m$. Accordingly, the sum of products $\Sigma_m a^{(j)}{}_m{}^* a^{(j)}{}_m$ remains invariant under r-transformations, as it must because it equals 1 owing to normalization.

In general, the r-transformations of a tensorial set need not be unitary. However, any tensorial set can be replaced, by a suitable linear substitution, with a set whose r-transformations are unitary. A proof of this statement is given in Appendix A. Once the r-transformations of a set are unitary, they remain unitary if the set experiences other unitary substitutions, because it follows from (2.11) that, if D and A are unitary, D' is unitary too. Henceforth we shall consider only sets whose r-transformations are unitary.

---

‡ Contragredience is also nontrivial in vector and tensor calculus where the space is non-euclidean or where the coordinates are curvilinear or oblique.

3

Irreducible Sets

When a tensorial set transforms, owing to a rotation of coordinate axes, according to $b_k = \Sigma_i D_{ki} a_i$, each b_k is in general a linear combination of all a_i. However, it may be possible to replace the set of a_i, by unitary substitution, with a new set of quantities

$$a'_r = \Sigma_i A_{ri} a_i \tag{3.1}$$

such that a rotation of coordinates transforms certain subsets of a'_r separately‡. That is, the r-transformation matrices of the new set,

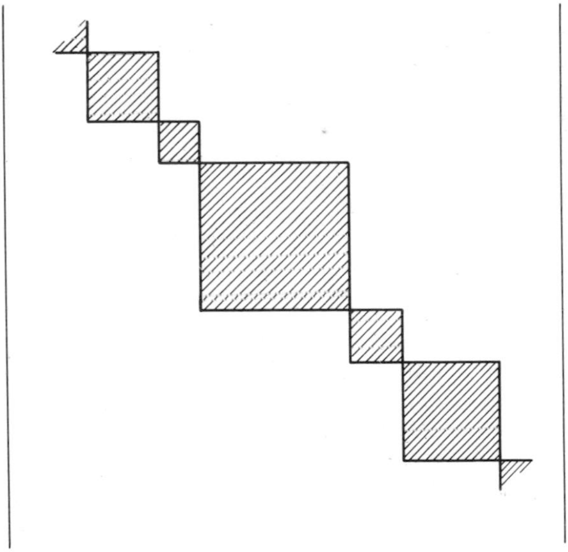

FIG. 1. Diagram of a transformation matrix in reduced form. All matrix elements outside the shaded regions vanish.

which are given by $D' = ADA^{-1}$ according to (2.11), have their non-vanishing elements concentrated in square blocks along the diagonal (see Fig. 1). In this event each of the subsets constitutes a separate

‡ It is implied here that if a subset transforms separately, the rest of the set also transforms separately. This is true because we deal with sets whose r-transformations are, or can be made, unitary.

tensorial set whose r-transformation matrix is one of the submatrices along the diagonal of D'.

This procedure of "reducing" a tensorial set into separate subsets has an ultimate limit. The ultimate subsets are called *irreducible tensorial sets*, and their r-transformations are called *irreducible r-transformations.*

When the a_i are regarded as the components of a vector in a representative space and their transformations are regarded as changes of coordinates in this space, the reduction procedure may be visualized as follows. A rotation of coordinate axes of the physical space brings about a change of axes of the representative space. This change intermixes all axes corresponding to the vector components a_i, but the axes corresponding to each subset of the new components a'_r intermix only among themselves and not with the axes corresponding to other subsets. In other words, the axes corresponding to each irreducible subset of a'_r span a subspace of the representative space which remains invariant under r-transformations. Each irreducible subset of a'_r may be regarded as the set of components of the projection of the initial vector into one invariant subspace.

The sets of $2j+1$ eigenstates $u^{(j)}{}_m$ of an atomic system, and the corresponding sets of coefficients such as the $a^{(j)}{}_m$ of the state function ψ_a in (2.3), are well known examples of irreducible sets. Because the quantum number j can take any integral or half-integral value, we have here examples of irreducible sets of all orders $2j+1 = 1, 2, 3 \ldots$ Indeed it was the classification of the energy levels of atomic particles in central fields which drew particular attention to irreducible sets. Quantum mechanics also offers a convenient point of view for considering the reduction procedure.

All eigenstates $u^{(j)}{}_m$ of an atomic system with the same value of j are eigenstates of the squared angular momentum, pertaining to the same eigenvalue $j(j+1)\hbar^2$. The angular momentum is introduced in elementary quantum mechanics as the moment-of-momentum of the motion of a particle about the origin of coordinate axes. Its matrices can also be introduced through the r-transformations experienced by the representations of quantum mechanical states. This alternate approach is more general, in that it applies to spin momenta as well as to orbital momenta. It utilizes the treatment of infinitesimal r-transformations of tensorial sets as given in Appendix B, which leads to the definition of hermitian matrices J_x, J_y, J_z, and $\mathbf{J}^2$ for any tensorial set.

For a set of quantum mechanical states, $\hbar^2\mathbf{J}^2$ represents the squared angular momentum. For any irreducible tensorial set of order $2j+1$, the matrix $\mathbf{J}^2$ is diagonal with all elements equal to $j(j+1)$. For a generic reducible tensorial set, $\mathbf{J}^2$ is a nondiagonal hermitian matrix; a unitary transformation which diagonalizes this matrix also resolves the set into subsets with separate r-transformations.

Appendix B shows how the matrices J_x, J_y, and J_z relate to infinitesimal r-transformations and how the geometrical properties of rotations determine the commutation rules of these matrices. The eigenvalues of these matrices are also determined.

The reduction of a tensorial set can be treated quite generally as an eigenvalue problem. Consider a hermitian matrix M which operates on a tensorial set but which is invariant under all r-transformations, i.e., such that $M = DMD^{-1}$ for all r-transformation matrices D of the set. This matrix M can be diagonalized by a suitable transformation B. The diagonal matrix $M' = BMB^{-1}$ and the r-transformations $D' = BDB^{-1}$ still give $M' = D'M'D'^{-1}$, that is $M'D' = D'M'$, which requires that all elements of D' connecting different eigenvalues of M' vanish. Thus diagonalizing M' breaks D' into blocks, one for each eigenvalue of M, in the manner of Fig. 1, and thereby reduces, at least partially, the initial set. (This theorem is made more complete in Appendix A.) The complete reduction of a tensorial set amounts, therefore, to the search of a maximal set of hermitian matrices invariant under r-transformations, and to the diagonalization of these matrices.

The matrix elements of irreducible r-transformations have important properties, reviewed in Appendix A. The most important of them is the orthogonality: if one takes the product of one matrix element D_{ki} and of the complex conjugate $D_{lj}{}^*$ of a different element, or of any element of a nonequivalent irreducible r-transformation, the average value of $D_{ki}D_{lj}{}^*$ for all r-transformations vanishes. It has also been shown that the matrix elements D_{ik} of the unitary irreducible r-transformations, as functions of the variables that identify a coordinate rotation, form a complete orthogonal set (Peter and Weyl, 1927) and are eigenfunctions of a system of partial differential equations (Casimir, 1931; see also Appendix E).

Even though various approaches have been indicated here to reduce a tensorial set, there is still no generally preferred procedure for solving this problem. In quantum mechanics, the reduction of the direct products of eigenstates $u^{(j)}{}_m v^{(j')}{}_{m'}$ is known as the addition of angular momenta (see Sections 7ff.). For the sets of components of ordinary tensors there is a traditional method of combining components so as to satisfy symmetry relations with respect to permutations of indices, and then proceeding by saturations of indices. See, e.g., Schouten (1924), Chapter 7, and Weyl (1939), Chapter VB.

The sets of components of ordinary tensors are reducible in general, except in the case of vectors (tensors of degree 1). Sets of base unit tensors are similarly reducible and in fact are reduced by a transformation contragredient to one which reduces tensor components. Irreducible sets obtained by reducing sets of tensor components and of unit base tensors serve to construct new tensors in various ways.

Consider first the simultaneous reduction of the set of components of an ordinary tensor T and of the corresponding set of base unit tensors. This operation splits the tensor into a sum of tensors each of which consists of an irreducible set of components and of an irreducible set of base tensors. Each of these tensors may accordingly be called an *irreducible tensor*. For example, a second degree tensor represented by

$$\mathsf{T} = \mathbf{ii}T_{xx} + \mathbf{ij}T_{xy} + \ldots + \mathbf{kk}T_{zz} \tag{3.2}$$

resolves into three parts

$$\mathsf{T} = \mathsf{T}^{(0)} + \mathsf{T}^{(1)} + \mathsf{T}^{(2)} \tag{3.3}$$

where

$$\mathsf{T}^{(0)} = \tfrac{1}{3}(\mathbf{ii} + \mathbf{jj} + \mathbf{kk})(T_{xx} + T_{yy} + T_{zz}), \tag{3.3a}$$

$$\mathsf{T}^{(1)} = \tfrac{1}{2}[(\mathbf{jk} - \mathbf{kj})(T_{yz} - T_{zy}) + (\mathbf{ki} - \mathbf{ik})(T_{zx} - T_{xz}) + (\mathbf{ij} - \mathbf{ji})(T_{xy} - T_{yx})], \tag{3.3b}$$

$$\mathsf{T}^{(2)} = \tfrac{1}{2}[\tfrac{1}{3}(2\mathbf{kk} - \mathbf{ii} - \mathbf{jj})(2T_{zz} - T_{xx} - T_{yy}) + (\mathbf{ii} - \mathbf{jj})(T_{xx} - T_{yy}) + (\mathbf{jk} + \mathbf{kj})(T_{yz} + T_{zy}) + (\mathbf{ki} + \mathbf{ik})(T_{zx} + T_{xz}) + (\mathbf{ij} + \mathbf{ji})(T_{xy} + T_{yx})] \tag{3.3c}$$

The form of the expressions (3.3) emphasizes the structure of the irreducible tensors $\mathsf{T}^{(0)}$, $\mathsf{T}^{(1)}$, and $\mathsf{T}^{(2)}$ in terms of irreducible sets. However, each of these tensors may also be written out in the form (3.2) and may thus be regarded as a tensor of second degree with nonindependent components. For example, $\mathsf{T}^{(0)}$ has, when so written out, only three nonvanishing components corresponding to $\mathbf{ii}$, $\mathbf{jj}$, and $\mathbf{kk}$ and all equal to $(T_{xx}+T_{yy}+T_{zz})/3$. In (3.3a), $\mathsf{T}^{(0)}$ is given as the product of two invariants $(\mathbf{ii}+\mathbf{jj}+\mathbf{kk})/\sqrt{3}$ and $(T_{xx}+T_{yy}+T_{zz})/\sqrt{3}$. The tensor $\mathsf{T}^{(0)}$ is called "isotropic" (Cisotti, 1930). The tensor $\mathsf{T}^{(1)}$ has, when written out in the form (3.2), six nonvanishing components that constitute an antisymmetric matrix. In the form (3.3b), $\mathsf{T}^{(1)}$ consists of a set of three components, $(T_{xy}-T_{yx})/\sqrt{2}$ etc., with the same r-transformations as a set of vector components, and of a set of base tensors with the same r-transformations as the set $\mathbf{i}$, $\mathbf{j}$, $\mathbf{k}$. The tensor $\mathsf{T}^{(2)}$ has, when written out in the form (3.2), a set of nine components which constitute a symmetric traceless matrix. In the form (3.3c), $\mathsf{T}^{(2)}$ consists of a set of five components and of a set of five unit base tensors. The base tensors, $(2\mathbf{kk}-\mathbf{ii}-\mathbf{jj})/\sqrt{6}$ etc., constitute the simplest set of irreducible unit base tensors of order five, analogous to the usual set of unit base vectors $\mathbf{i}$, $\mathbf{j}$, $\mathbf{k}$.

In general, the simplest set of irreducible unit base tensors of order $2n+1$ is the irreducible subset of highest order that results from the reduction of the *n-th* degree set $(\mathbf{i})^n, (\mathbf{i})^{n-1}\mathbf{j}, \ldots (\mathbf{k})^n$.

Irreducible tensors can be constructed by combining irreducible sets of unit tensors and of tensor components of different origin though contragredient to one another. In particular one may take an irreducible set of components derived from the components of a reducible tensor of degree n and combine it with a contragredient set of base tensors of degree lower than n. For example with the components of the second degree tensor T of (3.2) one can construct the ordinary scalar

$$\frac{1}{\sqrt{3}}(T_{xx} + T_{yy} + T_{zz}) \tag{3.4}$$

and the vector

$$\mathbf{V} = \frac{1}{\sqrt{2}}[\mathbf{i}(T_{yz} - T_{zy}) + \mathbf{j}(T_{zx} - T_{xz}) + \mathbf{k}(T_{xy} - T_{yx})] \tag{3.5}$$

which are irreducible tensors of order 1 and 3 respectively but do not coincide with $\mathsf{T}^{(0)}$ and $\mathsf{T}^{(1)}$ as given by (3.3). If the set of components of T is the direct product of the sets of components of vectors $\mathbf{a}$ and $\mathbf{b}$, i.e., if $T_{xx} = a_x b_x$ etc., (3.4) and (3.5) coincide respectively with $\mathbf{a}\cdot\mathbf{b}$ and $\mathbf{a}\times\mathbf{b}$, to within normalization constants. If $\mathbf{a}$ is the derivative vector operator ∇ and $\mathbf{b}$ a vector field $\mathbf{F}(x, y, z)$, i.e. if $\mathsf{T} = \nabla\mathbf{F}$, then (3.4) and (3.5) coincide respectively with div$\mathbf{F}$ and curl$\mathbf{F}$, to within normalization constants.

The importance of reducing tensorial sets is indicated by the following consideration. Because the laws of physics are independent of the choice of a coordinate system, the two sides of any equation representing a physical law must transform in the same way under coordinate rotations. It is, of course, convenient to cast both sides of the equations in the form of tensorial sets, so that their transformations will be linear. By resolving these sets into irreducible subsets one pushes the process of simplification to its limit, because one disentangles the physical equations into a maximum number of separate, independent equations.

Example. Consider an isotropic medium which is distorted elastically. The displacement experienced by each point (x, y, z) of the medium is indicated by a vector $\mathbf{s} = (u, v, w)$, and the distortion (strain) depends on the nine derivatives $\partial u/\partial x, \partial u/\partial y \ldots, \partial w/\partial z$, which constitute a tensorial set. The stress of the medium is represented by a symmetric tensor P with the six independent components $P_{xx}, P_{xy} = P_{yx}, \ldots P_{zz}$. The law of elasticity is usually expressed as a linear equation between the components of the strain and stress tensors

$$\begin{aligned}
\partial u/\partial x &= (1/E)P_{xx} - (\sigma/E)(P_{yy} + P_{zz}) & \partial v/\partial x + \partial u/\partial y &= (1+\sigma)(2/E)P_{xy} \\
\partial v/\partial y &= (1/E)P_{yy} - (\sigma/E)(P_{xx} + P_{zz}) & \partial u/\partial z + \partial w/\partial x &= (1+\sigma)(2/E)P_{zx} \\
\partial w/\partial z &= (1/E)P_{zz} - (\sigma/E)(P_{xx} + P_{yy}) & \partial w/\partial y + \partial v/\partial z &= (1+\sigma)(2/E)P_{yz}
\end{aligned} \tag{3.6}$$

where E indicates the Young modulus and σ the Poisson ratio.

The tensorial set $(\partial u/\partial x \ldots)$ resolves into the following irreducible sets: (a) a dilatation, represented by div s, which is a single-element set, i.e., a scalar; (*b*) a rotation of the medium, represented by the set of three components of the vector curl s; (*c*) a constant-volume deformation, indicated here by Θs and represented by the remaining five independent elements $[2\partial w/\partial z - \partial u/\partial x - \partial v/\partial y]/\sqrt{3}$, $\partial u/\partial x - \partial v/\partial y$, $\partial w/\partial y + \partial v/\partial z$, $\partial u/\partial z + \partial w/\partial x$, $\partial v/\partial x + \partial u/\partial y$, which are the components of a tensor of the type (3.3c). The stress tensor resolves into two irreducible sets: (a) the pressure $p = -\frac{1}{3}(P_{zz}+P_{xx}+P_{yy})$, and (b) the five independent components $[2P_{zz}-P_{xx}-P_{yy}]/\sqrt{3}, P_{xx}-P_{yy}, 2P_{yz}, 2P_{zx}, 2P_{xy}$ of a purely shearing stress, to be indicated here by Q.

The expression of the elasticity law in terms of irreducible sets derives directly from the following arguments. Because the law refers to small disturbances it relates the strain linearly to the stress. Because the law must be invariant under coordinate rotations and because the medium is isotropic, each irreducible subset of the strain can only be related to the corresponding subset of the stress. Because the stress contains only two irreducible subsets, there will be only two equations, containing one proportionality constant each. (The rotation of the medium, represented by curl s is not actually a part of the strain and is unrelated to the stress because it has no analog in the reduction of the stress tensor). One equation states that the contraction (negative dilatation) is proportional to the pressure

$$-\operatorname{div} \mathrm{s} = \varkappa p. \tag{3.7}$$

The other equation states that the constant volume deformation is proportional to the shearing stress

$$\Theta \mathrm{s} = \mathsf{Q}/\mu \tag{3.8}$$

The constant $\varkappa = 3(1-2\sigma)/E$ is the compressibility and $\mu = E/2(1+\sigma)$ is the shear modulus. Equation (3.7) and the equations among the elements of Θs and Q represented by (3.8) are often derived by linear combination of the usual equations (3.6).

4

Transition to Contragredience. Conjugation

Operations which change a tensorial set into one contragredient to itself are of importance to us for two purposes. In the first place when a set is changed into a contragredient one, all its unitary transformations A are changed into their complex conjugates $A^* = \tilde{A}^{-1}$. Therefore, in the construction of products of tensorial sets and in other operations, we may anticipate that the unitary matrix representing a certain operation is real if the operation is unaffected by changes to contragredience. In the second place, cogredient and contragredient pairs of sets may be combined equally well in the construction of products, if we know how to change a pair of cogredient sets into a contragredient pair, and vice versa.

Given a tensorial set of quantities a_i which possess complex conjugates‡ a_i^*, the set of a_i^* is contragredient to the initial set, because when the a_i are changed by an r-transformation into the $a'_r = \Sigma_i D_{ri} a_i$, the complex conjugates $a'_r{}^*$ are related to the a_i^* by the contragredient r-transformation $a'_r{}^* = \Sigma_i D_{ri}{}^* a_i^*$. It will be convenient to indicate complex conjugation in operator notation by K_o, so that $a_i^* = K_o a_i$ and similarly for a transformation matrix,

$$D^* = K_o D K_o^{-1}. \tag{4.1}$$

Notice that $K_o^{-1} = K_o$, because $K_o^2 = 1$. The operator K_o is not linear, because if c is a complex number, $K_o c a_i = c^* K_o a_i \neq c K_o a_i$.

Complex conjugation does not apply to all tensorial sets, but, as shown in Appendix C, any tensorial set can be changed into one contragredient to itself by a linear unitary substitution, which will be called U. According to (2.11), a substitution A changes each r-transformation

‡ Tensor components and the quantum mechanical coefficients $a^{(j)}{}_m$ of (2.3) are numbers and possess complex conjugates. However, the eigenstates, indicated by $u^{(j)}{}_m$ in (2.3), do not possess complex conjugates. In the notation of transformation theory $u^{(j)}{}_m$ is indicated by $|jm)$. The symbol $(jm|$ indicates the same state in a different representation and is *not* the complex conjugate of $|jm)$. In this notation transposition is equivalent to complex conjugation for transformation coefficients (i.e., for "brackets," not for "bras" and "kets"); e.g., $(xyz|jm)^* = (jm|xyz)$. In place of the symbol $(jm|$, we shall use in the first part of this book $u^{\dagger(j)}{}_m$. This set of eigenstate representatives $u^{\dagger(j)}{}_m$ is contragredient to the set of $u^{(j)}{}_m$ but is not obtained from it by complex conjugation.

matrix D into ADA^{-1}; therefore U causes a transition to contragredience if

$$UDU^{-1} = D^*. \tag{4.2}$$

The transformation U has the following properties, which derive from (4.2) and are discussed in detail in Appendix C:

a. The matrix U is identified by (4.2) to within multiplication by any matrix which commutes with all D. Therefore, for an irreducible set U is unique to within a phase factor.

b. The matrix U of an irreducible set is either symmetric or antisymmetric. The symmetry depends on the order $2j+1$ of the set and is even for integral j and odd for half-integral j.

c. The matrix U of a reducible set need not have a definite symmetry. If the set can be reduced into irreducible subsets with j values all integral (or all half-integral) it is possible and convenient to assign to it a symmetric (antisymmetric) U. This symmetry is invariant for unitary substitutions of the set.

d. When a tensorial set is replaced with a new one by a generic unitary substitution A, the U matrix of the new set is $U' = A^*UA^{-1}$ according to (2.8) with $B = A^*$. Thus the transformations U and U' are not equivalent, because they do not obey (2.10), except when A is real and A^*UA^{-1} coincides with AUA^{-1}. Conversely, all substitutions A for which U' is equivalent to U are real.

e. For the sets of tensor components of ordinary tensor algebra the r-transformations D are real and equal to D^*, and (4.2) is fulfilled by $U = 1$. Thus the operation U is nontrivial only for complex r-transformations. Sets which have a symmetric U can be transformed so that D becomes real and $U = 1$, sets which do not have a symmetric U cannot.

f. Whereas U cannot be reduced to unity in all cases of interest, it can be brought to coincide with a fixed nontrivial operation which is a rotation of 180° about a fixed arbitrary direction of space. The r-transformations corresponding to rotations about this axis will then be real. This axis is usually taken to be the y axis.

Accordingly, once a set has been transformed so that

$$U = D_y(\pi), \tag{4.3}$$

this equation remains unaffected by further real transformations; conversely, any transformation that preserves this equation is real. In particular a tensorial set is resolved into irreducible sets by real transformations, provided (4.3) holds for the initial set as well as for the final irreducible ones.

A tensorial set of quantities that possess complex conjugates can be changed by two successive transitions to contragredience, once by the operation U and once by K_o. This combined operation, represented by $K = K_o U$, yields a new set cogredient to the initial one. The initial and final sets will be called *conjugate*. Appendix C shows that this relationship of conjugation is reciprocal when U is symmetric and reciprocal to within a factor -1 when U is antisymmetric, and that it is invariant under all unitary transformations. Conjugation reduces to complex conjugation when the r-transformations are real and U is the identity operator‡. A tensorial set of real quantities with real r-transformations and $U = 1$ is self-conjugate because it is not modified by either K_o or U, and remains self-conjugate under unitary substitutions. Any tensorial set which is self-conjugate becomes real when its r-transformations are brought to real form, with $U = 1$.

‡ The quantum mechanical operation of time reversal (Wigner 1932; 1937; 1958) coincides formally with the conjugation operation.

5

Standard Sets

Different irreducible sets of the same order need not, of course, experience the same r-transformations when the coordinate system rotates. However, it is shown in Appendix B how any irreducible set of a given order can be replaced, by unitary substitution, with a set for which the matrices J_x, J_y, and J_z have a specified form. It is also shown that a generic r-transformation matrix can be expressed in terms of these three matrices. It is then possible to choose for irreducible sets of each order a standard form for the r-transformations and to replace any irreducible set with a set which transforms in the standard way and which will be called a *standard set.*

We model the standard r-transformations for irreducible sets of order $2j+1$ after those of the coefficients $a^{(j)}_m$ which identify in (2.3) a state of an atomic system with quantum number j. These transformations have usually two main features:

a. A rotation of φ radians about the z axis merely multiplies an element of the set by $\exp(im\varphi)$, where m is the index that identifies the element of the set and has one of the values j, $j-1 \ldots -j+1$, $-j$.

b. The r-transformations D_y corresponding to rotations about the y axis are real.

Additional conventions of phase normalization are required to complete the standardization.

The procedure which reduces a given tensorial set with given r-transformations and brings the irreducible subsets to standard form is the same as is followed in Appendix B to show how one can construct the matrixes J_x, J_y, and J_z for an irreducible r-transformation. If the set is reducible, one constructs its matrix $\mathbf{J}^2$ and diagonalizes it. Next one considers the subset corresponding to each eigenvalue $j(j+1)$ of $\mathbf{J}^2$ and one diagonalizes its matrix J_z. If the eigenvalues of J_z are still degenerate, that is, if more than one set element corresponds to a given pair of eigenvalues of $\mathbf{J}^2$ and J_z, the set is further reducible and splits up into a number of irreducible sets. These sets are identified by an index, called α in Appendix B, which may be regarded as representing the eigenvalues of a hermitian matrix M that commutes with $\mathbf{J}^2$, J_x, J_y, and J_z. The requirement of diagonalizing the hermitian matrices $\mathbf{J}^2$, J_z, and M identifies the unitary substitution to standard form except that the rows of the substitution matrix can be interchanged and each row can still be multiplied by an arbitrary phase factor.

Permutations of the rows of this matrix merely permute the sequence of eigenvalues of $\mathbf{J}^2$, J_z, and M. One usually removes the permutation arbitrariness by stipulating that the rows of the matrix be grouped in the first place according to the eigenvalues $j(j+1)$ of $\mathbf{J}^2$, then according to α (if there are different α) and finally arranged for each irreducible subset according to the eigenvalues m of J_z in descending order from j to $-j$.

The phase factors $\exp(i\gamma_m)$, by which one can multiply each row of the substitution matrix, have to be chosen so as to make the matrix J_x real, as discussed in Appendix C(f). For each irreducible set, there are $2j+1$ factors $\exp(i\gamma_m)$ to be chosen and $4j$ nonvanishing elements of the hermitian matrix J_x, which implies

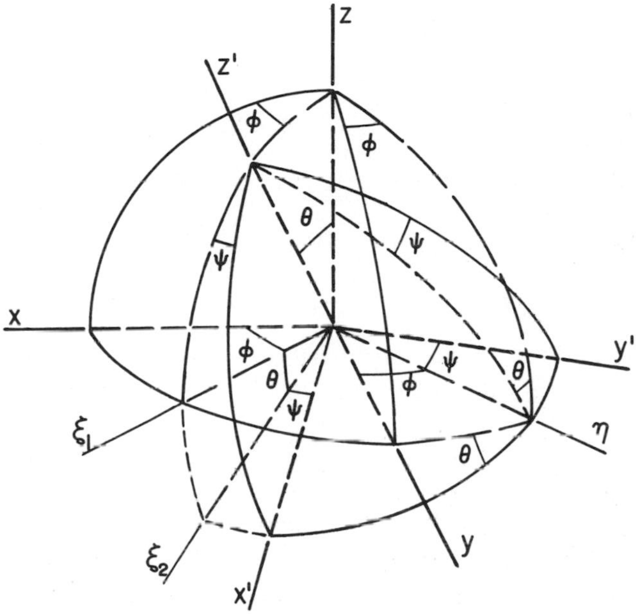

FIG. 2. Euler angles between two sets of coordinate axes (x, y, z) and (x', y', z'). The axes ξ_1 and ξ_2 are intermediate between x and x' and η between y and y'.

$2j$ independent phase factors left free after J_z is made diagonal. We choose the $2j$ *ratios* $\exp(i\gamma_m)/\exp(i\gamma_{m-1})$ so as to make each nonvanishing element of J_x not only real but *positive*, which is done by the substitution (B. 26). The standardization of the r-transformations is thereby completed‡. One phase factor, common to all $\exp(i\gamma_m)$, remains undetermined in the substitution matrix. It can be altered without changing the standard r-transformation, but not altogether without consequence after the matrix U has been chosen, as discussed below.

The standard form of the J matrices is thus determined to be

$$(J_z)_{\mu m} = m\, \delta_{\mu m}, \tag{5.1a}$$

‡ The sign of the elements of the matrix J_x is not standard throughout the literature on quantum mechanics. The choice made here, J_x positive, follows Condon and Shortley (1935).

$$(J_x)_{\mu m} = \tfrac{1}{2}\sqrt{j(j+1)-m(m-1)}\,\delta_{\mu,m-1} + \tfrac{1}{2}\sqrt{j(j+1)-m(m+1)}\,\delta_{\mu,m+1}$$
$$= \tfrac{1}{2}\sqrt{j(j+1)-\mu m}\,(\delta_{\mu,m-1} + \delta_{\mu,m+1}), \tag{5.1b}$$

$$(J_y)_{\mu m} = -i(\mu - m)\,(J_x)_{\mu m}, \tag{5.1c}$$

where (5.1c) derives from $J_zJ_x - J_xJ_z = iJ_y$.

The standard r-transformation matrix of an irreducible set of order $2j+1$ for any given rotation of the coordinate system can be described as a function of three Euler angles which identify the rotation, when it is decomposed into one rotation of φ radians about the z axis, a second one of θ radians about the y axis and finally one of ψ radians about the z axis (see Fig. 2). The matrix is calculated from the standard form (5.1) of the infinitesimal rotation matrices in Appendix D; alternate procedures are considered in Appendices E and F. The result is

$$\mathfrak{D}^{(j)}_{\mu m} = e^{i(\mu\psi + m\varphi)} \sum_r (-1)^r \sqrt{\frac{(j+\mu)!\,(j-\mu)!\,(j+m)!\,(j-m)!}{(j-\mu-r)!\,(j+m-r)!\,r!\,(r+\mu-m)!}} \times$$
$$(\cos\tfrac{1}{2}\theta)^{2j-\mu+m-2r}\,(\sin\tfrac{1}{2}\theta)^{2r+\mu-m}. \tag{5.2}$$

The functions $\mathfrak{D}^{(j)}_{\mu m}(\psi, \theta, \varphi)$ are harmonic functions of the Euler angles, known in quantum mechanics as eigenfunctions of the symmetrical top. The functions $\mathfrak{D}^{(j)}_{\mu m}$ with $\mu = 0$ or $m = 0$ are spherical harmonics, those with $\mu = m = 0$ are Legendre polynomials $P_j(\cos\theta)$. (See Appendix E).

Notations. We introduce a symbol to represent a whole set, rather than its individual elements, because our algebra deals with sets taken as a unit. A standard set or order $2j+1$ will be indicated with a bold face German letter and with a superscript in parenthesis, e.g. $\mathbf{\mathfrak{a}}^{(j)}$. Additional indexes, if any, which further identify the set may be indicated next to j, e.g., by writing $\mathbf{\mathfrak{a}}^{(\alpha j)}$. Individual elements of the set are indicated by the same symbol but not in bold face and with an additional subscript m whose value runs in integral steps from j to $-j$, e.g., $\mathfrak{a}^{(j)}_m$. The value of j is called the *degree* of the set, in agreement with the nomenclature of tensor algebra, where a vector, which has 3 components, is called a tensor of degree 1.

German type will be used for quantities pertaining to standard sets, e.g., for the matrix (5.2). The standard transformation formula is

$$\mathbf{\mathfrak{a}}'^{(j)} = \mathfrak{D}^{(j)}\,\mathbf{\mathfrak{a}}^{(j)} \tag{5.3}$$

or

$$\mathfrak{a}'^{(j)}_{\mu} = \Sigma_m\, \mathfrak{D}^{(j)}_{\mu m}\, \mathfrak{a}^{(j)}_m \tag{5.4}$$

A set contragredient to a standard set will be called *contrastandard* and will be indicated by the same symbol but with the superscript j

in brackets instead of parentheses, e.g., $\mathfrak{b}^{[j]}$. The r-transformation matrix for this set is $\mathfrak{D}^{[j]} = \mathfrak{D}^{(j)*} = \tilde{\mathfrak{D}}^{(j)-1}$ and the formula for contrastandard transformations is

$$\mathfrak{b}'^{[j]} = \mathfrak{D}^{[j]}\,\mathfrak{b}^{[j]} = \mathfrak{D}^{(j)*}\,\mathfrak{b}^{[j]} \tag{5.5}$$

or

$$\mathfrak{b}'^{[j]}_{\mu} = \Sigma_m\,\mathfrak{D}^{[j]}_{\mu m}\,\mathfrak{b}^{[j]}_{m} = \Sigma_m\,\mathfrak{D}^{[j]}_{\mu m}{}^{*}\,\mathfrak{b}^{[j]}_{m} \tag{5.6}$$

The equations (5.3) and (5.5) imply that the set elements are arranged as single-column matrices. The addition of a tilde will denote arrangement as single-row matrices, so that (5.5) may be written in the alternate form

$$\tilde{\mathfrak{b}}'^{[j]} = \tilde{\mathfrak{b}}^{[j]}\,\tilde{\mathfrak{D}}^{(j)*} = \tilde{\mathfrak{b}}^{[j]}\,\mathfrak{D}^{(j)-1}, \tag{5.7}$$

which emphasizes the contragredience to (5.3).

When a tensorial set of quantities a_i is transformed, as in (3.1), into a new set of b_k consisting of irreducible subsets, there is in general more than one subset of the same order $2j+1$. These subsets will be distinguished by an additional index α. If the subsets are obtained directly in their standard form, the generic element b_k of the new set may be indicated as $\mathfrak{b}^{(\alpha j)}_{m}$. In this event the matrix elements of the transformation A of (3.1) will be indicated by the transformation theory symbol $(\alpha jm|i)$ and (3.1) becomes

$$\mathfrak{b}^{(\alpha j)}_{m} = \Sigma_i(\alpha jm|i)\,a_i. \tag{5.8}$$

The reciprocal substitution

$$a_i = \Sigma_{\alpha jm}(i|\alpha jm)\,\mathfrak{b}^{(\alpha j)}_{m} \tag{5.9}$$

represents each element a_i of a reducible tensorial set as a linear combination of elements of irreducible standard sets $\mathfrak{b}^{(\alpha j)}$.

Standard form of the matrix U. The standard r-transformations fulfill (4.3), that is the standard form of U coincides with that of $\mathfrak{D}$ for the Euler angles $0, \pi, 0$,

$$\mathfrak{U}^{(j)} = \mathfrak{D}^{(j)}(0, \pi, 0), \tag{5.10}$$

or, by inserting the appropriate values in (5.2),

$$\mathfrak{U}^{(j)}_{\mu m} = (-1)^{j-\mu}\,\delta_{\mu,-m}, \tag{5.11}$$

$$\mathfrak{U}^{(j)} = \left\| \begin{matrix} \cdots\cdots\cdots & 0 & 0 & 0 & 1 \\ \cdots\cdots\cdots & 0 & 0 & -1 & 0 \\ \cdots\cdots\cdots & 0 & 1 & 0 & 0 \\ \cdots\cdots\cdots & -1 & 0 & 0 & 0 \\ \cdots\cdots\cdots & \cdots & \cdots & \cdots & \cdots \\ \cdots\cdots\cdots & \cdots & \cdots & \cdots & \cdots \end{matrix} \right\|. \tag{5.11'}$$

The standardization of $\mathfrak{U}^{(j)}$ restricts the phase normalization of standard sets. More specifically it prevents the replacement of a set $\mathfrak{a}^{(j)}$ with a set $c\mathfrak{a}^{(j)}$ which has the same standard transformation law as $\mathfrak{a}^{(j)}$, because multiplication by c, with $|c| = 1$, is a unitary transformation which changes $\mathfrak{U}^{(j)}$ into $c^2\mathfrak{U}^{(j)}$, according to (C.6). The new matrix $c^2\mathfrak{U}^{(j)}$ would still be a solution of the equation (4.2), $\mathfrak{U}^{(j)}\,\mathfrak{D}^{(j)}\,\mathfrak{U}^{(j)-1} = \mathfrak{D}^{(j)*}$, which defines $\mathfrak{U}^{(j)}$, but would no longer be identified with a rotation of 180° about y. However, $\mathfrak{U}^{(j)}$ remains invariant when $c = -1$.

Because (5.11) is real, we have

$$\mathfrak{U}^{[j]} = \mathfrak{U}^{(j)*} = \mathfrak{U}^{(j)}. \tag{5.12}$$

Standard sets of vector components. The ordinary components of a vector, V_x, V_y, and V_z constitute an irreducible set with real r-transformations and with $U = 1$. The set is brought to standard form by a unitary substitution of the type (5.8) which is identified to within a factor ± 1 by the condition that it changes D and U to standard form. The matrix of this substitution is indicated by $(1m|k)$ with $m = 1, 0, -1$ and $k = x, y, z$ and is

$$(1m|k) = \left\| \begin{matrix} i/\sqrt{2} & 1/\sqrt{2} & 0 \\ 0 & 0 & -i \\ -i/\sqrt{2} & 1/\sqrt{2} & 0 \end{matrix} \right\| \tag{5.13}$$

A standard set of vector components is, therefore,

$$\mathfrak{V}^{(1)}{}_1 = \frac{iV_x + V_y}{\sqrt{2}}, \qquad \mathfrak{V}^{(1)}{}_0 = -iV_z, \qquad \mathfrak{V}^{(1)}{}_{-1} = \frac{-iV_x + V_y}{\sqrt{2}}. \tag{5.14}$$

A contrastandard set of components is obtained by a substitution reciprocal to (5.13), with matrix elements $(k|1m) = (1m|k)^*$, and is given by

$$\mathfrak{V}^{[1]}{}_1 = \frac{-iV_x + V_y}{\sqrt{2}}, \qquad \mathfrak{V}^{[1]}{}_0 = iV_z, \qquad \mathfrak{V}^{[1]}{}_{-1} = \frac{iV_x + V_y}{\sqrt{2}}. \tag{5.15}$$

The unusual distribution of imaginary elements in (5.14) and (5.15), due to the standardization of U, is inconvenient in some respects, particularly in elementary problems, but explicit formulas like these should not be required too often in actual practice because calculations should be carried out mostly in set notation. The standardization conventions, which lead to (5.14) and (5.15), have the effect of making real most of the algebraic relationships among sets.

Standard sets of spherical harmonics. The adoption of the standard $\mathfrak{U}^{(j)}$ (5.11) also specifies a phase normalization of the spherical harmonic functions $Y_{lm}(\theta, \varphi)$. These functions represent in quantum mechanics the dependence on the polar coordinates θ and φ of the eigenfunctions of a particle in a central field. They are indicated by the transformation theory symbol $(\theta\varphi|lm)$. Accordingly, the spherical harmonics with fixed l and with $-l \leq m \leq l$ should constitute a contrastandard set of order $2l+1$.

Sets of spherical harmonics normalized according to Condon and Shortley (1935) have contrastandard r-transformations‡. It is desirable that such a set be self-conjugate, that is, that its elements become real when its r-transformations are brought to real form with $U=1$ (see Section 4, end, and Appendix C(i)). This requirement is not met by the Condon-Shortley normalization, because this normalization yields $K_o Y_{lm} - Y_{lm}{}^* = (-1)^m Y_{l,-m}$. On the other hand $\Sigma_{m'} \mathfrak{U}^{[l]}{}_{mm'} Y_{lm'} = (-1)^{l-m} Y_{l,-m}$, and therefore the effects of K_o and $\mathfrak{U}^{[j]}$ on the set differ by a factor $(-1)^l$.

The contrastandard, self-conjugate spherical harmonics will be indicated as $\mathfrak{Y}^{[l]}{}_m(\theta, \varphi)$. They fulfill the normalization condition

$$\int_0^{2\pi} d\varphi \int_0^{\pi} \sin\theta \, d\theta \, |\mathfrak{Y}^{[l]}{}_m(\theta, \varphi)|^2 = 1 \tag{5.16}$$

and have their phase normalized so that

$$\mathfrak{Y}^{[l]}{}_0(\theta, 0) = i^l \sqrt{\frac{2l+1}{4\pi}} P_l(\cos\theta). \tag{5.17}$$

The factor i^l is somewhat inconvenient, like the factor i in $\mathfrak{V}^{[1]}{}_0$ which may be regarded as a special case of it, but it has compensating advantages§. These sperical harmonics are related to the standard r-transformation functions by

$$\mathfrak{Y}^{[l]}{}_m(\theta, \varphi) = i^l \sqrt{\frac{2l+1}{4\pi}} \mathfrak{D}^{(l)}{}_{0m}(0, \theta, \varphi). \tag{5.18}$$

---

‡ The normalization of spherical harmonics varies considerably in common usage. In the literature on quantum mechanics the spherical harmonics are usually defined so that their r-transformations have the features indicated in (*a*) and (*b*) in Section 5. However, some normalizations differ from that of Condon and Shortley by factors -1 which have the effect of making some or all elements of the matrix J_x negative instead of positive.

§ The coefficients of the expansion of a plane wave into spherical waves become real after the i^l factor is absorbed into $\mathfrak{Y}^{[l]}{}_0(\theta, \varphi)$. We are indebted to Prof. Biedenharn for indicating to us the advantages of the normalization (5.17) for tensorial algebra applications and for the related considerations of time reversal.

In the calculation of multipole moments it is convenient to utilize spherical harmonics normalized like Legendre polynomials, rather than according to (5.16). We indicate these harmonics by the letter $\mathfrak{C}$ and require their set to be contrastandard and self-conjugate; we define then

$$\mathfrak{C}^{[k]}{}_m(\theta, \varphi) = \sqrt{\frac{4\pi}{2l+1}}\, \mathfrak{Y}^{[l]}{}_m(\theta, \varphi) = i^l\, \mathfrak{D}^{(l)}{}_{0m}(0, \theta, \varphi). \tag{5.19}$$

6

Invariant Products of Two Sets

A bilinear combination $\Sigma_{ik} t_{ik} a_i b_k$ of the elements a_i and b_k of two tensorial sets, which does not vary when the space coordinates rotate, is called an invariant product of the two sets. The term "product" is understood here in the general meaning indicated in Section 2. Various types of invariant products are rather well known, but their relationships are less generally known. Their nomenclature is also ill-defined and we shall attempt to standardize it.

Inner Product. Given any two sets of quantities c_i and d_k of the same order and contragredient to one another, the sum of products of their corresponding elements,

$$\Sigma_i c_i d_i, \tag{6.1}$$

remains invariant under r-transformations, because these transformations change the d_i into $d'_r = \Sigma_i D_{ri} d_i$ and the c_i into $c'_r = \Sigma_i D_{ri}{}^* c_i = \Sigma_i c_i D_{ir}{}^{-1}$. The expression (6.1) will be called the *inner product* of the initial sets.

Indeed the concept of contragredience originates in Section 2 from the remark that the expressions (2.2), $\mathbf{V} = \mathbf{i}V_x + \mathbf{j}V_y + \mathbf{k}V_z$, and (2.3), $\psi_a = \Sigma_m u^{(j)}{}_m a^{(j)}{}_m$, which are special cases of (6.1), must remain invariant when the space coordinates rotate.

The inner product of a contrastandard set $\mathfrak{a}^{[j]}$ and of a standard set $\mathfrak{b}^{(j)}$ may be indicated, in set notation, as

$$\tilde{\mathfrak{a}}^{[j]}\, \mathfrak{b}^{(j)} = \Sigma_m \mathfrak{a}^{[j]}{}_m \mathfrak{b}^{(j)}{}_m. \tag{6.2}$$

The inner product (6.1) of two reducible contragredient sets resolves into a sum of inner products of standard sets (6.2), when the initial sets are reduced to aggregates of standard sets. If the d_i are expressed in terms of elements of standard sets by (5.9),

$$d_i = \Sigma_{\alpha j m} (i|\alpha j m)\, \mathfrak{b}^{(\alpha j)}{}_m$$

and the c_i are expressed by the contragredient transformation

$$c_i = \Sigma_{\alpha' j' m'} \mathfrak{a}^{[\alpha' j']}{}_{m'} (\alpha' j' m'|i),$$

(6.1) becomes‡

‡ A special case of this formula has been presented by Cohen (1954). Notice that the explicit use of contragredient formalism and the restriction to unitary transformations has led us to define $\mathfrak{b}^{(\alpha j)}$ and $\mathfrak{a}^{[\alpha j]}$ so that no numerical coefficients appear in the last sum.

$$\Sigma_i \left[\Sigma_{\alpha'j'm'} \mathfrak{a}^{[\alpha'j']}{}_{m'} (\alpha'j'm'|i)\right] \left[\Sigma_{\alpha jm}(i|\alpha jm)\, \mathfrak{b}^{(\alpha j)}{}_m\right]$$
$$= \Sigma_{\alpha'j'm'\alpha jm}\, \mathfrak{a}^{[\alpha'j']}{}_{m'}\, \delta_{\alpha'\alpha}\, \delta_{j'j}\, \delta_{m'm}\, \mathfrak{b}^{(\alpha j)}{}_m = \Sigma_{\alpha j}\, \tilde{\mathfrak{a}}^{[\alpha j]}\, \mathfrak{b}^{(\alpha j)}. \tag{6.3}$$

The splitting of a tensor into a sum of irreducible tensors in (3.2) is a special case of (6.3).

Scalar product. Given two tensorial sets of quantities a_i and b_k of the same order and having the same r-transformations (i.e., cogredient), an invariant product can be constructed by changing one of them into a contragredient set by the transformation U introduced in Section 4 and taking the inner product of the new set and the other one. We call *scalar product* the invariant

$$\Sigma_k(\Sigma_i U_{ki} a_i) b_k = \Sigma_{ik} a_i \tilde{U}_{ik} b_k. \tag{6.4}$$

The scalar product so defined is not unique, insofar as the transformation U itself is not unique, unless standardization conventions are adopted. For standard sets, U has the standard form (5.11) and the scalar product will be indicated by

$$\mathfrak{a}^{(j)} \cdot \mathfrak{b}^{(j)} = \widetilde{\mathfrak{U}^{(j)}\, \mathfrak{a}^{(j)}}\, \mathfrak{b}^{(j)} = \tilde{\mathfrak{a}}^{(j)}\, \tilde{\mathfrak{U}}^{(j)}\, \mathfrak{b}^{(j)} = \Sigma_m (-1)^{j-m}\, \mathfrak{a}^{(j)}{}_{-m}\, \mathfrak{b}^{(j)}{}_m. \tag{6.5}$$

For irreducible non-standard sets the scalar product is unique to within a phase factor. For reducible sets whose reduced form contains no two subsets with the same j, the scalar product resolves, like the inner product (6.3), into a sum of the scalar products of the irreducible subsets, but each of these has an arbitrary phase factor. When the reduced form includes subsets with the same j, there are several scalar products of subsets with the same j, and the scalar product of the complete sets may be defined as any of various linear combinations of the subproducts.

If U is symmetric or antisymmetric (see Section 4 and Appendix C (g) and (h)), the scalar product is even or odd with respect to permutation of its factors.

The scalar product and the inner product coincide only for sets that are self-contragredient, i.e., when their r-transformations are real and $U = 1$. The distinction between the two products is seldom emphasized because the special case of real r-transformations is encountered most frequently.

The scalar product of two sets of eigenstates of atomic systems, $\mathfrak{u}^{[j]} \cdot \mathfrak{v}^{[j]}$ represents (except for normalization, see Section 7) an eigenstate of the two systems combined with zero angular momentum.

Hermitian product. Given two tensorial sets of quantities a_i and b_k, of the same order, having the same r-transformations (i.e., cogredient) and of which at least one possesses a complex conjugate, the inner product of the complex conjugate of one and of the other,

$$\Sigma_i a_i{}^* b_i, \tag{6.6}$$

is called their *hermitian product*. The hermitian product of two standard sets is

$$\widetilde{(\mathfrak{a}^*)^{[j]}}\,\mathfrak{b}^{(j)} = \Sigma_m (\mathfrak{a}^*)^{[j]}{}_m\, \mathfrak{b}^{(j)}{}_m = \Sigma_m \mathfrak{a}^{(j)}{}_m{}^* \mathfrak{b}^{(j)}{}_m. \tag{6.7}$$

Permutation of the factors of a hermitian product changes it into its complex conjugate.

When two quantum mechanical states are represented, as in (2.3), by $\psi_a = \Sigma_m \mathfrak{u}^{[j]}{}_m \mathfrak{a}^{(j)}{}_m = \widetilde{\mathfrak{u}}^{[j]}\mathfrak{a}^{(j)}$ and by $\psi_b = \widetilde{\mathfrak{u}}^{[j]}\mathfrak{b}^{(j)}$ respectively, the hermitian product (6.7) of the sets of coefficients represents the amplitude with which the state a is "contained" in the state b, that is, the quantity indicated by the transformation theory symbol $(a|b)$.

The hermitian product of two sets coincides with their scalar product only when the first set, namely a_i, is selfconjugate (see Appendix C (i)). In the ordinary algebra of real tensors there is only one kind of invariant product.

Sets related to different frames of reference. Tensorial sets are often conveniently defined with respect to a particular frame of reference. This may occur because the components of the set assume thereby a particularly simple form or anyhow when the tensorial set represents properties of a macroscopic body and it becomes relevant to have a frame of reference attached to the body. A familiar example is given by the components of the moment of inertia of a body, which reduce to three nonvanishing ones, namely I_{xx}, I_{yy}, and I_{zz}, when the coordinate axes coincide with the principal axes of inertia of the body. Less familiar examples are the tensorial sets representing properties of macroscopic laboratory apparatus (magnets, radiation detectors, etc.) which may interact with microscopic systems.

The equations given in this section, which express invariant products of two sets in terms of the set elements, were constructed with the implied understanding that the two sets relate to the same frame of reference. When the sets relate to different frames of reference, the construction of the product includes a preliminary r-transformation of one set, corresponding to the coordinate rotation which brings its frame of reference to coincide with that of the other set. The equations (6.2), (6.5), and (6.7) take then respectively the more general forms:

$$\tilde{\mathfrak{a}}^{[j]}\,\mathfrak{D}^{(j)}\,\mathfrak{b}^{(j)} = \Sigma_{\mu m}\,\mathfrak{a}^{[j]}{}_{\mu}\,\mathfrak{D}^{(j)}{}_{\mu m}(\psi, \theta, \varphi)\,\mathfrak{b}^{(j)}{}_{m}, \tag{6.8}$$

$$\mathfrak{a}^{(j)}.\mathfrak{D}^{(j)}\,\mathfrak{b}^{(j)} = \Sigma_{\mu m}(-1)^{j-\mu}\,\mathfrak{a}^{(j)}{}_{-\mu}\,\mathfrak{D}^{(j)}{}_{\mu m}(\psi, \theta, \varphi)\,\mathfrak{b}^{(j)}{}_{m}, \tag{6.9}$$

$$\tilde{\mathfrak{a}}^{*[j]}\,\mathfrak{D}^{(j)}\,\mathfrak{b}^{(j)} = \Sigma_{\mu m}\,\mathfrak{a}^{*[j]}{}_{\mu}\,\mathfrak{D}^{(j)}{}_{\mu m}(\psi, \theta, \varphi)\,\mathfrak{b}^{(j)}{}_{m}. \tag{6.10}$$

In these formulas, ψ, θ, and φ indicate the Euler angles of the rotation R which brings the frame of reference of $\mathfrak{b}^{(j)}$ to coincide with the frame of the other set. Since $\mathfrak{D}^{(j)}(R) = \tilde{\mathfrak{D}}^{(j)*}(R^{-1}) = \tilde{\mathfrak{D}}^{[j]}(R^{-1})$, each of these formulas can be also regarded as describing an r-transformation of the first set corresponding to the rotation R^{-1} which brings its frame of reference to coincide with that of $\mathfrak{b}^{(j)}$.

Sets $\mathfrak{a}^{(j)}$ which represent physical quantities with cylindrical symmetry (e.g., the moment of a magnetic needle, a constant field, or the sensitivity of a radiation detector with a cylindrical collimator and no polarization analyzing device) are reduced to a single nonvanishing component, $\mathfrak{a}^{(j)}{}_{0}$, by taking the axis of symmetry as z-axis. If one of the sets in the products (6.8 – 6.10) has this property, one of the summations reduces to a single term with $m = 0$, or $\mu = 0$, and the functions $\mathfrak{D}^{(j)}{}_{\mu m}$ reduce to spherical harmonics. If both tensorial sets have cylindrical symmetry, the double sums reduce to a single term, with $m = \mu = 0$, and the relevant $\mathfrak{D}^{(j)}{}_{\mu m}$ reduces to the Legendre polynomial $P_j(\cos\theta)$. For example the scalar product becomes

$$\mathfrak{a}^{(j)}.\mathfrak{D}^{(j)}\,\mathfrak{b}^{(j)} = (-1)^{j}\,\mathfrak{a}^{(j)}{}_{0}\,\mathfrak{b}^{(j)}{}_{0}\,P_j(\cos\theta). \tag{6.11}$$

The familiar formula for the energy of a magnetic needle, $-\mathbf{M}\cdot\mathbf{H} = -MH\cos\theta$ where $\mathbf{M}$ is the moment of the needle, $\mathbf{H}$ the magnetic field, and θ the angle between their directions, is a special case of (6.11). If the z axis is taken parallel to the magnetic field, the set $\mathfrak{H}^{(1)}$ of field components has a single nonvanishing element, namely $\mathfrak{H}^{(1)}{}_{0} = -iH$, according to (5.14). Similarly the set $\mathfrak{M}^{(1)}$ referred to a z-axis along the needle has the single nonvanishing component $\mathfrak{M}^{(1)}{}_{0} = -iM$.

Expansions into series of invariant products. Consider a physical quantity such as the potential energy of a system of electric charges in an electric field. This quantity is independent of the orientation of the coordinate system, but depends on the mutual orientation of the system of charges and of the field. This functional dependence is often conveniently analyzed into a series of harmonic functions of the angles ψ, θ, φ. The potential energy is then represented as a series of invariant products of tensorial sets, like (6.8). Expansions of this type may arise whenever one deals with a function of the orientation of a physical system with respect to a fixed frame of reference or with a function of the mutual orientation of two systems.

For purpose of illustration, the example of the potential energy is worked out here somewhat further. In terms of the polar coordinates of the charges e_i with respect to their center of mass, the energy is $U = \Sigma_i e_i V(r_i, \theta_i, \varphi_i)$. Because the function V obeys the potential equation, it can be expanded into harmonic functions. We utilize the spherical harmonics normalized according to (5.19) and write the expansion

$$V(r, \theta, \varphi) = \Sigma_{lm} r^l \mathfrak{A}^{(l)}{}_m \mathfrak{C}^{[l]}{}_m(\theta, \varphi), \tag{6.12}$$

The expansion coefficients $\mathfrak{A}^{(l)}{}_m$ involve l-fold derivatives of $V(r, \theta, \varphi)$ at the point $r = 0$ and must constitute standard sets contragredient to the sets $\mathfrak{C}^{[l]}$; the sum of the series is the invariant function $V(r, \theta, \varphi)$. The energy of all the charges is then

$$\begin{aligned} U &= \Sigma_i e_i \Sigma_{lm} r_i{}^l \mathfrak{A}^{(l)}{}_m \mathfrak{C}^{[l]}{}_m(\theta_i, \varphi_i) \\ &= \Sigma_{lm} [\Sigma_i e_i r_i{}^l \mathfrak{C}^{[l]}{}_m(\theta_i, \varphi_i)] \mathfrak{A}^{(l)}{}_m = \Sigma_l \widetilde{\mathfrak{M}}^{[l]} \mathfrak{A}^{(l)}, \end{aligned} \tag{6.13}$$

where the contrastandard set

$$\mathfrak{M}^{[l]} = \Sigma_i e_i r_i{}^l \mathfrak{C}^{[l]}(\theta_i, \varphi_i) \tag{6.14}$$

represents the components of the 2^l-pole moment of the electric charges.

If the sets of components of the multipole moments are referred to coordinates attached to the system of charges, the products in (6.13) take the form (6.8) and we have

$$U = \Sigma_l \widetilde{\mathfrak{M}}^{[l]} \mathfrak{D}^{(l)}(\psi, \theta, \varphi) \mathfrak{A}^{(l)}, \tag{6.15}$$

which represents the dependence of the energy on the mutual orientation of the system of charges and of the fixed field.

7

Irreducible Products of Two Standard Sets. Wigner Coefficients

The set of all pairs of elements, $a_i b_k$, of two tensorial sets has been called in Section 2 the "direct product" of the two sets. The direct product is, in general, a reducible set even when the initial sets are irreducible. We are interested here in a complete analysis of the direct product of two standard sets, namely in its reduction to an aggregate of standard sets, each of which is called an *irreducible product* of the initial sets. This reduction is a basic operation of the algebra of tensorial sets.

Some examples of the reduction of direct products are familiar. For example, given two ordinary vectors $\mathbf{a}$ and $\mathbf{b}$, the direct product of their components is a set consisting of 9 elements $(a_x b_x, a_x b_y \ldots a_z b_z)$, which are the components of an ordinary second-degree tensor. As indicated in Section 3, the reduction of this set resolves it into: (1) the invariant $a_x b_x + a_y b_y + a_z b_z$, which is the usual scalar product $\mathbf{a}\cdot\mathbf{b}$ of the two vectors, (2) the set of three elements $a_x b_y - a_y b_x$ etc., which are the components of the usual vector product $\mathbf{a}\times\mathbf{b}$, (3) the five components $[2a_z b_z - a_x b_x - a_y b_y]/\sqrt{3}$, $a_x b_x - a_y b_y$, $a_y b_z + a_z b_y$, $a_z b_x + a_x b_z$, $a_x b_y + a_y b_x$, of an irreducible tensor of degree two.

In quantum mechanics, given two systems with quantum numbers j_1 and j_2 and sets of eigenstates $\mathfrak{u}^{[j_1]}{}_{m_1}$ and $\mathfrak{v}^{[j_2]}{}_{m_2}$, the two systems combined have a set of states $\mathfrak{u}^{[j_1]}{}_{m_1}\mathfrak{v}^{[j_2]}{}_{m_2}$ which is the direct product $\mathfrak{u}^{[j_1]}\mathfrak{v}^{[j_2]}$. The states $\mathfrak{u}^{[j_1]}{}_{m_1}$ are eigenstates of the operators $\mathbf{J}_1{}^2$ and J_{1z}, which are the angular momentum operators of system 1 divided respectively by $\hbar^2$ and $\hbar$. Similarly the $\mathfrak{v}^{[j_2]}{}_{m_2}$ are eigenstates of $\mathbf{J}_2{}^2$ and J_{2z}. Therefore the states $\mathfrak{u}^{[j_1]}{}_{m_1}\mathfrak{v}^{[j_2]}{}_{m_2}$ of the combined system are eigenstates of all four operators $\mathbf{J}_1{}^2$, J_{1z}, $\mathbf{J}_2{}^2$, and J_{2z}. The direct product set is reducible because its elements are not eigenstates of the operator $\mathbf{J}^2 = (\mathbf{J}_1 + \mathbf{J}_2)^2$ of the combined system. The reduction of the product set consists of a unitary transformation that replaces the states $\mathfrak{u}^{[j_1]}{}_{m_1}\mathfrak{v}^{[j_2]}{}_{m_2}$ with eigenstates of $\mathbf{J}^2$. This operation is commonly known as *addition of angular momenta*.

The reduction of the direct product of any two standard sets $\mathfrak{a}^{(j_1)}$ and $\mathfrak{b}^{(j_2)}$ is presented here as a straightforward generalization of the procedure for the addition of angular momenta. Because we wish the irreducible products to be in standard form, the reduction will be expressed as in (5.8) in terms of a transformation matrix $(\alpha j m|i)$. The index i corresponds to the elements of the set to be reduced, and must be replaced here by the pair of indices (m_1, m_2), eigenvalues of J_{1z} and J_{2z}, which label the elements of the direct product $\mathfrak{a}^{(j_1)}\mathfrak{b}^{(j_2)}$. The indices (αjm) correspond to the elements of the irreducible product sets; m labels one element of a particular product set, j the degree of the product set, and α further identifies the product set, if required. In practice α is not required to identify irreducible products of two standard sets, but at this point we do not know yet which irreducible products are generated.

The reduction problem consists first of enumerating the irreducible products and thus of specifying the indices α and j, and then of actually constructing the matrix

$$(\alpha jm|m_1 m_2). \tag{7.1}$$

This task is facilitated by the standardization conventions of Section 5, which have the intended effect of simplifying the structure of the matrix (7.1).

The reducing matrix is real. Section 5 prescribes that standard sets have the property (4.3), namely,

$$U = D_y(\pi). \tag{7.2}$$

This property remains valid for the direct product of standard sets because the direct product has U and D matrices that are the direct (Kronecker) product of those of its factors. The r-transformations of the irreducible products must also obey (7.2) because we require them to be standard. Thus the reducing transformation $(\alpha jm|m_1 m_2)$ preserves (7.2) and therefore must be real, according to Section 4.

The reducing matrix resolves into submatrices. Item (a) of Section 5 prescribes that each element $\mathfrak{a}^{(j_1)}{}_{m_1}$ or $\mathfrak{b}^{(j_2)}{}_{m_2}$ is simply multiplied by $\exp(im_1\varphi)$ or respectively $\exp(im_2\varphi)$, when the coordinates rotate by φ radians about the z axis. Therefore the product $\mathfrak{a}^{(j_1)}{}_{m_1}\,\mathfrak{b}^{(j_2)}{}_{m_2}$ is multiplied by $\exp[i(m_1+m_2)\varphi]$ and is an eigenelement of the matrix‡ $J_z = J_{1z}+J_{2z}$ pertaining to the eigenvalue $m = m_1+m_2$. After the reduction operation, the new standard sets must still consist of eigenelements of

‡ When a matrix operating on a set is applied to the direct product of this and other sets, it is understood that the matrix is Kronecker-multiplied by the unit matrixes of the other sets. In particular $J_{1z}+J_{2z}$ stands for $J_{1z}\times 1_2+1_1\times J_{2z}$.

J_z. Therefore, each group of elements of the direct product set with equal values of m_1+m_2 experiences a separate transformation which yields the elements with $m = m_1+m_2$ of different irreducible product sets. Each of the separate transformation submatrices must be unitary if the complete matrix is to be unitary.

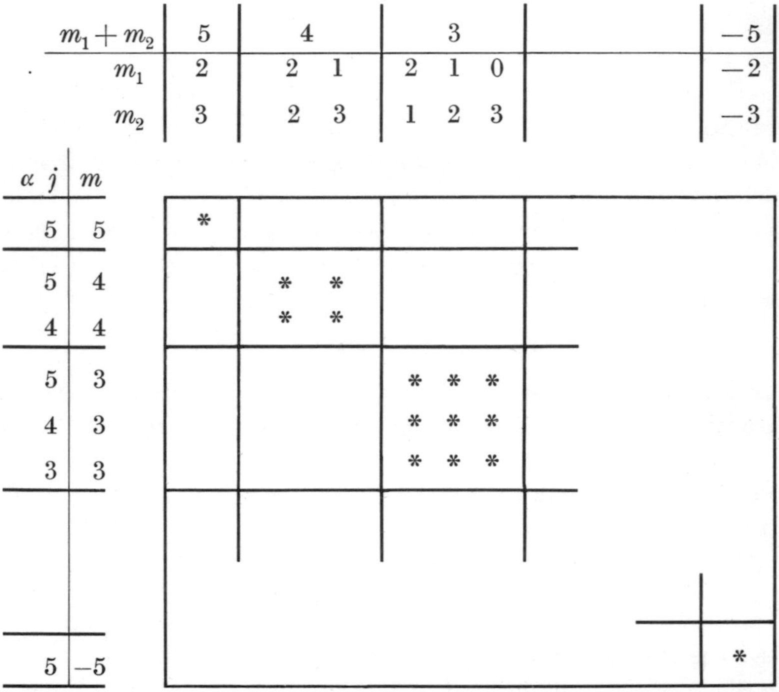

FIG. 3. Diagram of the matrix of Wigner coefficients which reduces the direct product of two irreducible sets of degrees $j_1 = 2$ and $j_2 = 3$. Matrix elements not indicated by an asterisk vanish.

The separate submatrices can be disentangled and laid out along the diagonal of the complete matrix by the following procedure, which is illustrated in Fig. 3 for the example $j_1 = 2$, $j_2 = 3$. Each column of the matrix is labeled by a pair of indices (m_1, m_2). Columns with the same value of m_1+m_2 will be grouped together and groups of columns with successive values of m_1+m_2 (5, 4, 3 in Fig. 3) will be laid out in succession. The rows of the complete matrix will similarly be laid out in groups of rows with equal m, and the groups will follow one another, just like the groups of columns with equal m_1+m_2. To each group of columns with a certain value of m_1+m_2 must correspond a group of as many rows labeled with $m = m_1+m_2$, because each submatrix is unitary and therefore square. The elements of the complete matrix vanish unless $m = m_1+m_2$, and therefore the nonvanishing elements remain concentrated in the square submatrices at the intersection of each group of columns with the corresponding group of rows.

Enumeration of the irreducible products. As shown in the figure, the largest value of m can be obtained only by taking $m_1 = j_1$, $m_2 = j_2$. Therefore: (a) there is no irreducible product set with $j > j_1+j_2$ because some of its elements would have $m > j_1+j_2$; (b) the submatrix for $m = j_1+j_2$ has one column only and hence only one row, which must correspond to the element $m = j_1+j_2$ of an irreducible product set of degree $j = j_1+j_2$. This set must have elements with all values of m from j_1+j_2 down to $-(j_1+j_2)$. Therefore each of the submatrices with these values of m must have one row corresponding to an element of the irreducible product with $j = j_1+j_2$.

Consider now the submatrix for $m = j_1+j_2-1$. There are two pairs (m_1, m_2) with $m_1+m_2 = j_1+j_2-1$ namely j_1, j_2-1 and j_1-1, j_2, so that the submatrix has two columns and two rows. One row is taken by the element with $m = j_1+j_2-1$ of the product set with $j = j_1+j_2$. The remaining row with $m = j_1+j_2-1$ must pertain to an element of a different set with j smaller than j_1+j_2 and no smaller than j_1+j_2-1, i.e., with $j = j_1+j_2-1$. Proceeding to lower and lower m one keeps demonstrating the existence of one additional irreducible product set for each value of j in descending integral steps down to $j = |j_1-j_2|$. All rows of the reducing matrix are accounted for by the elements of these sets.

This determination of the values of j for the irreducible product sets is represented by the equations

$$j_1 + j_2 - j = \text{integer}, \tag{7.3a}$$

$$j_1 + j_2 \geqslant j \geqslant |j_1-j_2|. \tag{7.3b}$$

Equation (7.3b) is called the *triangular condition* because it corresponds to the limitation on the magnitudes of two vectors and of their sum in the addition of vectors. Notice that, given any three integers or half-integers a, b, and c, if $a + b + c = \text{integer}$, also $a + b - c$ is integer, and that, if $a+b \geqslant c \geqslant |a-b|$, also $b+c \geqslant a \geqslant |b-c|$ and $c+a \geqslant b \geqslant |c-a|$. For future reference it is convenient to write (7.3) in the generic notation

$$a + b + c = \text{integer}, \tag{7.4a}$$

$$a + b \geqslant c \geqslant |a-b|. \tag{7.4b}$$

The index α on the left of the symbol $(\alpha jm|m_1 m_2)$ turns out to be superfluous, because, among the irreducible products of *two* standard sets, there are *no two with the same j*.

Values of the matrix elements. The elements of the matrix $(jm|m_1 m_2)$ have been calculated by Wigner and later by various authors and by various techniques which are discussed in Appendix G. They are called Wigner coefficients and have the algebraic expression

$$(jm|m_1 m_2) = \delta_{m,m_1+m_2} \sqrt{2j+1}\, \Delta(j_1, j_2, j) \sum_p (-1)^p \times \tag{7.5}$$

$$\frac{[(j+m)!(j-m)!(j_1+m_1)!(j_1-m_1)!(j_2+m_2)!(j_2-m_2)!]^{\frac{1}{2}}}{p!(j_1+j_2-j-p)!(j_1-m_1-p)!(j-j_2+m_1+p)!(j_2+m_2-p)!(j-j_1-m_2+p)!}$$

where

$$\Delta(a,b,c) = [(a+b-c)!(b+c-a)!(c+a-b)!/(a+b+c+1)!]^{\frac{1}{2}} \tag{7.6}$$

and the sum runs over all integral p. (However, no contribution to the sum accrues from values of p for which any factorial has a negative argument and therefore yields an infinite factor in the denominator.) Numerical values of all matrix elements for $j_1, j_2, j \leqslant 9/2$ have been tabulated (Simon, 1954).

The Wigner coefficients (7.5) may be written with the indices j_1 and j_2 explicitly indicated in the body of the matrix symbol, because the matrix elements are functions of j_1 and j_2,

$$(j_1 j_2 jm|j_1 m_1, j_2 m_2), \tag{7.7}$$

or, as in Condon and Shortley (1935), p. 73,

$$(j_1 j_2 jm|j_1 j_2 m_1 m_2). \tag{7.8}$$

Wigner indicated them with $s^{(j_1 j_2)}_{jm_1 m_2}$ and notations like $C^{(j_1 j_2 j)}_{m_1 m_2 m}$ have also been widely used. In this book the form $(jm|m_1 m_2)$ will be used except where the more explicit form (7.7) appears desirable.

Definition and notation. In conclusion, given two standard sets $\mathfrak{a}^{(j_1)}$ and $\mathfrak{b}^{(j_2)}$ one can construct one irreducible standard *product* set of *degree j* (i.e. of order $2j+1$) for each value of j consistent with (7.3). This product will be indicated as

$$[\mathfrak{a}^{(j_1)} \times \mathfrak{b}^{(j_2)}]^{(j)}; \tag{7.9}$$

its elements are

$$[\mathfrak{a}^{(j_1)} \times \mathfrak{b}^{(j_2)}]^{(j)}_m = \Sigma_{m_1 m_2} (jm|m_1 m_2)\, \mathfrak{a}^{(j_1)}_{m_1} \mathfrak{b}^{(j_2)}_{m_2}. \tag{7.10}$$

Symmetry. Irreducible products have a definite symmetry (even or odd) with respect to permutation of their factors. The symmetry alternates for successive values of j, beginning with "even" for the largest value, $j = j_1+j_2$, as indicated by the formula

$$[\mathfrak{b}^{(j_2)} \times \mathfrak{a}^{(j_1)}]^{(j)} = (-1)^{j_1+j_2-j}[\mathfrak{a}^{(j_1)} \times \mathfrak{b}^{(j_2)}]^{(j)}. \tag{7.11}$$

This property derives from the structure of (7.5), and can be verified by replacing, in the equation, p with j_1+j_2-j-p, which yields

$$(j_1 j_2 jm|j_1 m_1, j_2 m_2) = (-1)^{j_1+j_2-j}(j_2 j_1 jm|j_2 m_2, j_1 m_1). \tag{7.12}$$

From (7.9) it follows that many products of a set with itself vanish (provided the set elements are commutable):

$$[\mathfrak{a}^{(j_1)} \times \mathfrak{a}^{(j_1)}]^{(j)} = 0 \qquad \text{for } 2j_1 - j \text{ odd}, \tag{7.13}$$

which is a generalization of the vector formula $\mathfrak{a} \times \mathfrak{a} = 0$.

Product of degree zero. The product of degree zero, which exists only when $j_2 = j_1$ owing to (7.3b), reduces to the simple form

$$[\mathfrak{a}^{(j_1)} \times \mathfrak{b}^{(j_1)}]^{(0)}{}_0 = \frac{\sum_{m_1}(-1)^{j_1-m_1}\mathfrak{a}^{(j_1)}{}_{m_1}\mathfrak{b}^{(j_1)}{}_{-m_1}}{\sqrt{2j_1+1}}, \tag{7.14}$$

because (7.5) gives

$$(j_1 j_2 00|j_1 m_1, j_2 m_2) = \frac{(-1)^{j_1-m_1}}{\sqrt{2j_1+1}}\delta_{j_1 j_2}\delta_{m_1,-m_2}. \tag{7.15}$$

Thus it coincides with the scalar product (6.5) except for the normalization factor $(-1)^{2j_1}/\sqrt{2j_1+1}$‡.

Extension to contrastandard sets. The definition of the irreducible products of two standard sets extends immediately to products of contrastandard sets $\mathfrak{c}^{[j_1]}$, $\mathfrak{d}^{[j_2]}$. The transformation that reduces the direct product $\mathfrak{c}^{[j_1]}\mathfrak{d}^{[j_2]}$ is contragredient to (7.5), but actually coincides with (7.5) because it is real. We indicate the irreducible product of degree j of $\mathfrak{c}^{[j_1]}$ and $\mathfrak{d}^{[j_2]}$ as

$$[\mathfrak{c}^{[j_1]} \times \mathfrak{d}^{[j_2]}]^{[j]}. \tag{7.16}$$

‡ In our definition of scalar product the *first* factor is made contrastandard to match the prevailing practice in the definition of hermitian product. On the other hand the sign of the irreducible product of degree zero follows from the usual convention (G.3) or (G.5), in which a negative sign is connected with the m of the *second* factor. The factor $(-1)^{2j_1}$ in the connection between (6.5) and (7.15) follows from this difference of approach. The factor $\sqrt{2j_1+1}$ in the denominator of (7.15) follows from the requirement that all irreducible products be obtained by a unitary transformation of the direct product.

Its elements are

$$[\mathfrak{c}^{[j_1]} \times \mathfrak{d}^{[j_2]}]^{[j]}{}_m = \Sigma_{m_1 m_2}(jm|m_1 m_2)\, \mathfrak{c}^{[j_1]}{}_{m_1} \mathfrak{d}^{[j_2]}{}_{m_2}$$
$$= \Sigma_{m_1 m_2} \mathfrak{c}^{[j_1]}{}_{m_1} \mathfrak{d}^{[j_2]}{}_{m_2}(m_1 m_2|jm). \qquad (7.17)$$

The matrix elements $(m_1 m_2|jm)$ are identical with $(jm|m_1 m_2)$ but are written in transposed form to emphasize the contragredience by the appropriate notation.

The definition of irreducible product also extends readily to a pair of sets contragredient to one another, $\mathfrak{a}^{[j_1]}$ and $\mathfrak{b}^{(j_2)}$. The sets are first made cogredient by applying to one of them the transformation $\mathfrak{U}$ and then are multiplied according to (7.10) or (7.17). There are two kinds of products of $\mathfrak{a}^{[j_1]}$ and $\mathfrak{b}^{(j_2)}$, contragredient to one another, namely

$$[\mathfrak{U}^{[j_1]}\, \mathfrak{a}^{[j_1]} \times \mathfrak{b}^{(j_2)}]^{(j)} \qquad (7.18)$$

and

$$[\mathfrak{a}^{[j_1]} \times \mathfrak{U}^{(j_2)}\mathfrak{b}^{(j_2)}]^{[j]}. \qquad (7.19)$$

The elements of these product sets are obtained from (7.10) or (7.17) and from the expression (5.11) of $\mathfrak{U}^{(j)}$ and are

$$[\mathfrak{U}^{[j_1]}\, \mathfrak{a}^{[j_1]} \times \mathfrak{b}^{(j_2)}]^{(j)}{}_m = \Sigma_{m_1 m_2}(jm|-m_1 m_2)\,(-1)^{j_1+m_1}\, \mathfrak{a}^{[j_1]}{}_{m_1} \mathfrak{b}^{(j_2)}{}_{m_2}, \qquad (7.20)$$

$$[\mathfrak{a}^{[j_1]} \times \mathfrak{U}^{(j_2)}\mathfrak{b}^{(j_2)}]^{[j]}{}_m = \Sigma_{m_1 m_2}(-1)^{j_2+m_2}\, \mathfrak{a}^{[j_1]}{}_{m_1} \mathfrak{b}^{(j_2)}{}_{m_2}(m_1, -m_2|jm). \qquad (7.21$$

Examples of irreducible products in quantum mechanics. As indicated at the beginning of this section, when $\mathfrak{u}^{[j_1]}$ and $\mathfrak{v}^{[j_2]}$ are sets of eigenstates of two quantum mechanical systems, their product $[\mathfrak{u}^{[j_1]} \times \mathfrak{v}^{[j_2]}]^{[j]}$ consists of eigenstates of the combined system with total angular momentum quantum number j. When $\mathfrak{a}^{(j_1)}$ and $\mathfrak{b}^{(j_2)}$ consist of the components of the state functions ψ_{a_1} and ψ_{b_2} of the two systems, their product $[\mathfrak{a}^{(j_1)} \times \mathfrak{b}^{(j_2)}]^{(j)}$ consists of the components of the state function ψ_{a_1} ψ_{b_2} of the combined system in the scheme of eigenstates $[\mathfrak{u}^{[j_1]} \times \mathfrak{v}^{[j_2]}]^{[j]}{}_m$.

Tensor products. With sets $\mathfrak{S}^{(k_1)}$ and $\mathfrak{T}^{(k_2)}$ consisting of the components of two irreducible tensors one can construct products $[\mathfrak{S}^{(k_1)} \times \mathfrak{T}^{(k_2)}]^{(k)}$, whose elements may be interpreted as the components of new irreducible tensors. The initial tensors may be indicated by $\mathsf{S}^{(k_1)} = \tilde{\mathfrak{e}}^{[k_1]}\, \mathfrak{S}^{(k_1)}$ and $\mathsf{T}^{(k_2)} = \tilde{\mathfrak{e}}^{[k_2]}\, \mathfrak{T}^{(k_2)}$, where the sets $\mathfrak{e}^{[k]}$ consist of base unit irreducible tensors of degree k such as were considered in Section 3. These sets are analogous to the set of base vectors **i**, **j**, **k**, except for standardization. We define then the *irreducible tensor product* of degree k according to

$$[\mathsf{S}^{(k_1)} \times \mathsf{T}^{(k_2)}]^{(k)} = \tilde{\mathfrak{e}}^{[k]}\, [\mathfrak{S}^{(k_1)} \times \mathfrak{T}^{(k_2)}]^{(k)}. \qquad (7.22)$$

Notice that the set of components of this tensor product is a product of the sets of components of $\mathfrak{S}^{(k_1)}$ and $\mathfrak{T}^{(k_2)}$, but that the set of unit tensors

$\mathbf{e}^{[k]}$ is not obtained by reduction of the direct product of $\mathbf{e}^{[k_1]}$ and $\mathbf{e}^{[k_2]}$. This definition agrees with the definition of vector product $\mathbf{a}\times\mathbf{b}$ in which the base vectors **i**, **j**, **k** of the product are not obtained by reduction of the products of the base vectors of **a** and **b**. As a matter of fact, when $\mathsf{S}^{(k_1)}$ and $\mathsf{T}^{(k_2)}$ are vectors, i.e. when $k_1 = k_2 = 1$, their product (7.22) of degree $k = 1$ coincides with the ordinary vector product $\mathbf{S}\times\mathbf{T}$ to within a factor $-1/\sqrt{2}$. Tensors of equal degree $k_1 = k_2 = k$ have a tensor product (7.22) of degree zero which coincides with the ordinary scalar product $\mathsf{S}^{(k)}\cdot\mathsf{T}^{(k)}$ to within a factor $\sqrt{2k+1}$.

8

Irreducible Multiple Products of Standard Sets

Irreducible products of n standard sets, $\mathfrak{a}^{(j_1)}$, $\mathfrak{b}^{(j_2)}$, $\mathfrak{c}^{(j_3)} \ldots \mathfrak{p}^{(j_n)}$ can be constructed stepwise by applying the procedure of the preceding section to two factors at a time. For example, one can construct the irreducible product set

$$\Big[[[\mathfrak{a}^{(j_1)} \times \mathfrak{b}^{(j_2)}]^{(j_{12})} \times \mathfrak{c}^{(j_3)}]^{(j_{123})} \times \ldots \times \mathfrak{p}^{(j_n)}\Big]^{(j)} \tag{8.1}$$

by multiplying first $\mathfrak{a}^{(j_1)}$ and $\mathfrak{b}^{(j_2)}$, taking their irreducible product of degree j_{12}, multiplying this product and $\mathfrak{c}^{(j_3)}$, taking their irreducible product of degree j_{123}, etc. until the n factors are exhausted and one has a product set of degree j.

This construction is a stepwise reduction of the direct product $\mathfrak{a}^{(j_1)}$ $\mathfrak{b}^{(j_2)}$ $\mathfrak{c}^{(j_3)} \ldots \mathfrak{p}^{(j_n)}$ of the initial standard sets. The direct product consists of $(2j_1+1)(2j_2+1)(2j_3+1)\ldots(2j_n+1)$ elements, $\mathfrak{a}^{(j_1)}_{m_1}$ $\mathfrak{b}^{(j_2)}_{m_2}$ $\mathfrak{c}^{(j_3)}_{m_3} \ldots \mathfrak{p}^{(j_n)}_{m_n}$, each of which is characterized by the set of indices $(m_1 m_2 m_3 \ldots m_n)$.

The elements of the irreducible product set (8.1) are given in terms of the direct product elements by linear combinations (5.8), in which the generic index i is indicated specifically by $m_1 m_2 m_3 \ldots m_n$ and the generic index α by $j_{12} j_{123} \ldots$,

$$\begin{aligned}&\Big[[[\mathfrak{a}^{(j_1)} \times \mathfrak{b}^{(j_2)}]^{(j_{12})} \times \mathfrak{c}^{(j_3)}]^{(j_{123})} \times \ldots \times \mathfrak{p}^{(j_n)}\Big]^{(j)}_m \\ &\quad = \Sigma_{m_1 m_2 m_3 \ldots m_n} (j_{12} j_{123} \ldots jm|m_1 m_2 m_3 \ldots m_n)\, \mathfrak{a}^{(j_1)}_{m_1} \mathfrak{b}^{(j_2)}_{m_2} \mathfrak{c}^{(j_3)}_{m_3} \ldots \mathfrak{p}^{(j_n)}_{m_n}.\end{aligned} \tag{8.2}$$

The coefficients of this combination are constructed with Wigner coefficients (7.5) according to the definition (8.1),

$$\begin{aligned}&(j_{12} j_{123} \ldots jm|m_1 m_2 m_3 \ldots m_n) \\ &\quad = \Sigma_{m_{12} m_{123} \ldots m_{12 \ldots n-1}} (jm|m_{12 \ldots n-1} m_n) \ldots (j_{123} m_{123}|m_{12} m_3)(j_{12} m_{12}|m_1 m_2).\end{aligned} \tag{8.3}$$

This sum reduces to a single term, owing to the δ factor in (7.5), and moreover vanishes unless $m = m_1+m_2+\ldots+m_n$. Thus we have

$$\begin{aligned}&(j_{12} j_{123} \ldots jm|m_1 m_2 \ldots m_n) \\ &\qquad = (jm|m_1+\ldots+m_{n-1}, m_n) \ldots \times \\ &\qquad\quad (j_{123}, m_1+m_2+m_3|m_1+m_2, m_3)(j_{12}, m_1+m_2|m_1 m_2).\end{aligned} \tag{8.4}$$

The definition of multiple products of standard sets according to the preceding formulas can be extended to multiple products of sets contragredient to them, or to multiple mixed products, according to the pattern of Eqs. (7.16 — 7.21).

Multiple products with two or more identical factors may vanish for symmetry reasons, like the double product (7.13). In particular, all irreducible products of n identical sets $\mathfrak{a}^{(\frac{1}{2})}$ vanish except the product with $j = n/2$ (see Appendix F).

Any reducible tensorial set whose r-transformations coincide with those of a direct product $\mathfrak{a}^{(j_1)}\mathfrak{b}^{(j_2)}\mathfrak{c}^{(j_3)}\ldots$ is reduced to an aggregate of standard sets by the transformation (8.4). This applies particularly to the sets of components of ordinary tensors of degree n, whose r-transformations are the same as those of direct products of n sets of vector components. (Prior to application of (8.2) the tensor components must be substituted according to (5.13) so that their r-transformations coincide with those of the direct product of *standard* sets of degree 1.) Thus one obtains a general procedure for reducing ordinary tensors. This approach can also be followed on a qualitative basis to determine the number and degrees of irreducible tensors $\mathsf{T}^{(\alpha j)}$ contained in a general tensor of degree n. In the language of spectroscopy one may say that the number of tensors of degree j equals the number of terms with $L = j$ in the spectrum of n p-electrons without spin or Pauli principle (Racah, 1933).

Coupling scheme classification of multiple products. The irreducible multiple product (8.1) is characterized by the indices $j_{12}, j_{123}, \ldots j_{12\ldots n\text{-}1}$ in addition to the index j. These "j-numbers" indicate that the elements (8.3) of the product set are eigenelements of the operators $\mathbf{J}_{12}{}^2 = (\mathbf{J}_1 + \mathbf{J}_2)^2$, $\mathbf{J}_{123}{}^2 = (\mathbf{J}_1 + \mathbf{J}_2 + \mathbf{J}_3)^2, \ldots, \mathbf{J}_{12\ldots n-1}{}^2 = (\sum_{i=1}^{n-1} \mathbf{J}_i)^2$, pertaining to their respective eigenvalues $j_{12}(j_{12}+1)$, $j_{123}(j_{123}+1)\ldots$. An irreducible product of n sets constructed according to (8.1) is thus characterized by $n-1$ j-numbers corresponding to eigenvalues of the $n-1$ operators $\mathbf{J}_{12\ldots r}{}^2 = (\sum_{i=1}^{r} \mathbf{J}_i)^2$, where r ranges from 2 to n.

The procedure indicated above for constructing irreducible products can be altered, for example by replacing (8.1) with

$$\Big[\big[\mathfrak{a}^{(j_1)} \times [\mathfrak{b}^{(j_2)} \times \mathfrak{c}^{(j_3)}]^{(j_{23})}\big]^{(j_{123})} \times \ldots\Big]^{(j)}. \tag{8.5}$$

The elements of a product set constructed according to this scheme are eigenelements of $\mathbf{J}_{23}{}^2$, and, in general, are *not* eigenelements of $\mathbf{J}_{12}{}^2$, because the operators $\mathbf{J}_{12}{}^2$ and $\mathbf{J}_{23}{}^2$ do not commute. Any two operators $(\sum_i \mathbf{J}_i)^2$ and $(\sum_k \mathbf{J}_k)^2$ commute if, and only if: either the sum with the larger number of terms includes the other sum entirely or the two sums have no common term. It follows that, out of n operators $\mathbf{J}_1, \mathbf{J}_2, \ldots \mathbf{J}_n$, one can construct in different ways groups of commuting operators $(\sum_i \mathbf{J}_i)^2, (\sum_k \mathbf{J}_k)^2 \ldots$ A complete group always consists of $n-1$ commuting operators, in addition to the individual $\mathbf{J}_i^2$. Each complete group includes the operator $(\sum_{i=1}^n \mathbf{J}_i)^2 = \mathbf{J}^2$, but there is considerable latitude in the choice of the remaining $n-2$ operators‡. The group of operators $\mathbf{J}_{12\ldots r}{}^2$ with $2 \leqslant r \leqslant n$, which was implicitly selected in construction of the product (8.1), is an obvious but special choice.

Notice that the rows and the columns of the transformation matrix (8.4), which reduces a direct product of n standard sets, are identified by equal numbers of indices. Each column is identified by the n indices $m_1, m_2 \ldots m_n$, and each row by $n-1$ j-numbers and by the value of $m = m_1 + m_2 \ldots + m_n$.

A prescription for constructing irreducible products of n standard sets should contain the order of the factors and a choice of $n-2$ commuting operators $(\sum_i \mathbf{J}_i)^2$ in addition to $\mathbf{J}^2$. We call such a prescription a *coupling scheme*. A coupling scheme is identified by the order of the factors and by the groups of values of i included in each $\sum_i$. Each of these groups may, in turn, be indicated by the subscripts of one j-number in the symbol that represents the coupling scheme. For example, the quadruple product $[[\mathfrak{a}^{(j_1)} \times \mathfrak{b}^{(j_2)}]^{(j_{12})} \times [\mathfrak{c}^{(j_3)} \times \mathfrak{d}^{(j_4)}]^{(j_{34})}]^{(j)}$ consists of eigenelements of the operators $\mathbf{J}_{12}{}^2 = (\mathbf{J}_1 + \mathbf{J}_2)^2$ and $\mathbf{J}_{34}{}^2 = (\mathbf{J}_3 + \mathbf{J}_4)^2$. We indicate its coupling scheme by the symbol (j_{12}, j_{34}). The subscripts $_{12}$ and $_{34}$ actually identify the coupling scheme, whereas the *values* of j_{12}, j_{34}, and j identify a particular product constructed according to this coupling scheme.

The word "coupling scheme" originates from the addition, or coupling, of angular momenta in atomic physics. Consider, for example, two atomic electrons, whose orbital eigenstates constitute two standard sets indicated respectively as $\mathfrak{u}^{[l_1]}$ and $\mathfrak{v}^{[l_2]}$ and whose spin eigenstates constitute respectively standard sets $\mathfrak{g}^{[\frac{1}{2}]}$ and $\mathfrak{h}^{[\frac{1}{2}]}$. The Russell-Saunders

---

‡ To construct a complete group one can arrange the sum $\mathbf{J} = \sum_{i=1}^n \mathbf{J}_i$, with the $\mathbf{J}_i$ in an arbitrary order. The sum is then separated into partial sums by $n-1$ cuts in arbitrary succession. Each cut produces two new partial sums extending to the next preceding cut on its left or on its right. The squares of the $2(n-1)$ partial sums generated in this way constitute a group of commuting operators. This group contains the individual $\mathbf{J}_i^2$ and $n-2$ nontrivial operators which, together with $\mathbf{J}^2$, characterize an irreducible multiple product.

(or "*LS*") coupling of orbital and spin momenta yields the set of combined eigenstates

$$[[\mathfrak{g}^{[\frac{1}{2}]} \times \mathfrak{h}^{[\frac{1}{2}]}]^{[S]} \times [\mathfrak{u}^{[l_1]} \times \mathfrak{v}^{[l_2]}]^{[L]}]^{[J]}; \tag{8.6}$$

the "*jj*"-coupling yields instead

$$[[\mathfrak{g}^{[\frac{1}{2}]} \times \mathfrak{u}^{[l_1]}]^{[j_1]} \times [\mathfrak{h}^{[\frac{1}{2}]} \times \mathfrak{v}^{[l_2]}]^{[j_2]}]^{[J]}. \tag{8.7}$$

The elements of the product (8.6) are eigenstates of $\mathbf{S}^2 = (\mathbf{s}_1+\mathbf{s}_2)^2$, $\mathbf{L}^2 = (\mathbf{l}_1+\mathbf{l}_2)^2$ and of $\mathbf{J}^2 = (\mathbf{s}_1+\mathbf{s}_2+\mathbf{l}_1+\mathbf{l}_2)^2$, those of (8.7) are eigenstates of $\mathbf{j}_1{}^2 = (\mathbf{s}_1+\mathbf{l}_1)^2$, $\mathbf{j}_2{}^2 = (\mathbf{s}_2+\mathbf{l}_2)^2$ and of $\mathbf{J}^2$. The states indicated by (8.6) and (8.7) represent substantially different physical situations even for equal values of $\mathbf{J}$; the *LS* coupling state represents a situation where the electrostatic interaction between the two orbits is much stronger than the interaction between orbits and spins, and the *jj* coupling corresponds to strong spin-orbit coupling for each electron and weak interaction between electrons.

9

Transformations Between Coupling Schemes

The elements of all irreducible product sets belonging to any given coupling scheme constitute together a complete set of products, that is, a set of linearly independent elements of the same order as the direct product set, because the reduction transformation matrix (8.4) is unitary. The elements of irreducible sets obtained by different coupling schemes constitute alternate complete sets. Because each complete set is related to the direct product by a unitary transformation, the complete sets belonging to different coupling schemes also go into one another by unitary transformations.

As mentioned in Section 3, the reduction of a direct product may be visualized as a change of coordinate axes in a representative vector space. For example, the reduction of a direct triple product $[[\mathfrak{a}^{(j_1)}\times\mathfrak{b}^{(j_2)}]^{(j_{12})}\times\mathfrak{c}^{(j_3)}]^{(j)}$ according to (8.2) may be regarded as a change from a set of axes labeled by $(m_1 m_2 m_3)$ to a set labeled by $(j_{12} jm)$. To the irreducible products $[\mathfrak{a}^{(j_1)}\times[\mathfrak{b}^{(j_2)}\times\mathfrak{c}^{(j_3)}]^{(j_{23})}]^{(j)}$ of a different coupling scheme corresponds still another set of axes, labeled by $(j_{23} jm)$.

The unitary matrix that transforms a complete set of triple product elements labeled by $(j_{12} jm)$ into a complete set labeled by $(j_{23} jm)$ may be indicated by $(j_{23} j'm'|j_{12} jm)$. In general a unitary transformation between two coupling schemes may be indicated by $(\alpha' j'm'|\alpha jm)$, where α' and α represent different sets of j-numbers, as e.g., $(j_{12} j_{123})$ or $(j_{13} j_{24})$, which characterize the two coupling schemes. This transformation can be defined as the product of two transformations of the type (8.4),

$$(\alpha' j'm'|\alpha jm) = \Sigma_{m_1 m_2 \ldots m_n} (\alpha' j'm'|m_1 m_2 \ldots m_n)(m_1 m_2 \ldots m_n|\alpha jm). \qquad (9.1)$$

The transformations between coupling schemes are *real*, because both factors on the right of (9.1) are real. Anyhow they meet the requirement for reality indicated in Section 4, for the reasons discussed in the case of the matrix $(jm|m_1 m_2)$ in Section 7.

The elements of the irreducible products belonging to different coupling schemes are eigenelements of different groups of operators, but these groups have at least $\mathbf{J}^2 = (\Sigma_{\text{all}\, i}\, \mathbf{J}_i)^2$ and $J_z = \Sigma_{\text{all}\, i}\, J_{iz}$ in common. Accordingly the recoupling transformation does not intermix irreducible products of different degree j, nor does it intermix elements of these product sets whose m are different. It merely intermixes elements with equal j and m of products belonging to a given scheme but with different values of other j-numbers. That is, the recoupling matrix resolves into separate submatrices, much like the matrices of Fig. 1 or Fig. 3, and each submatrix pertains to a specific value of j and a specific value of m, which is expressed by writing

$$(\alpha' j' m' | \alpha j m) = (\alpha' j m | \alpha j m)\, \delta_{j'j}\, \delta_{m'm}. \tag{9.2}$$

In the picture of the representative vector space, recoupling may be regarded as a change of axes within each subspace with fixed j and m.

Moreover, the irreducible products of degree j, which are intermixed by recoupling transformations, experience equal standard r-transformations $\mathfrak{D}^{(j)}$. That is, recoupling transformations commute with all r-transformations. Because r-transformations intermix elements with equal j and different m, it follows that submatrices of (9.2) pertaining to equal j and different m must be identical and that the matrix elements (9.2) are in fact independent of m. Thus recoupling transformations are *relationships among sets* rather than among set elements and are wholly independent of the choice of coordinate axes.

Coupling schemes in which the order of factors differs but the choice of the $(\sum_i \mathbf{J}_i)^2$ is the same are related by very simple *reordering transformations*. These transformations consist only of permutations of the two factors of some partial products and therefore merely multiply the product by ± 1. Examples are the transformations from the scheme $(j_{12} j_{34})$ to $(j_{34} j_{12})$ or $(j_{12} j_{43})$.

Notations. Since the matrix element $(\alpha' j m | \alpha j m)$ has the same index j on both sides, and since the index m is irrelevant, it may be indicated more briefly as

$$(\alpha' | \alpha)^{(j)}. \tag{9.3}$$

The superscript (j) may be omitted when its value is clearly understood, or is irrelevant.

Unequivocal characterization of a recoupling coefficient for n-fold products requires in general that the "α" on each side of (9.3) consist of $2n-2$ j-numbers. These include the j-numbers that represent the degree of each of the n factors, in the proper order, and the $n-2$ j-numbers that represent the degree of each partial product. The j-numbers pertaining to the factors of each partial product should be enclosed in parentheses, followed by the j-number which indicates the degree of that partial product. For example we should write

$$([(j_1 j_2) j_{12} j_3] j_{123} j_4 | (j_1 j_4) j_{14} (j_2 j_3) j_{23})^{(j)}. \tag{9.4}$$

However, in any specific application it is desirable to omit as many of the j-numbers and of the parentheses as possible without equivocation. As indicated in Section 8, the order of the indices attached to the j-number of a partial product is often adequate to specify the order of the factors. For example, the coefficient (9.4) may be given in the simpler form

$$(j_{12}j_{123}j_4|j_{14}j_{23}). \tag{9.5}$$

The j_4 on the left may be dropped only if there is no doubt about the order of the factors.

The j-numbers of individual factors or of partial products are not always indicated by the letter j with subscripts. The procedure of indicating the order of factors by subscripts is then limited. This procedure is also inconvenient in a case such as

$$(j_{12}j_{123}j_4|j_{23}j_{231}j_4) \tag{9.6}$$

where j_{123} and j_{231} have different subscripts but must have the same numerical value in order that the coefficient does not vanish.

Factorization of recoupling transformations. Alternate coupling schemes exist for all products of three or more irreducible sets. All changes of coupling can be resolved into a succession of recouplings each of which involves only three sets, allowing for the fact that an irreducible product may be treated as a single set. For example a recoupling of quadruple products may be decomposed as indicated in the following equation

$$(j_{12}j_{34}|j_{13}j_{24})^{(j)} = \Sigma_{j_{123}}(j_{12}j_{34}|j_{12}j_{123}j_4)^{(j)}\,(j_{12}j_3|j_{13}j_2)^{(j_{123})}\,(j_{13}j_{132}j_4|j_{13}j_{24})^{(j)}. \tag{9.7}$$

The first and third factors on the right are triple product transformations, because the two-set products of degree j_{12} and, respectively, j_{13} are treated there as single factors. Notice also that j_{132} is numerically equal to j_{123}.

This factorization of recoupling transformations is analogous to the factorization (8.4) of the reduction of multiple direct products by stepwise reduction of one two-set product at a time.

Therefore, recoupling transformations of triple products have a central position with regard to all recouplings, analogous to the position of the Wigner coefficients with regard to the construction of all irreducible products. These transformations of triple products will be treated in Section 11.

Recouplings of quadruple products are of special importance for practical applications, especially those of the type $(j_{12}j_{34}|j_{13}j_{24})^{(j)}$ which include the change from *LS*- to *jj*-coupling in atomic structure. Therefore, these transformations are treated in Section 12 even though they can be resolved according to (9.7) into a sequence of triple product recouplings.

Recoupling transformations of products of increasing multiplicity can also be studied in detail and some progress has been made in this direction (Jahn and Hope, 1954; Ord-Smith, 1954; Elliott and Flowers, 1955).

Comparison with identities of vector algebra. Whereas the irreducible products have been presented as generalizations of the vector product, recoupling transformation formulas do not include as a special case any of the familiar vector identities. Vector products obtained with different couplings are related, for example, by the identity $(\mathbf{a}\times\mathbf{b})\times\mathbf{c} = (\mathbf{a}\cdot\mathbf{c})\,\mathbf{b}-\mathbf{a}\,(\mathbf{b}\cdot\mathbf{c})$, but the two vectors on the right of this equation belong not to the same coupling scheme but respectively, to couplings $(j_{13}j_2)$ and (j_1j_{23}).

From the standpoint of this section, a recoupling transformation of triple products of sets of vector components is

$$\left[[\mathfrak{a}^{(1)}\times\mathfrak{b}^{(1)}]^{(1)}\times\mathfrak{c}^{(1)}\right]^{(1)} = \gamma_0\left[\mathfrak{a}^{(1)}\times[\mathfrak{b}^{(1)}\times\mathfrak{c}^{(1)}]^{(0)}\right]^{(1)} + \gamma_1\left[\mathfrak{a}^{(1)}\times[\mathfrak{b}^{(1)}\times\mathfrak{c}^{(1)}]^{(1)}\right]^{(1)} + \gamma_2\left[\mathfrak{a}^{(1)}\times[\mathfrak{b}^{(1)}\times\mathfrak{c}^{(1)}]^{(2)}\right]^{(1)}, \tag{9.8}$$

where the γ_i are the recoupling coefficients $(j_{12}j_3|j_1j_{23})^{(j)}$ for $j_1=j_2=j_3=j_{12}=j=1$ and $j_{23}=i$. The first term on the right coincides, to within normalization, with the set of components of $\mathbf{a}(\mathbf{b}\cdot\mathbf{c})$ and the second with that of $\mathbf{a}\times(\mathbf{b}\times\mathbf{c})$, but the third contains the product $[\mathfrak{b}^{(1)}\times\mathfrak{c}^{(1)}]^{(2)}$ which is not used in vector algebra.

Products of invariant products. The recoupling of multiple invariant products like $[\mathfrak{a}^{(j_1)}\times\mathfrak{b}^{(j_1)}]^{(0)}[\mathfrak{c}^{(j_2)}\times\mathfrak{d}^{(j_2)}]^{(0)}\ldots$ is particularly simple. This can be shown most conveniently starting from inner (or scalar or hermitian) products which are equivalent to irreducible products of degree zero. For example the product of three inner products

$$(\tilde{\mathfrak{a}}^{[j_1]}\,\mathfrak{b}^{(j_1)})\,(\tilde{\mathfrak{c}}^{[j_2]}\,\mathfrak{d}^{(j_2)})\,(\tilde{\mathfrak{e}}^{[j_3]}\,\mathfrak{f}^{(j_3)}) \tag{9.9}$$

is equivalent to the inner product of two direct products

$$(\tilde{\mathfrak{a}}^{[j_1]}\,\tilde{\mathfrak{c}}^{[j_2]}\,\tilde{\mathfrak{e}}^{[j_3]})\,(\mathfrak{b}^{(j_1)}\,\mathfrak{d}^{(j_2)}\,\mathfrak{f}^{(j_3)}), \tag{9.10}$$

which are reducible sets. The general reduction formula (6.3) for the inner product of reducible sets shows that (9.10) equals the sum of inner products

$$\Sigma_{j_{12}j}\,[[\tilde{\mathfrak{a}}^{[j_1]}\times\tilde{\mathfrak{c}}^{[j_2]}]^{[j_{12}]}\times\tilde{\mathfrak{e}}^{[j_3]}]^{[j]}\,[[\mathfrak{b}^{(j_1)}\times\mathfrak{d}^{(j_2)}]^{(j_{12})}\times\mathfrak{f}^{(j_3)}]^{(j)}. \tag{9.11}$$

It also equals the corresponding sum constructed with irreducible products of any alternate coupling scheme, as e.g., (j_1j_{23}) instead of $(j_{12}j_3)$.

10

Invariant Triple Products. $\bar{V}$ Coefficients

In the study of recoupling, as in other tensorial problems, it is convenient to pay particular attention to the construction of invariants, mainly because it points up symmetries which might otherwise be overlooked or appear accidental. In this section we consider the triple product of degree zero, $[[\mathfrak{a}^{(j_1)}\times\mathfrak{b}^{(j_2)}]^{(j_{12})}\times\mathfrak{c}^{(j_3)}]^{(0)}$.

The triangular conditions (7.4) allow only one value for j_{12}, namely $j_{12}=j_3$. That is, in the reduction of the direct product of three standard sets $\mathfrak{a}^{(j_1)}\,\mathfrak{b}^{(j_2)}\,\mathfrak{c}^{(j_3)}$ according to the coupling scheme identified by the j-number j_{12} one finds only one irreducible product set of degree zero. This set consists of course of the single element $m=0$. Thus the representative vector space of these triple products contains no more than one axis which remains fixed under r-transformations, and this axis exists only if j_1, j_2, and j_3 obey the triangular conditions (7.4). Therefore, whichever coupling scheme is followed in constructing a triple product of degree zero, one will always arrive at the same result. Only a factor ± 1 may be changed by recoupling the product in any possible way. The scalar triple product of vectors $\mathfrak{a}\times\mathfrak{b}\cdot\mathfrak{c}=\mathfrak{a}\cdot\mathfrak{b}\times\mathfrak{c}$ coincides, to within a normalization factor, with the product $[[\mathfrak{a}^{(1)}\times\mathfrak{b}^{(1)}]^{(1)}\times\mathfrak{c}^{(1)}]^{(0)}$ of the standard sets of vector components.

To find the sign relationship between $[[\mathfrak{a}^{(j_1)}\times\mathfrak{b}^{(j_2)}]^{(j_3)}\times\mathfrak{c}^{(j_3)}]^{(0)}$ and $[\mathfrak{a}^{(j_1)}\times[\mathfrak{b}^{(j_2)}\times\mathfrak{c}^{(j_3)}]^{(j_1)}]^{(0)}$, we write out the reduction matrix elements which serve to construct the product of degree zero as a linear combination of elements of the direct product,

$$[[\mathfrak{a}^{(j_1)}\times\mathfrak{b}^{(j_2)}]^{(j_{12})}\times\mathfrak{c}^{(j_3)}]^{(0)}_0=\Sigma_{m_1m_2m_3}(j_{12}00|m_1\,m_2\,m_3)\,\mathfrak{a}^{(j_1)}_{m_1}\,\mathfrak{b}^{(j_2)}_{m_2}\,\mathfrak{c}^{(j_3)}_{m_3}. \tag{10.1}$$

Equations (8.4) and (7.15) give for $j_{12}=j_3$

$$(j_{12}00|m_1\,m_2\,m_3)=\Sigma_{m_{12}}(j_{12}\,j_3 00|j_{12}\,m_{12},\,j_3\,m_3)\,(j_1\,j_2\,j_{12}\,m_{12}|j_1\,m_1,\,j_2\,m_2)$$

$$=\frac{(-1)^{j_3+m_3}}{\sqrt{2j_3+1}}\,(j_1\,j_2\,j_3\,-m_3|j_1\,m_1,\,j_2\,m_2). \tag{10.2}$$

If one follows, instead, the coupling scheme characterized by the j-number $j_{23}=j_1$, he finds in the place of (10.2)

$$(j_{23}00|m_1 m_2 m_3) = \Sigma_{m_{23}}(j_1 j_{23}00|j_1 m_1, j_{23} m_{23})(j_2 j_3 j_{23} m_{23}|j_2 m_2, j_3 m_3)$$
$$= \frac{(-1)^{j_1-m_1}}{\sqrt{2j_1+1}}(j_2 j_3 j_1 -m_1|j_2 m_2, j_3 m_3). \tag{10.3}$$

The transformation coefficients (10.2) and (10.3) are indeed identical, as seen by entering in them the Wigner coefficient expressions (7.5) for $(j_3 -m_3|m_1 m_2)$ and $(j_1 -m_1|m_2 m_3)$. Notice in the first place that the divisors $\sqrt{2j_3+1}$ and $\sqrt{2j_1+1}$ in (10.2) and (10.3) respectively cancel the most obviously asymmetric feature of the Wigner coefficient (7.5), namely its first factor $\sqrt{2j+1}$. Replacing the running index p in the expression of $(j_3 -m_3|m_1 m_2)$ with $p-j_3+j_1-m_1-m_3$, it is then seen that (10.2) and (10.3) are identical.

We conclude that the triple product of degree zero possesses the associative property

$$[[\mathfrak{a}^{(j_1)} \times \mathfrak{b}^{(j_2)}]^{(j_3)} \times \mathfrak{c}^{(j_3)}]^{(0)} = [\mathfrak{a}^{(j_1)} \times [\mathfrak{b}^{(j_2)} \times \mathfrak{c}^{(j_3)}]^{(j_1)}]^{(0)}, \tag{10.4}$$

and may be written, without indication of coupling scheme, in the form

$$[\mathfrak{a}^{(j_1)} \times \mathfrak{b}^{(j_2)} \times \mathfrak{c}^{(j_3)}]^{(0)}. \tag{10.5}$$

Both coefficients (10.2) and (10.3) may then be indicated by the single symbol

$$(00\,|m_1 m_2 m_3), \tag{10.6}$$

or, in more detailed notation corresponding to (7.7),

$$(00|j_1 m_1, j_2 m_2, j_3 m_3), \tag{10.7}$$

which represents a coefficient of the expansion of (10.5) in terms of direct-product elements.

The product (10.5), like the ordinary product of two sets, does not possess the commutative property. As long as all j are integral (symmetric U), (10.5) is invariant under circular permutations of the factors, but even this property fails when there are half-integral j (anti-symmetric U). It follows from (7.11) that

$$[\mathfrak{c}^{(j_3)} \times \mathfrak{a}^{(j_1)} \times \mathfrak{b}^{(j_2)}]^{(0)} = (-1)^{2j_3}[\mathfrak{a}^{(j_1)} \times \mathfrak{b}^{(j_2)} \times \mathfrak{c}^{(j_3)}]^{(0)}, \tag{10.8}$$

and

$$[\mathfrak{b}^{(j_2)} \times \mathfrak{c}^{(j_3)} \times \mathfrak{a}^{(j_1)}]^{(0)} = (-1)^{2j_1}[\mathfrak{a}^{(j_1)} \times \mathfrak{b}^{(j_2)} \times \mathfrak{c}^{(j_3)}]^{(0)}. \tag{10.9}$$

Considering (7.4a), i.e., $j_1+j_2+j_3 =$ integer, the results (10.8) and (10.9) are summarized by stating that a circular permutation changes the sign of the triple product if, and only if, it changes the j of the middle factor from an integer to a half-integer or vice versa. Therefore the expression

$$(-1)^{2j_2}\,[\mathfrak{a}^{(j_1)} \times \mathfrak{b}^{(j_2)} \times \mathfrak{c}^{(j_3)}]^{(0)} \tag{10.10}$$

is invariant under circular permutation of its factors. It is easily verified that an odd permutation of the factors of (10.10) multiplies it by $(-1)^{j_1+j_2+j_3}$.

It has been considered whether the sign conventions in the definition of the Wigner coefficients could be changed so that the triple product would possess the same high symmetry as (10.10). However, the symmetry given by (7.11) for $j=0$, like the symmetry of the scalar product (6.5), depends only on the symmetry of U. Therefore the sign in (10.8) and (10.9) depends only on the symmetry of U and on the associative property (10.4); the circular permutability and the associative property cannot be combined in the definition of a triple product. The singling out of j_2 in (10.10) relates to the special position of $\mathfrak{b}^{(j_2)}$ in (10.4).

It is convenient, especially for applications, to express the matrix elements of coupling and recoupling transformations so as to keep all their symmetries in the foreground. Therefore we define a new set of high symmetry coefficients, which are the coefficients $(-1)^{2j_2}$ $(00|j_1 m_1, j_2 m_2, j_3 m_3)$ of the expansion of (10.10) in terms of direct-product elements. These coefficients are functions of three pairs of indices $a\alpha$, $b\beta$, and $c\gamma$, corresponding to the $j_i m_i$ of (10.7). We define

$$\overline{V}\begin{pmatrix} a\; b\; c \\ \alpha\; \beta\; \gamma \end{pmatrix} = (-1)^{2b}\,(00|a\alpha, b\beta, c\gamma). \tag{10.11}$$

A single row arrangement of the indices, $\overline{V}(abc;\alpha\beta\gamma)$, may serve for typographical convenience.

The coefficients $\overline{V}$ differ from the "3-j-symbols" of Wigner (1937) by a factor $(-1)^{a+b+c}$. The bar distinguishes $\overline{V}$ from the related but less symmetric coefficients of Racah (1942, Eq. 16′), namely

$$V = (-1)^{2(b-c)}\,\overline{V}. \tag{10.12}$$

Owing to (10.2) and (10.11), any Wigner coefficient may be expressed in terms of $\overline{V}$,

$$(j_1 j_2 j m|j_1 m_1, j_2 m_2) = (-1)^{2j_2+j-m}\sqrt{2j+1}\;\overline{V}\begin{pmatrix} j_1 & j_2 & j \\ m_1 & m_2 & -m \end{pmatrix}. \tag{10.13}$$

Whereas the definition of the Wigner coefficients implied only some symmetry with respect to permutations of $j_1 m_1$ and $j_2 m_2$, their connection with the $\overline{V}$ implies also an inherent symmetry with respect to permutations of all three pairs of indices $j_1 m_1$, $j_2 m_2$ and jm. The gain of symmetry relates to the circumstance that j_1, j_2, and j are treated equally in (10.7) whereas in a Wigner coefficient j is singled out.

From (10.13) and (7.5) follows the explicit form of $\overline{V}$,

$$\overline{V}\begin{pmatrix} a\,b\,c \\ \alpha\,\beta\,\gamma \end{pmatrix} = \delta_{\alpha+\beta+\gamma,0}\, \Delta(a,b,c) \sum_p (-1)^{2b+c+\gamma+p} \times \tag{10.14}$$
$$\frac{[(a+\alpha)!\,(a-\alpha)!\,(b+\beta)!\,(b-\beta)!\,(c+\gamma)!\,(c-\gamma)!]^{1/2}}{p!\,(a+b-c-p)!\,(a-\alpha-p)!\,(c-b+\alpha+p)!\,(b+\beta-p)!\,(c-a-\beta+p)!},$$

where $\Delta(a,b,c)$ is defined in (7.6). As we know, these coefficients are unaffected by even permutations of the sequence of columns of variables $a\alpha$, $b\beta$, and $c\gamma$, and are multiplied by $(-1)^{a+b+c}$ for odd permutations. This symmetry is not immediately apparent in (10.14) but can be verified by taking as a summation index instead of p the argument of any of the other five factorials in the denominator of (10.14). To make (10.14) manifestly symmetric, one must introduce redundant summation indices analogous to q and r in (G.8).

For reversal of the sign of the indices α, β, and γ, $\overline{V}$ has the same parity as for an odd permutation,

$$\overline{V}\begin{pmatrix} a & b & c \\ -\alpha & -\beta & -\gamma \end{pmatrix} = (-1)^{a+b+c}\, \overline{V}\begin{pmatrix} a\,b\,c \\ \alpha\,\beta\,\gamma \end{pmatrix}. \tag{10.15}$$

This equation results from the identity $\overline{V}(bac;\beta\alpha\gamma) = \overline{V}(abc;-\alpha\,-\beta\,-\gamma)$, which is apparent by inspection of (10.14). Equation (10.15) also follows from the transformation of (10.1) under a coordinate rotation of 180° about the y axis. The left side is invariant. The sum on the right side becomes

$$\Sigma_{m_1 m_2 m_3}(00|m_1\,m_2\,m_3)\,(-1)^{j_1+j_2+j_3-m_1-m_2-m_3}\, \mathfrak{a}^{(j_1)}{}_{-m_1}\, \mathfrak{b}^{(j_2)}{}_{-m_2}\, \mathfrak{c}^{(j_3)}{}_{-m_3},$$

where $m_1+m_2+m_3 = 0$ in the exponent. This transformation leaves the sum invariant only if (10.15) is fulfilled. It follows from (10.15) that $\overline{V}$ vanishes for $\alpha = \beta = \gamma = 0$ and $a+b+c$ odd, whereas, for $a+b+c=2g$ even, it has been shown (Racah 1942, Eq. 22) that

$$\overline{V}\begin{pmatrix} a\,b\,c \\ 0\,0\,0 \end{pmatrix} = \Delta(a,b,c) \frac{(-1)^g g!}{(g-a)!\,(g-b)!\,(g-c)!}. \tag{10.16}$$

The Wigner coefficients, as elements of a unitary matrix, have orthonormality properties which can be carried over to the $\overline{V}$ in the form

$$\sum_{\alpha\beta} \overline{V}\begin{pmatrix} a\,b\,c \\ \alpha\,\beta\,\gamma \end{pmatrix} \overline{V}\begin{pmatrix} a\,b\,c' \\ \alpha\,\beta\,\gamma' \end{pmatrix} = \frac{\delta_{cc'}\,\delta_{\gamma\gamma'}\,\delta(a,b,c)}{2c+1}, \tag{10.17}$$

$$\sum_{c\gamma}(2c+1)\,\overline{V}\begin{pmatrix} a & b & c \\ \alpha & \beta & \gamma \end{pmatrix}\overline{V}\begin{pmatrix} a & b & c \\ \alpha' & \beta' & \gamma \end{pmatrix} = \delta_{\alpha\alpha'}\,\delta_{\beta\beta'}, \tag{10.18}$$

where

$$\delta(a, b, c) = 1 \text{ or } 0 \tag{10.19}$$

depending on whether a, b, and c do or do not obey the triangular conditions (7.4). Further summation of (10.17) over γ yields

$$\sum_{\alpha\beta\gamma}\overline{V}\begin{pmatrix} a & b & c \\ \alpha & \beta & \gamma \end{pmatrix}^2 = \delta(a, b, c), \tag{10.20}$$

which is equivalent to the normalization property $\Sigma(00|m_1 m_2 m_3)^2 = 1$.

Equation (10.17) will be applied in particular for $c' = 0$ and $b = a$, in which case it reduces to

$$\sum_{\alpha\beta}(-1)^{a+\alpha}\,\overline{V}\begin{pmatrix} a & a & c \\ \alpha & \beta & \gamma \end{pmatrix} = \sqrt{2a+1}\,\delta_{c0}\,\delta_{\gamma 0}\,. \tag{10.21}$$

11

Recoupling of Triple Products. $\overline{W}$ Coefficients

The matrix elements of recoupling transformations can be calculated in straightforward manner starting from the definition (9.1) of recoupling as a product of two different reductions of a direct product. In the special case of triple products each reduction matrix element is a product of two Wigner coefficients, according to (8.4). Thus a typical recoupling matrix element for triple products takes the form

$$\begin{aligned}(j_{12}j_3|j_1j_{23})^{(j)} &= \Sigma_{m_1m_2m_3}(j_{12}jm|m_1m_2m_3)\,(m_1m_2m_3|j_{23}jm)\\ &= \Sigma_{m_1m_2m_3}(jm|m_1+m_2m_3)\,(j_{12}m_1+m_2|m_1m_2)\times\\ &\qquad (m_2m_3|j_{23}m_2+m_3)\,(m_1m_2+m_3|jm)\end{aligned} \tag{11.1}$$

of a sum of products of four Wigner coefficients.

All recoupling transformations of triple products can be decomposed into a sequence of transformations, one of which is of the type (11.1) and the others are simple reordering transformations, i.e., diagonal in all j-numbers and with matrix elements ± 1. For example we have

$$\begin{aligned}(j_{12}j_3|j_{13}j_2) &= (j_{12}j_3|j_{21}j_3)\,(j_{21}j_3|j_2j_{13})\,(j_2j_{13}|j_{13}j_2)\\ &= (-1)^{j_{12}+j_{13}-j_1-j}(j_{21}j_3|j_2j_{13}),\end{aligned} \tag{11.2}$$

$$(j_1j_{23}|j_{13}j_2) = (j_1j_{23}|j_1j_{32})\,(j_1j_{32}|j_{13}j_2) = (-1)^{j_{23}-j_2-j_3}(j_1j_{32}|j_{13}j_2). \tag{11.3}$$

Therefore it is adequate to consider the single type of transformation (11.1).

On the right of (11.1) the sum over m_1, m_2, and m_3 is effectively twofold, because of the condition $m_1+m_2+m_3 = m$, and each Wigner coefficient is expressed by (7.5) as a sum over an index p. Therefore the calculation of the recoupling coefficient appears to require a sixfold sum. Actually this calculation can be reduced to a single sum and its result is a highly symmetric function of the six parameters j_1, j_2, j_3, j_{12}, j_{23}, and j.

Formally, the symmetry is brought out by replacing in (11.1) the Wigner coefficients with $\overline{V}$ coefficients, according to (10.13)

$$\begin{aligned}(j_{12}j_3|j_1j_{23})^{(j)} &= \sum_{m_1m_2m_3}(-1)^{2j_3+j-m}\sqrt{2j+1}\,\overline{V}\begin{pmatrix} j_{12} & j_3 & j\\ m_{12} & m_3 & -m\end{pmatrix}\times\\ &(-1)^{2j_2+j_{12}-m_{12}}\sqrt{2j_{12}+1}\,\overline{V}\begin{pmatrix} j_1 & j_2 & j_{12}\\ m_1 & m_2 & -m_{12}\end{pmatrix}(-1)^{2j_3+j_{23}-m_{23}}\sqrt{2j_{23}+1}\,\overline{V}\begin{pmatrix} j_2 & j_3 & j_{23}\\ m_2 & m_3 & -m_{23}\end{pmatrix}\times\\ &(-1)^{2j_{23}+j-m}\sqrt{2j+1}\,\overline{V}\begin{pmatrix} j_1 & j_{23} & j\\ m_1 & m_{23} & -m\end{pmatrix},\end{aligned} \tag{11.4}$$

and by simplifying this expression utilizing the symmetry properties of $\overline{V}$.

In the combined exponent of -1, the quantities $4j_3$ and $2(j-m)$ are even numbers and can be dropped. The factor $2j+1$ may be replaced by extending the summation to all values of m, because there are $2j+1$ such values and the transformation coefficient must be the same for every m according to Section 9. We may make the summation fully symmetric by extending it also to m_{12} and m_{23}. This formal extension does not change the result because the second $\overline{V}$ vanishes unless $m_{12}=m_1+m_2$ and the third unless $m_{23}=m_2+m_3$.

Each of the six j-numbers appears in (11.4) in two of the four $\overline{V}$. Among these numbers, j_1 and j_3 never appear in the same $\overline{V}$, nor do j_2 and j, nor j_{12} and j_{23}. Permutations among the columns of the $\overline{V}$ may then bring the j of each pair in the same position in the four $\overline{V}$, e.g., bring the three pairs respectively in the first, second, and third column. This arrangement is achieved by a circular permutation of the columns of the first $\overline{V}$, and by an interchange of two columns in each of the last two $\overline{V}$. If we reverse simultaneously the sign of the m in the last two $\overline{V}$, the whole operation causes no change of sign owing to (10.15).

The exponent of -1 was $2j_2+j_{12}-m_{12}+j_{23}-m_{23}+2j_{23}$ after the initial simplification. To this we add $2(j_3-m_3)$ and $2(j+j_1-j_{23})$ which are even integers, and also $m_1+m_2+m_3-m$ which vanishes.

It follows from these operations that (11.1) reduces to

$$(j_{12}j_3|j_1j_{23})^{(j)} = \sqrt{(2j_{12}+1)(2j_{23}+1)}\,(-1)^{j_1+j_2+j_3+j} \times$$
$$\sum_{all\ m}(-1)^{j_1+j_2+j_3+j+j_{12}+j_{23}+m_1+m_2-m_3-m-m_{12}-m_{23}} \times$$
$$\overline{V}\begin{pmatrix} j_1 & j_2 & j_{12} \\ m_1 & m_2 & -m_{12}\end{pmatrix}\overline{V}\begin{pmatrix} j_1 & j & j_{23} \\ -m_1 & m & -m_{23}\end{pmatrix}\overline{V}\begin{pmatrix} j_3 & j_2 & j_{23} \\ -m_3 & -m_2 & m_{23}\end{pmatrix}\overline{V}\begin{pmatrix} j_3 & j & j_{12} \\ m_3 & -m & m_{12}\end{pmatrix}. \qquad (11.5)$$

The sum in this formula is a function of the six j-numbers which will be indicated by $\overline{W}\begin{pmatrix} j_1 j_2 j_{12} \\ j_3 j\ j_{23}\end{pmatrix}$, where

$$\overline{W}\begin{pmatrix} a\,b\,c \\ d\,e\,f\end{pmatrix} = \sum_{\alpha\beta\gamma\delta\varepsilon\varphi}(-1)^{a-\alpha+b-\beta+c-\gamma+d-\delta+e-\varepsilon+f-\varphi} \times \qquad (11.6)$$
$$\overline{V}\begin{pmatrix} a & b & c \\ -\alpha & -\beta & -\gamma\end{pmatrix}\overline{V}\begin{pmatrix} a & e & f \\ \alpha & \varepsilon & -\varphi\end{pmatrix}\overline{V}\begin{pmatrix} d & b & f \\ -\delta & \beta & \varphi\end{pmatrix}\overline{V}\begin{pmatrix} d & e & c \\ \delta & -\varepsilon & \gamma\end{pmatrix}.$$

The variables may be arranged in a single row, $\overline{W}(abc/def)$, for typographical convenience. The function $\overline{W}$ coincides with the 6-j-symbol of Wigner (1937). The bar distinguishes $\overline{W}$ from the related but less symmetric coefficients of Racah (1942, Eq. 36′), namely,

$$W(abcd;ef) = (-1)^{a+b+c+d}\,\overline{W}\,(abe/dcf). \qquad (11.7)$$

In terms of the function $\overline{W}$ the recoupling coefficient (11.5) becomes

$$(j_{12}j_3|j_1j_{23})^{(j)} = (-1)^{j_1+j_2+j_3+j}\sqrt{(2j_{12}+1)(2j_{23}+1)}\,\overline{W}\begin{pmatrix} j_1 & j_2 & j_{12} \\ j_3 & j & j_{23} \end{pmatrix} \tag{11.8}$$

The function $\overline{W}$ is a function of six numbers grouped in four triads (abc), (aef), (dbf), and (dec). All numbers may be integral or half-integral and the numbers of each triad must fulfil the triangular conditions (7.4). Each triad contains one index drawn from each of the three columns of variables of $\overline{W}$. One triad has all indices taken from the first row, the others consist ot two indices of the second row and the remaining one from the first row. Each index is included in two triads.

Permutations of the three triads (aef), (dbf), and (dec) are represented by permutations of the columns of indices of $\overline{W}$. Permutation of any of these three triads with (abc) is represented by a permutation of the upper and lower indices in *two* columns of indices. All these permutations leave $\overline{W}$ invariant, but it takes some manipulation to verify this property from (11.6). However the symmetry of $\overline{W}$ with respect to permutations of all triads becomes fully manifest when $\overline{W}$ is expressed as a single sum (Racah, 1942)

$$\overline{W}\begin{pmatrix} a & b & c \\ d & e & f \end{pmatrix} = \Delta(a,b,c)\,\Delta(d,e,c)\,\Delta(d,b,f)\,\Delta(a,e,f)\sum\nolimits'_q\{(-1)^q(q+1)!\times$$
$$[(q-a-b-c)!(q-d-e-c)!(q-d-b-f)!(q-a-e-f)!\times$$
$$(a+b+d+e-q)!(a+c+d+f-q)!(b+c+e+f-q)!]^{-1}\} \tag{11.9}$$

where $\Delta(a,b,c)$ is given by (7.6). Notice that the variables appear in (11.9) either in triads or grouped by columns.

The symmetry of $\overline{W}$ with respect to permutations of its variables is the symmetry of a tetrahedron with respect to permutations of its edges. Figure 4 shows a vector diagram in which the operators $\mathbf{J}_1$, $\mathbf{J}_2$, $\mathbf{J}_3$, $\mathbf{J}_{12}$, $\mathbf{J}_{23}$, and $\mathbf{J} = \mathbf{J}_1+\mathbf{J}_2+\mathbf{J}_3$ are indicated as ordinary vectors, that is, as angular momenta are treated in classical mechanics. The diagram represents a tetrahedron. The edges of each triangular face are labeled by $\mathbf{J}$ vectors whose j-numbers constitute a triad in the $\overline{W}$ of (11.8) and fulfil the triangular conditions. The three pairs of opposite edges of the tetrahedron correspond to the pairs of j-numbers in the three columns of the $\overline{W}$ of (11.8). Another type of diagram, which represents recoupling relationships with their full symmetry, is described in Appendix H.

The function $\overline{W}$, or rather the W, has been tabulated over rather extended ranges of its variables, by Biedenharn (1952), Simon *et al.* (1954), Obi *et al.* (1953, 1954, 1955), and Sharp *et al.* (1953).

Recoupling of quadruple products of degree zero. The correspondence between two-set products and triple products of degree zero, discussed in Section 10, exists also between n-set products and $(n+1)$-set products of degree zero. For example, for products of degree zero the coupling schemes $((j_1 j_2)(j_3 j_4))$ and $([(j_1 j_2)j_3]j_4)$ coincide as shown by applying the

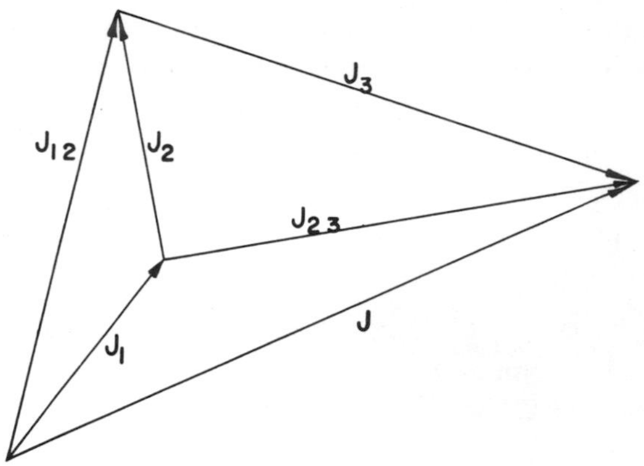

FIG. 4. Vector diagram of infinitesimal rotation operators in the recoupling of triple products.

associative property (10.4) to the product of degree zero of the sets of degree j_{12}, j_3, and j_4. Therefore, the recoupling between products with the coupling schemes $(j_{12} j_{34}) = ((j_{12} j_3) j_4)$ and $(j_{13} j_{24}) = ((j_{13} j_2) j_4)$ reduces to the recoupling $(j_{12} j_3 | j_{13} j_2)$. Notice that the invariance of the quadruple product requires, owing to the triangular conditions, that the j-numbers j_{12} and j_{34} be equal, and similarly that $j_{13} = j_{24}$.

We have, then, from (11.2) and (11.8),

$$
\begin{aligned}
(j_{12} j_{34} | j_{13} j_{24})^{(0)} &= (j_{12} j_3 | j_{13} j_2)^{(j_4)} = (-1)^{j_{12}+j_{13}-j_1-j_4} (j_{21} j_3 | j_2 j_{13})^{(j_4)} \\
&= \sqrt{(2j_{12}+1)(2j_{13}+1)}\, (-1)^{j_{12}+j_{13}+j_2+j_3}\, \overline{W}\begin{pmatrix} j_1 j_2 j_{12} \\ j_4 j_3 j_{13} \end{pmatrix}. \qquad (11.10)
\end{aligned}
$$

The four j-numbers j_1, j_2, j_3, and j_4 have equivalent positions in the recoupling transformation (11.10), whereas j has a position different from j_1, j_2, and j_3 in the recoupling of triple products. The correspondence between j and j_4, which follows from the correspondence between triple products and invariant quadruple products, illustrates why j occupies a position equivalent to those of j_1, j_2, and j_3 in the $\overline{W}$ of (11.8).

Recoupling transformation having the full symmetry of $\overline{\mathbf{W}}$. One may ask at this point whether $\overline{W}$ itself represents a recoupling transformation in which all of its six variables have equivalent position. A transformation with this high symmetry is found to occur in a very special type of recoupling of twelvefold products. This is the transformation between a product of *four triple* products of degree zero and a product of *six* products of degree zero of *two* sets each. In the definition (11.6) of $\overline{W}$ the four $\overline{V}$ represent the transformation from a direct product of twelve sets to the product of four invariant triple products; the factors $(-1)^{a-\alpha}$ represent, to within normalization factors, the transformation to the product of six two-set products of degree zero. One verifies that

$$\overline{W}\begin{pmatrix} a\,b\,c \\ d\,e\,f \end{pmatrix} = [(2a+1)\,(2b+1)\ldots(2f+1)]^{\frac{1}{2}} \times \tag{11.11}$$

$$((abc)0, (aef)0, (dbf)0, (dec)0 \mid (aa)0, (bb)0, (cc)0, (dd)0, (ee)0, (ff)0)^{(0)}.$$

Properties of the $\overline{\mathbf{W}}$. The $\overline{W}$ coefficients reduce to very simple form whenever one of their variables vanishes,

$$\overline{W}\begin{pmatrix} a\,b\,c \\ d\,e\,0 \end{pmatrix} = \Delta(aa0)\,\Delta(bb0)(-1)^{a+b+c}\delta_{ae}\,\delta_{bd} = \frac{(-1)^{a+b+c}\,\delta_{ae}\,\delta_{bd}\,\delta(a,b,c)}{\sqrt{(2a+1)\,(2b+1)}} \tag{11.12}$$

where $\delta(a,b,c)$ is given by (10.19). This was to be expected because the recoupling of triple products of degree zero amounts at most to a change of sign as discussed in Section 10.

The recoupling transformations are unitary

$$\Sigma_{j_{23}}(j_{12}\,j_3|j_1\,j_{23})\,(j_1\,j_{23}|j_{12}'\,j_3) = \delta_{j_{12}j_{12}'}, \tag{11.13}$$

and have the associative property (group property)

$$\Sigma_{j_{13}}(j_{12}\,j_3|j_{13}\,j_2)^{(j)}(j_{13}\,j_2|j_1\,j_{23})^{(j)} = (j_{12}\,j_3|j_1\,j_{23})^{(j)}. \tag{11.14}$$

From these properties follow, respectively, the following sum rules for $\overline{W}$,

$$\sum_c (2c+1)\,\overline{W}\begin{pmatrix} a\,b\,c \\ d\,e\,f \end{pmatrix}\overline{W}\begin{pmatrix} a\,b\,c \\ d\,e\,g \end{pmatrix} = \frac{\delta_{fg}\,\delta(a,e,f)\,\delta(d,b,f)}{2f+1}, \tag{11.15}$$

$$\sum_c (-1)^{c+f+g}(2c+1)\,\overline{W}\begin{pmatrix} a\,b\,c \\ d\,e\,f \end{pmatrix}\overline{W}\begin{pmatrix} a\,b\,c \\ e\,d\,g \end{pmatrix} = \overline{W}\begin{pmatrix} a\,e\,f \\ b\,d\,g \end{pmatrix}. \tag{11.16}$$

Equations involving $\overline{V}$ and $\overline{W}$. A recoupling transformation relates the transformations (8.4) which reduce a direct product according to different coupling schemes. For example we have

$$(j_{12}jm|m_1m_2m_3) = \Sigma_{j_{23}}(j_{12}j_3|j_1j_{23})^{(j)}(j_{23}jm|m_1m_2m_3). \qquad (11.17)$$

The reducing transformations on each side are products of Wigner coefficients, according to (8.4), e.g., $(j_{12}jm|m_1m_2m_3) = (jm|m_{12}m_3)(j_{12}m_{12}|m_1m_2)$. By replacing these Wigner coefficients with $\overline{V}$ by means of (10.13), expressing $(j_{12}j_3|j_1j_{23})^{(j)}$ in terms of $\overline{W}$ by means of (11.8), and utilizing the symmetry properties of the $\overline{V}$, we find that

$$\sum_{\varphi}\overline{V}\begin{pmatrix} d\,b\,f \\ \delta\,\beta\,\varphi \end{pmatrix}\overline{V}\begin{pmatrix} a\ e\ f \\ \alpha\ \varepsilon\ \text{-}\varphi \end{pmatrix}$$
$$= \sum_{c\gamma}(-1)^{c+f-\alpha-\delta}(2c+1)\overline{W}\begin{pmatrix} a\,b\,c \\ d\,e\,f \end{pmatrix}\overline{V}\begin{pmatrix} a\,b\,c \\ \alpha\,\beta\,\gamma \end{pmatrix}\overline{V}\begin{pmatrix} d\ e\ c \\ \delta\ \varepsilon\ \text{-}\gamma \end{pmatrix}. \qquad (11.18)$$

Multiplying this equation by $(-1)^{c+f-\alpha-\delta}\,\overline{V}(dec';\delta\varepsilon\,\text{-}\gamma)$, summing over δ and ε, and considering the symmetry and orthonormality properties of the $\overline{V}$, yields

$$\sum_{\delta\varepsilon\varphi}(-1)^{d-\delta+e-\varepsilon+f-\varphi}\,\overline{V}\begin{pmatrix} a\ e\ f \\ \alpha\ \varepsilon\ \text{-}\varphi \end{pmatrix}\overline{V}\begin{pmatrix} d\ b\ f \\ \text{-}\delta\ \beta\ \varphi \end{pmatrix}\overline{V}\begin{pmatrix} d\ \ e\,c \\ \delta\ \text{-}\varepsilon\ \gamma \end{pmatrix}$$
$$= \overline{W}\begin{pmatrix} a\,b\,c \\ d\,e\,f \end{pmatrix}\overline{V}\begin{pmatrix} a\,b\,c \\ \alpha\,\beta\,\gamma \end{pmatrix}. \qquad (11.19)$$

Equations (11.18) and (11.19), or equivalent equations in terms of V and W like (41) of Racah (1942), have been applied frequently to simplify expressions involving sums over products of $\overline{V}$. However, these equations are not needed if calculations are carried out entirely through recoupling operations without explicit use of $\overline{V}$.

12

Recoupling of Quadruple Products. X Coefficients

The coupling schemes of irreducible quadruple products and their recoupling transformations are classified conveniently with reference to the corresponding quintuple products of degree zero. Given the coupling scheme of any quadruple product such as $(j_{12}j_{34})$, the corresponding scheme of quintuple product is $((j_{12}j_{34})j_5)$ which may be indicated simply by $(j_{12}j_{34}j_5)$, owing to the associative property of invariant triple products. To a quadruple product scheme $((j_{12}j_3)j_{123}j_4)$, there corresponds the scheme $([(j_{12}j_3)j_{123}j_4]j_5)$, which is equivalent to $((j_{12}j_3)(j_4j_5))$, i.e., $(j_{12}j_3j_{45})$.

Any quintuple product of degree zero may be described as the triple product of degree zero of two two-set products and of a single set. The different coupling schemes differ only in the pairing of the sets into the two-set products and in the ordering of the sets. Apart from reorderings, there are 15 coupling schemes, because two pairs of sets, e.g., 1, 2, and 4, 5, can be chosen out of five sets in 15 ways.

Apart again from reorderings, the transformations among the 15 coupling schemes of quintuple products of degree zero fall into three groups, typified by

$$(j_{12}j_{34}j_5|j_{12}j_3j_{45})^{(0)}, \tag{12.1}$$

$$(j_{12}j_{34}j_5|j_1j_{23}j_{45})^{(0)}, \tag{12.2}$$

$$(j_{12}j_{34}j_5|j_{13}j_{24}j_5)^{(0)}. \tag{12.3}$$

The transformations of type (12.1) leave the pairing of two sets, j_{12} in the example, unchanged. The pair of sets behaves as a single set and the transformation reduces to that of a quadruple product of degree zero or to the equivalent triple product transformation $(j_{34}j_5|j_3j_{45})^{(j_{12})}$.

The transformations of type (12.2) involve a recoupling of the two pairs and of the single set. They are products of two transformations of type (12.1), for example

$$\begin{aligned}(j_{12}j_{34}j_5|j_1j_{23}j_{45})^{(0)} &= (j_{12}j_{34}j_5|j_{12}j_3j_{45})^{(0)}\,(j_{12}j_3j_{45}|j_1j_{23}j_{45})^{(0)}\\ &= (j_{34}j_5|j_3j_{45})^{(j_{12})}\,(j_{12}j_3|j_1j_{23})^{(j_{45})}.\end{aligned} \tag{12.4}$$

The transformations of type (12.3) resolve only in products of three recouplings of triple products. Moreover the degree of the intermediate recouplings is not fixed by the j-numbers of the initial or final coupling but may take a number of values to be summed over in the multiplication of the triple product transformation matrices. The example (12.3) corresponds to a main recoupling transformation of quadruple products, namely $(j_{12}j_{34}|j_{13}j_{24})$. This transformation can be resolved in the form

$$(j_{12}j_{34}j_5|j_{13}j_{24}j_5)^{(0)} = \Sigma_{j_{45}}(j_{34}j_5|j_3j_{45})^{(j_{12})}\,(j_{12}j_3|j_{13}j_2)^{(j_{45})}\,(j_2j_{45}|j_{24}j_5)^{(j_{13})}, \quad (12.5)$$

which is equivalent to

$$(j_{12}j_{34}|j_{13}j_{24})^{(j)} = \Sigma_{j_{123}}(j_{12}j_{34}|j_{12}j_{123}j_4)^{(j)}\,(j_{12}j_3|j_{13}j_2)^{(j_{123})}\,(j_{13}j_{132}j_4|j_{13}j_{24})^{(j)}. \quad (12.6)$$

The transformation (12.6) can also be approached by resolving it into the product of two different reductions of the quadruple direct products, according to (9.1), namely

$$(j_{12}j_{34}|j_{13}j_{24})^{(j)} = \Sigma_{m_1m_2m_3m_4}(j_{12}j_{34}jm|m_1m_2m_3m_4)\,(m_1m_2m_3m_4|j_{13}j_{24}jm). \quad (12.8)$$

Each of the reduction transformations on the right of this equation factors out, according to (8.4), into three Wigner coefficients. Therefore the recoupling coefficient $(j_{12}j_{34}|j_{13}j_{24})^{(j)}$ can be expressed as a sum of products of six Wigner coefficients, like the recoupling of triple products is expressed by (11.1) in terms of four Wigner coefficients.

To bring out the symmetry of $(j_{12}j_{34}|j_{13}j_{24})^{(j)}$ one may replace here, as in Section 11, each Wigner coefficient with a $\overline{V}$ multiplied by a power of -1 and by a factor of the type $\sqrt{2a+1}$. Of the six factors $\sqrt{2a+1}$, two have $a=j$ and combine to yield $2j+1$, and this factor can be replaced by extending the sum in (12.8) over all values of m. The sum in (12.8) can also be extended formally over m_{12}, m_{34}, m_{13}, and m_{24} because all values of these parameters except $m_{12}=m_1+m_2$, etc., yield no contribution. The product of powers of -1 contributed by the six Wigner coefficients contains in the exponent: (a) a term $2(j_2+j_4+j_{24}+j_3+j_4+j_{34})$ which is an even number, owing to triangular conditions, and therefore drops out; (b) a term $-(m_{12}+m_{34}+m+m_{13}+m_{24}+m) = -4m$, which is also even and drops out; (c) two terms $(j_{12}+j_{34}+j)$ and $(j_{13}+j_{24}+j)$ which are removed according to (10.15) by reversing the signs of all m in the coefficients $\overline{V}(j_{12}j_{34}j;m_{12}m_{34}\text{-}m)$ and $\overline{V}(j_{13}j_{24}j;m_{13}m_{24}\text{-}m)$.

It follows from these considerations that (12.8) reduces to

$$(j_{12}j_{34}|j_{13}j_{24})^{(j)} = [(2j_{12}+1)\,(2j_{34}+1)\,(2j_{13}+1)\,(2j_{24}+1)]^{1/2} \times \quad (12.9)$$
$$\sum_{\text{all}\,m} \overline{V}\begin{pmatrix} j_1 & j_2 & j_{12} \\ m_1 & m_2 & -m_{12}\end{pmatrix} \overline{V}\begin{pmatrix} j_3 & j_4 & j_{34} \\ m_3 & m_4 & -m_{34}\end{pmatrix} \overline{V}\begin{pmatrix} j_{12} & j_{34} & j \\ -m_{12} & -m_{34} & m\end{pmatrix} \overline{V}\begin{pmatrix} j_1 & j_3 & j_{13} \\ m_1 & m_3 & -m_{13}\end{pmatrix} \times$$
$$\overline{V}\begin{pmatrix} j_2 & j_4 & j_{24} \\ m_2 & m_4 & -m_{24}\end{pmatrix} \overline{V}\begin{pmatrix} j_{13} & j_{24} & j \\ -m_{13} & -m_{24} & m\end{pmatrix}.$$

The sum in this formula is a function of the nine variables j_1, j_2, j_3, j_4, j_{12}, j_{34}, j_{13}, j_{24}, and j. This function will be indicated by

$$X\begin{pmatrix} a\,b\,c \\ d\,e\,f \\ g\,h\,k \end{pmatrix} = \sum_{\alpha\beta\gamma\delta\varepsilon\varphi\eta\theta\varkappa} \overline{V}\begin{pmatrix} a\,b\,c \\ \alpha\,\beta\,\gamma \end{pmatrix} \overline{V}\begin{pmatrix} d\,e\,f \\ \delta\,\varepsilon\,\varphi \end{pmatrix} \overline{V}\begin{pmatrix} g\,h\,k \\ \eta\,\theta\,\varkappa \end{pmatrix} \overline{V}\begin{pmatrix} a\,d\,g \\ \alpha\,\delta\,\eta \end{pmatrix} \overline{V}\begin{pmatrix} a\,d\,g \\ \beta\,\varepsilon\,\theta \end{pmatrix} \overline{V}\begin{pmatrix} c\,f\,k \\ \gamma\,\varphi\,\varkappa \end{pmatrix}, \tag{12.10}$$

which coincides with the Wigner 9-j-symbol‡. Each $\overline{V}$ contains one triad of j-numbers which constitutes one row or one column in the layout of the variables of X. The flattened layout $X(abc/def/ghk)$ may be utilized for typographical convenience.

In terms of the function X, the recoupling coefficient expression (12.9) becomes

$$(j_{12}j_{34}|j_{13}j_{24})^{(j)} = [(2j_{12}+1)\,(2j_{34}+1)\,(2j_{13}+1)\,(2j_{24}+1)]^{\frac{1}{2}}\, X\begin{pmatrix} j_1\;j_2\;j_{12} \\ j_3\;j_4\;j_{34} \\ j_{13}\,j_{24}\,j \end{pmatrix}. \tag{12.11}$$

The function X is invariant with respect to circular (even) permutations of its rows or columns, which is apparent from the corresponding invariance of $\overline{V}$. From the behavior of $\overline{V}$ under odd permutations, it follows that interchange of two rows or two columns multiplies X by $(-1)^{a+b+c+d+e+f+g+h+k}$. Interchange of the rows with the columns, i.e., transposition of the 3×3 pattern, leaves X unchanged.

The function X is calculated most conveniently as a sum of products of three $\overline{W}$. The necessary formula can be derived by combining (12.11) with (12.6) and (11.8) and is

$$X\begin{pmatrix} a & b & c \\ d & e & f \\ g & h & k \end{pmatrix} = \sum_r (-1)^{2r}\,(2r+1)\,\overline{W}\begin{pmatrix} a & b & c \\ f & k & r \end{pmatrix} \overline{W}\begin{pmatrix} d & e & f \\ b & r & h \end{pmatrix} \overline{W}\begin{pmatrix} g & h & k \\ r & a & d \end{pmatrix}. \tag{12.12}$$

The connection between (12.10) and (12.12) may also be established analytically by means of (11.18) and (11.19). Tables of X have been prepared by Sharp *et al.* (1953), Kennedy *et al.* (1954), Matsunobu and Takebe (1955), Smith and Stephenson (1957).

---

‡ The function (12.8) was first considered by Wigner (1937) and then independently in other unpublished reports (Fano, 1951; Hope, 1952; Schwinger, 1952). Systematic discussions were published by Jahn and Hope (1954) and by Arima, *et al.* (1954). The Wigner notation is abandoned here in favor of a regular function notation.

In analogy to the representation (11.11) of $\overline{W}$, one may seek a recoupling transformation which has the full symmetry of X. Inspection of (12.10), having in mind the connection of $\overline{V}$ with invariant triple products, shows that X coincides with a special type of recoupling coefficient for nine-set products of degree zero

$$X\begin{pmatrix} a & b & c \\ d & e & f \\ g & h & k \end{pmatrix} = ((abc)0,\ (def)0,\ (ghk)0 \mid (adg)0,\ (beh)0,\ (cfk)0). \tag{12.13}$$

The X function reduces to a single $\overline{W}$ when any one of its variables vanishes, because the recoupling corresponding to it reduces in effect to a triple product recoupling. The variable equal to zero can always be brought to the lower right corner by permutations of rows and columns and it is therefore sufficient to consider (12.10) for $k = 0$. Owing to (11.12) we have

$$X\begin{pmatrix} a & b & c \\ d & e & f \\ g & h & 0 \end{pmatrix} = \frac{(-1)^{b+c+d+g}\,\delta_{cf}\,\delta_{gh}}{\sqrt{(2c+1)\,(2g+1)}}\,\overline{W}\begin{pmatrix} a & b & c \\ e & d & g \end{pmatrix}. \tag{12.14}$$

Indeed, the $\overline{W}$ function appears often in applications as a special case of X.

Sum rules for the X coefficients, analogous to those of the $\overline{W}$, follow like (11.15) and (11.16) from the unitary character and the associative property of the recoupling transformations,

$$\sum_{gh}(2g+1)\,(2h+1)\,X\begin{pmatrix} a & b & c \\ d & e & f \\ g & h & k \end{pmatrix} X\begin{pmatrix} a & b & c' \\ d & e & f' \\ g & h & k \end{pmatrix} = \frac{\delta_{cc'}\,\delta_{ff'}\,\delta(a,b,c)\,\delta(d,e,f)\,\delta(c,f,k)}{(2c+1)\,(2f+1)}, \tag{12.15}$$

$$\sum_{gh}(2g+1)\,(2h+1)\,X\begin{pmatrix} a & b & c \\ d & e & f \\ g & h & k \end{pmatrix} X\begin{pmatrix} a & d & g \\ e & b & h \\ l & m & k \end{pmatrix} = X\begin{pmatrix} a & b & c \\ e & d & f \\ l & m & k \end{pmatrix}, \tag{12.16}$$

where $\delta(a,b,c)$ is given by (10.19).

PART II

QUANTUM MECHANICAL APPLICATIONS

Quantum mechanics is the field where multiple products of tensorial sets have been encountered most frequently, and which therefore has stimulated the development of recoupling transformations.

Multiple tensorial products occur in the analysis of atomic systems consisting of many particles, when each particle has a "good" — or approximately good — quantum number j. The states of the complete system are then conveniently represented in terms of products of one-particle states, each of which is an element of an irreducible set. The energy eigenstates of the complete system are usually eigenstates of the squared total angular momentum $\hbar^2 \mathbf{J}^2$, and therefore are irreducible products of irreducible sets of one-particle states. Transformations between states constructed according to different coupling schemes are required for the determination of antisymmetric states and of energy eigenstates. These applications will be reviewed in Section 13.

The multiplicity of products is enhanced by the circumstance that the quantum mechanical expression of interaction energies, transition probabilities, etc., involves products of two, or more, states (loosely speaking, a ψ^* usually appears besides a ψ). Therefore, even for single-particle systems, tensorial algebra may be applied for analyzing the matrices which represent operators A in a scheme of states with quantum numbers (jm). The matrix elements $(jm|A|j'm')$ depend on the orientation of a coordinate system through *two* magnetic quantum numbers, m and m' (corresponding respectively to ψ^* and ψ). A further dependence on the coordinate system, with a corresponding further increase of the multiplicity of products, arises when the operator itself belongs to a tensorial set of operators.

The recoupling transformations have proven particularly useful in the treatment of operator products, where they reduce a variety of seemingly unrelated problems to a few standard operations. Moreover, the technique of dealing with irreducible sets and with their products, rather than with individual set elements, eliminates summations over quantum numbers m and the irrelevant dependence of the formalism upon the orientation of coordinates.

Most of the applications have been concerned with problems that are easily formulated in terms of tensorial operators. The algebra of these operators is developed in Sections 14 and 15 and its immediate applications are reviewed in Sections 16 and 17.

The treatment of tensorial operators may be extended to other operators, in essence by expanding them into sums of tensorial operators (Section 18). This expansion has been applied to the analysis of angular correlations of nuclear radiations and of other directional distributions of nuclear or atomic radiations (Section 19).

In the applications the results are often expressed as sums over invariant products of the types considered in Section 6. Interactions of atomic systems are expanded into multipole interactions of different orders, directional distributions, and angular correlations into series of functions $\mathfrak{D}^{(j)}(\psi, \theta, \varphi)$. Because atomic systems and their constituents have, usually, low angular momenta, i.e., low values of the quantum numbers j, the series expansions reduce to a few terms of low degree, which makes the expansions particularly convenient.

The notations of transformation theory will be fully utilized in this second part. In particular the angular momentum eigenstates will be indicated by Dirac symbols $|\alpha jm)$ and $(\alpha jm|$ instead of $\mathfrak{u}^{[\alpha j]}{}_m$ and $\mathfrak{u}^{\dagger(\alpha j)}{}_m$. Sets of these eigenstates will be indicated by symbols $|\alpha j\}$ and $\{\alpha j|$ instead of $\mathbf{u}^{[\alpha j]}$ and $\mathbf{u}^{\dagger(\alpha j)}$.

13

Coupling and Recoupling of Atomic and Nuclear States

Two-particle eigenstates. The first application to atomic spectroscopy of the concept of irreducible products was the calculation of the so-called "zero-order eigenfunctions" of a two-electron system. This basic problem actually led Wigner to the calculation of his coefficients, and was the starting point of the whole subject of this book.

If we have a single particle in a spherically symmetric potential in a state characterized by a principal quantum number n and an azimuthal quantum number l, this state will be a superposition of eigenstates $|nlm)$, which are the elements of the irreducible contrastandard tensorial set $|nl\}$ of order $2l+1$.

If we have two particles in a spherically symmetric potential, one in a state with quantum numbers $(n_a l_a)$ and the other with quantum numbers $(n_b l_b)$, any state of the two-particle system will be a superposition of the states

$$|n_a l_a m_a)\,|n_b l_b m_b) = |n_a l_a m_a, n_b l_b m_b) \tag{13.1}$$

which are eigenstates of the operators $\mathbf{l}_1^2$, $\mathbf{l}_2^2$, l_{1z}, l_{2z}.

These eigenstates are the elements of a reducible tensorial set, which is the direct product of the irreducible sets $|n_a l_a\}$ and $|n_b l_b\}$.

If we want to classify the states of the system according to the eigenvalues of the total angular momentum, i.e., according to the eigenvalues of the operator $\mathbf{L}^2 = (\mathbf{l}_1 + \mathbf{l}_2)^2$, we have to replace the states (13.1) with the states

$$|n_a l_a n_b l_b LM) = \Sigma_{m_a m_b} |n_a l_a m_a)\,|n_b l_b m_b)\,(m_a m_b|LM), \tag{13.2}$$

which are the elements of the irreducible products

$$|n_a l_a n_b l_b L\} = [\,|n_a l_a\} \times |n_b l_b\}]^{[L]} \tag{13.3}$$

defined in Section 7.

Three-particle eigenstates. In the case of three particles the reduction of the set of eigenfunctions is not unique, because the reduction of the direct product $|n_a l_a\}\,|n_b l_b\}\,|n_c l_c\}$ depends on the choice of a particular coupling scheme. If the first two sets are coupled first, the eigenstates will be elements of the sets

$$|n_a l_a n_b l_b n_c l_c, L_{ab} L\} = [\,|n_a l_a n_b l_b L_{ab}\} \times |n_c l_c\}]^{[L]}, \tag{13.4}$$

if the last two sets are coupled first the eigenstates will be elements of the sets

$$|n_a l_a n_b l_b n_c l_c, L_{bc} L\} = [\,|n_a l_a\} \times |n_b l_b n_c l_c\, L_{bc}\}]^{[L]}. \tag{13.5}$$

The first set may also be coupled with the third one.

From the mathematical point of view the three coupling schemes are completely equivalent. The eigenstates of each scheme constitute a complete set of orthogonal states and the eigenstates of any one scheme may be expressed as linear superpositions of the eigenstates of another scheme. The unitary substitution which connects for example (13.4) and (13.5) has already been given in (11.8):

$$\begin{aligned}(n_a l_a n_b l_b n_c l_c, L_{ab} L | n_a l_a n_b l_b n_c l_c, L_{bc} L) \qquad (13.6)\\ = (-1)^{l_a+l_b+l_c+L} \sqrt{(2L_{ab}+1)(2L_{bc}+1)}\, \overline{W}\begin{pmatrix} l_a l_b L_{ab} \\ l_c L L_{bc} \end{pmatrix}.\end{aligned}$$

From the physical point of view the three coupling schemes are not equivalent, but describe different situations. States of a three-particle system, which are eigenstates of the energy, do not in general belong to any of these coupling schemes, because the matrix of the interaction energy between the particles is not diagonal in any of the three coupling schemes. However, if the interaction between the particles in the states a and b is much stronger than the interaction with the third one, the energy eigenstates will be very near to the states (13.4). This happens in general, *but not always*, when the particles in the states a and b are more tightly bound in the potential field than the particle in the state c, and constitute the "core" of the configuration. The state of the core to which the outer particle is added and which is characterized by the quantum number L_{ab} is called the *parent* of the state (13.4).

Eigenstates of a particle with spin. Another application of the concept of irreducible product is found in the problem of a spinning particle in a spherically symmetric potential. If we consider separately the spin orientation and the orbital motion, we take as a basis the eigenstates $|nlm_s m_l)$ of the operators $\mathbf{l}^2$, s_z, l_z, which are elements of the direct product of the set $|\frac{1}{2}\}$ of spin states and the set $|nl\}$ of orbital states. But if we want to classify these states according to the eigenvalues of the total angular momentum, we take as a basis the states

$$|nljm) = \Sigma_{m_s m_l} |nlm_s m_l)\,(m_s m_l|jm) \tag{13.7}$$

which are elements of the irreducible products

$$|nlj\} = [\,|\tfrac{1}{2}\} \times |nl\}]^{[j]}. \tag{13.8}$$

Eigenstates of two particles with spin. The situation is more complicated if we want to reduce the set of eigenstates of a system of two spinning particles. In this case we have to reduce the product of four irreducible sets and the reduction is not unique, but depends on the choice of a particular coupling scheme. To understand the properties of a given system not only analytically but also from the physical and geometrical point of view, it is convenient to choose a coupling scheme whose eigenstates are as near as possible to the eigenstates of the energy.

The Russell-Saunders, or LS-coupling scheme is the most familiar one. Its eigenstates are elements of the sets

$$|n_a l_a n_b l_b, SLJ\} = [[\,|\tfrac{1}{2}\} \times |\tfrac{1}{2}\}]^{[S]} \times [\,|n_a l_a\} \times |n_b l_b\}]^{[L]}]^{[J]}. \qquad (13.9)$$

They are eigenstates of $\mathbf{S}^2 = (\mathbf{s}_1+\mathbf{s}_2)^2$ and $\mathbf{L}^2 = (\mathbf{l}_1+\mathbf{l}_2)^2$ and approximate the eigenstates of the energy when the electrostatic interaction between the particles is much larger than the spin-orbit coupling of each particle.

When the spin-orbit coupling is stronger than the interaction between the particles, as happens in most of the nuclei and for the electrons of heavy atoms, the appropriate scheme is the jj-coupling scheme, whose eigenstates are characterized by the eigenvalues of $\mathbf{j}_1{}^2 = (\mathbf{s}_1+\mathbf{l}_1)^2$ and $\mathbf{j}_2{}^2 = (\mathbf{s}_2+\mathbf{l}_2)^2$. These eigenstates are elements of the sets

$$|n_a l_a j_a, n_b l_b j_b, J\} = [[\,|\tfrac{1}{2}\} \times |n_a l_a\}]^{[j_a]} \times [\,|\tfrac{1}{2}\} \times |n_b l_b\}]^{[j_b]}]^{[J]}. \qquad (13.10)$$

In the excited states of many two-electron atomic spectra one electron is tightly bound to the atom and another much more loosely. It may then happen that the electrostatic interaction between the two electrons is smaller than the spin-orbit coupling of the inner electron, but larger than that of the outer one. Then a good approximation to the energy eigenstates is given by the jl-coupling scheme, where the eigenstates are characterized by the eigenvalues of $\mathbf{j}_1{}^2 = (\mathbf{l}_1+\mathbf{s}_1)^2$ and $\mathbf{K}^2 = (\mathbf{j}_1+\mathbf{l}_2)^2$. These eigenstates are elements of the sets

$$|n_a l_a j_a, n_b l_b, KJ\} = \Big[[[\,|\tfrac{1}{2}\} \times |n_a l_a\}]^{[j_a]} \times |n_b l_b\}]^{[K]} \times |\tfrac{1}{2}\}\Big]^{[J]}. \qquad (13.11)$$

The transformations between these three coupling schemes are a good illustration of quadruple-product recoupling transformations considered in Section 12. The transformation from jj-coupling to jl-coupling is the simplest one, because j_a does not change, and we have actually as in (12.1) only a triple-product recoupling with the transformation matrix

$$\begin{aligned}(j_a j_b|j_a K) &= (j_a, (s_b l_b) j_b|(j_a l_b)K, s_b)^{(J)} \\ &= (-1)^{j_a+j_b+J} \sqrt{(2j_b+1)\,(2K+1)}\; \overline{W}\begin{pmatrix} \frac{1}{2} & l_b & j_b \\ j_a & J & K \end{pmatrix}. \end{aligned} \qquad (13.12)$$

The transformation from LS-coupling to jl-coupling, which is of the type (12.2), is the result of two triple-product recouplings,

$$(SL|j_aK) = ((s_as_b)S, L|(s_aL)K, s_b)^{(J)} (s_a, (l_al_b)L|(s_al_a)j_a, l_b)^{(K)}$$
$$= (-1)^{s_a+s_b+l_a+l_b+S+L+2K} \sqrt{(2j_a+1)(2L+1)(2S+1)(2K+1)} \times$$
$$\overline{W}\begin{pmatrix} \frac{1}{2} \, l_a \, j_a \\ l_b K L \end{pmatrix} \overline{W}\begin{pmatrix} S L J \\ K \frac{1}{2} \frac{1}{2} \end{pmatrix}. \tag{13.13}$$

The transformation from jj-coupling to LS-coupling is of the type (12.3), and according to (12.11) may be expressed by an X coefficient,

$$(j_aj_b|SL) = \sqrt{(2j_a+1)(2j_b+1)(2S+1)(2L+1)} \; X\begin{pmatrix} \frac{1}{2} \, l_a \, j_a \\ \frac{1}{2} \, l_b \, j_b \\ S L J \end{pmatrix}. \tag{13.14}$$

This transformation may also be considered as the result of a transformation from jj- to jl-coupling and a transformation for jl- to LS-coupling,

$$(j_aj_b|SL) = \Sigma_K (j_aj_b|j_aK)\,(j_aK|SL). \tag{13.15}$$

Substitution of (13.12) and (13.13) into (13.15) and comparison with (13.14) provides a physical example of (12.12), which gives the X coefficient as a sum of products of three $\overline{W}$-coefficients. The actual values of the X coefficient in (13.14) are fairly simple, because two of the parameters are equal to one half. Explicit expressions for the matrix elements (13.14) have been given by Racah (1950) and numerical values of these X coefficients for $j \leq 7/2$, and $L, J \leq 4$ have been calculated by Matsunobu and Takebe (1955).

Antisymmetrization. The eigenfunction of a system of two or more identical particles must have a well defined symmetry with respect to permutations of the coordinates. The Pauli principle requires the eigenfunctions of identical particles with spin $\frac{1}{2}$ to be antisymmetric with respect to permutations of the position and spin coordinates. We consider here the construction of such eigenfunctions.

The eigenfunctions represent the eigenstates in terms of the position and spin coordinates and are indicated by bracket symbols in the notation of transformation theory. We indicate all the coordinates of the nth particle by the numeral n. Sets of eigenfunctions corresponding to the sets of states (13.3) are then written, for example, in the form

$$(12|n_al_an_bl_bL\} = [(1|n_al_a\} \times (2|n_bl_b\}]^{[L]}. \tag{13.16}$$

Permutation of the particle coordinates in these eigenfunctions yields the alternative sets

$$(21|n_a l_a n_b l_b L\} = [(2|n_a l_a\} \times (1|n_b l_b\}]^{[L]}. \tag{13.17}$$

The symmetry property (7.11) of the irreducible product yields

$$[(2|n_a l_a\} \times (1|n_b l_b\}]^{[L]} = (-1)^{l_a+l_b-L} [(1|n_b l_b\} \times (2|n_a l_a\}]^{[L]}, \tag{13.18}$$

and therefore

$$(21|n_a l_a n_b l_b L\} = (-1)^{l_a+l_b-L} (12|n_b l_b n_a l_a L\} \tag{13.19}$$

In the particular case $(n_a l_a) = (n_b l_b)$, the eigenfunction on the right side of (13.19) coincides with (13.16) and therefore $(12|nl,nl,L\}$ is symmetric or antisymmetric according to the parity of $2l-L$, which is the same as the parity of L. In the general case $(n_a l_a) \neq (n_b l_b)$ the eigenfunction on the right side of (13.19) is different from, and actually orthogonal to, the eigenfunction (13.16), and neither of them has a definite symmetry. We may, however, construct symmetric or antisymmetric eigenfunctions, by taking a symmetric or antisymmetric combination of (13.16) and (13.19),

$$\frac{1}{\sqrt{2}} [(12|n_a l_a n_b l_b L\} \pm (21|n_a l_a n_b l_b L\}]$$
$$= \frac{1}{\sqrt{2}} [(12|n_a l_a n_b l_b L\} \pm (-1)^{l_a+l_b-L} (12|n_b l_b n_a l_a L\}], \tag{13.20}$$

where the factor $\frac{1}{\sqrt{2}}$ preserves the normalization.

We indicate sets of antisymmetric eigenfunctions with the notation $(12]\!] n_a l_a n_b l_b L\}$, and write

$$(12]\!] n_a l_a n_b l_b L\} = \frac{1}{\sqrt{2}} [(12|n_a l_a n_b l_b L\} - (21|n_a l_a n_b l_b L\}] \tag{13.21}$$

or

$$(12]\!] n_a l_a n_b l_b L\} = \frac{1}{\sqrt{2}} [(12|n_a l_a n_b l_b L\} - (-1)^{l_a+l_b-L} (12|n_b l_b n_a l_a L\}]. \tag{13.21$'$}$$

Notice that for $(n_a l_a) = (n_b l_b) = (nl)$ the right side of these equations would vanish for even L and would have the wrong normalization for odd L. In this case we must write instead

$$(12]\!](nl)^2 L\} = (12|(nl)^2 L\}, \qquad (L \text{ odd}); \tag{13.22}$$

$(12]\!](nl)^2 L\}$ does not exist for even L.

The equation

$$(12]\!]\, n_a l_a n_b l_b L\} = -(-1)^{l_a+l_b-L}(12]\!]\, n_b l_b n_a l_a L\} \tag{13.23}$$

holds independently of whether $(n_a l_a)$ coincides with $(n_b l_b)$.

Equations (13.21) and (13.22) are immediately extended to spinning electrons in any coupling scheme. In LS-coupling we have

$$(12]\!]\, n_a l_a n_b l_b, SLJ\} = \frac{1}{\sqrt{2}}[(12|n_a l_a n_b l_b, SLJ\} - (21|n_a l_a n_b l_b, SLJ\}] \tag{13.24}$$

or

$$(12]\!]\, n_a l_a n_b l_b, SLJ\} = \frac{1}{\sqrt{2}}[(12|n_a l_a n_b l_b, SLJ\} - (-1)^{s_a+s_b+l_a+l_b-S-L}(12|n_b l_b n_a l_a, SLJ\}] \tag{13.24'}$$

for $(n_a l_a) \neq (n_b l_b)$, and

$$(12]\!]\, (nl)^2\, SLJ\} = (12|(nl)^2 SLJ\} \qquad (L+S \text{ even}) \tag{13.25}$$

for $(n_a l_a) = (n_b l_b) = (nl)$. In jj-coupling we have

$$(12]\!]\, n_a l_a j_a, n_b l_b j_b, J\} = \frac{1}{\sqrt{2}}[(12|n_a l_a j_a, n_b l_b j_b, J\} - (21|n_a l_a j_a, n_b l_b j_b, J\}] \tag{13.26}$$

or

$$(12]\!]\, n_a l_a j_a, n_b l_b j_b, J\} = \frac{1}{\sqrt{2}}[(12|n_a l_a j_a, n_b l_b j_b, J\} - (-1)^{j_a+j_b-J}(12|n_b l_b j_b, n_a l_a j_a, J\}] \tag{13.26'}$$

for $(n_a l_a j_a) \neq (n_b l_b j_b)$, and

$$(12]\!]\, (nlj)^2 J\} = (12|(nlj)^2 J\} \qquad (J \text{ even}) \tag{13.27}$$

for $(n_a l_a j_a) = (n_b l_b j_b) = (nlj)$. In jl-coupling only the equation

$$(12]\!]\, n_a l_a j_a, n_b l_b, KJ\} = \frac{1}{\sqrt{2}}[(12|n_a l_a j_a, n_b l_b, KJ\} - (21|n_a l_a j_a, n_b l_b, KJ\}] \tag{13.28}$$

is important, because the analog of (13.21′) is not interesting and (13.22) has no analog, as jl-coupling does not exist for $(n_a l_a) = (n_b l_b)$.

The recoupling transformations (13.12) to (13.14) are not affected by the antisymmetrization for $(n_a l_a) \neq (n_b l_b)$, because the right sides of Eqs. (13.24), (13.26), and (13.28) are combinations of two terms, each of which undergoes the same recoupling transformations. For $(n_a l_a) = (n_b l_b)$ there is only the transformation $((nl)^2 SLJ|nlj_a, nlj_b, J)$ which connects (13.25) with (13.26) for $j_a \neq j_b$ and with (13.27) for $j_a = j_b$. The matrix elements of the transformation coincide again with those of (13.14) for $j_a = j_b$, but for $j_a \neq j_b$ the superposition of the matrix elements connecting (13.25) to the two terms of (13.26) yields the matrix element of (13.14) multiplied by $\sqrt{2}$.

Antisymmetrization of three-particle eigenfunctions. We discuss in detail the antisymmetrization of orbital eigenfunctions because the extension to particles with spin is almost immediate.

For nonequivalent particles, i.e., for $(n_a l_a) \neq (n_b l_b) \neq (n_c l_c)$, the analog of (13.21) is

$$(123]\!]\, n_a l_a n_b l_b n_c l_c, L_{ab} L\} = \frac{1}{\sqrt{6}}\Big((123|n_a l_a n_b l_b n_c l_c, L_{ab}L\} - (213|n_a l_a n_b l_b n_c l_c, L_{ab}L\} + (231|n_a l_a n_b l_b n_c l_c, L_{ab}L\} - (321|n_a l_a n_b l_b n_c l_c, L_{ab}L\} + (312|n_a l_a n_b l_b n_c l_c, L_{ab}L\} - (132|n_a l_a n_b l_b n_c l_c, L_{ab}L\}\Big), \tag{13.29}$$

or also, owing to (13.4) and (13.21),

$$(123]\!]\, n_a l_a n_b l_b n_c l_c, L_{ab} L\} = \frac{1}{\sqrt{3}}\Big([(12]\!]\, n_a l_a n_b l_b, L_{ab}\} \times (3|n_c l_c\}]^{[L]} + [(23]\!]\, n_a l_a n_b l_b, L_{ab}\} \times (1|n_c l_c\}]^{[L]} + [(31]\!]\, n_a l_a n_b l_b, L_{ab}\} \times (2|n_c l_c\}]^{[L]}\Big). \tag{13.30}$$

The analog of (13.21′) is much more complicated here because the permutation of the factors of the triple products involves a recoupling (13.6) instead of a simple reordering (13.19).

Similar antisymmetrized eigenfunctions can be constructed in coupling schemes with the j-numbers L_{bc} or L_{ac} instead of L_{ab}. The recoupling transformations between the different coupling schemes are the same as for non-antisymmetrized eigenfunctions.

When $(n_a l_a) = (n_b l_b)$ but is different from $(n_c l_c)$, the sets of antisymmetric normalized eigenfunction are still given by (13.30), with the understanding that the sets of two-particle eigenfunctions of degree L_{ab} are given by (13.22) instead of (13.21). Coupling schemes with the j-numbers L_{bc} or L_{ac} do not occur in this case.

For $(n_a l_a) = (n_b l_b) = (n_c l_c) = (nl)$ the three terms on the right side of (13.30) are no longer orthogonal, and therefore (13.30) is not normalized.

In order to construct normalized antisymmetric eigenfunctions we start from the set of eigenfunctions

$$[(12]\!\!](nl)^2L_0\} \times (3|nl\}]^{[L]} = [(12|(nl)^2L_0\} \times (3|nl\}]^{[L]} \quad (L_0 \text{ odd}), \tag{13.31}$$

which are antisymmetric only with respect to the first two particles, and apply to it an antisymmetrization operator A defined by

$$\begin{aligned} A[(12]\!\!](nl)^2L_0\} \times (3|nl\}]^{[L]} & \\ = \tfrac{1}{3}\Big([(12]\!\!](nl)^2L_0\} \times (3|nl\}]^{[L]} &+ [(23]\!\!](nl)^2L_0\} \times (1|nl\}]^{[L]} + \\ & [(31]\!\!](nl)^2L_0\} \times (2|nl\}]^{[L]}\Big). \end{aligned} \tag{13.32}$$

In order to normalize the function (13.32) we first reduce all three terms on the right side to the same coupling scheme as the first one. The second term is

$$\begin{aligned} [(23]\!\!](nl)^2L_0\} \times (1|nl\}]^{[L]} = \sum_{L'}(-1)^{L_0}\sqrt{(2L_0+1)(2L'+1)}\,\overline{W}\begin{pmatrix} l\ l\ L_0 \\ l\ L\ L' \end{pmatrix} \times & \\ [(12]\!\!](nl)^2L'\} \times (3|nl\}]^{[L]} & \end{aligned} \tag{13.33a}$$

and the third term is

$$\begin{aligned} [(31]\!\!](nl)^2L_0\} \times (2|n\}]^{[L]} = \sum_{L'}(-1)^{L'}\sqrt{(2L_0+1)(2L'+1)}\,\overline{W}\begin{pmatrix} l\ l\ L_0 \\ l\ L\ L' \end{pmatrix} \times & \\ [(12]\!\!](nl)^2L'\} \times (3|nl\}]^{[L]}. & \end{aligned} \tag{13.33b}$$

The contributions of these two terms are equal if $L'-L_0$ is even, and opposite if $L'-L_0$ is odd. Since L_0 is itself odd, the expansion of (13.32) contains only terms with L'odd, as it must. Introducing (13.33a) and (13.33b) into (13.32) we get

$$\begin{aligned} A[(12]\!\!](nl)^2L_0\} \times (3|nl\}]^{[L]} & \\ = \tfrac{1}{3}\sum_{L'\text{ odd}}\left[\delta_{L_0L'} - 2\sqrt{(2L_0+1)(2L'+1)}\,\overline{W}\begin{pmatrix} l\ l\ L_0 \\ l\ L\ L' \end{pmatrix}\right] \times & \\ [(12|(nl)^2L'\} \times (3|nl\}]^{[L]}. & \end{aligned} \tag{13.33}$$

This equation may also be written in the form

$$\begin{aligned} A[(12]\!\!](nl)^2L_0\} \times (3|nl)\}]^{[L]} & \\ = \Sigma_{L'}[(12]\!\!](nl)^2L'\} \times (3|nl\}]^{[L]}(L'|A(L)|L_0), & \end{aligned} \tag{13.34}$$

with

$$\begin{aligned} (L'|A(L)|L_0) &= (L_0|A(L)|L') \\ &= \tfrac{1}{3}\,\delta_{L'L_0} - \tfrac{2}{3}\sqrt{(2L_0+1)(2L'+1)}\,\overline{W}\begin{pmatrix} l\ l\ L' \\ l\ L\ L_0 \end{pmatrix} \qquad (L', L_0 \text{ odd}), \end{aligned} \tag{13.35}$$

and shows that the antisymmetric eigenfunctions are linear combinations of the eigenfunctions (13.31).

No antisymmetric eigenfunctions of three particles exist for those values of L for which every $(L'|A(L)|L_0)$ vanishes. (For example, this is always the case for $L = 3l-1$, $3l-2$, and $3l-4$; Weyl, 1931, p. 377). When these eigenfunctions exist, the (13.34) are still not normalized and have to be divided by $\sqrt{N_{L_0}(L)}$, where

$$N_{L_0}(L) = \Sigma_{L'}(L'|A(L)|L_0)^2. \tag{13.36}$$

This sum may be immediately carried out because (13.32) shows that the antisymmetrization operator A leaves invariant an eigenfunction which is already antisymmetric, and therefore satisfies the equation

$$A^2 = A. \tag{13.37}$$

Eq. (13.36) becomes now

$$N_{L_0}(L) = (L_0|A(L)|L_0), \tag{13.38}$$

and the eigenfunctions

$$(123]\!](nl)^3(L_0)L\} \tag{13.39}$$
$$= (L_0|A(L)|L_0)^{-\frac{1}{2}}\,\Sigma_{L'}[(12]\!](nl)^2L'\} \times (3|nl\}]^{[L]}(L'|A(L)|L_0)$$

are therefore normalized antisymmetric eigenfunctions of the configuration $(nl)^3$.

It should be emphasized that for different values of L_0 these eigenfunctions are not orthogonal or even linearly independent. In many cases states constructed from two-particle eigenfunctions with different L_0 are actually identical. This fact is easy to understand, because Eq. (13.37) shows that the operator A is a projection operator, i.e., an operator which transforms every eigenfunction into its orthogonal projection in the subspace of the antisymmetric eigenfunctions. It is then evident that by projecting into a subspace a complete set of orthogonal vectors of the whole space, we get a set of vectors which are linearly dependent.

The set of linearly dependent eigenfunctions (13.39) can be replaced with an orthogonal set by well known orthogonalization procedures of vector algebra. One needs only to know the projections of the eigenfunctions (13.39) on one another, which are

$$\frac{\Sigma_{L'}(L_0|A(L)|L')\,(L'|A(L)|L_0')}{\sqrt{(L_0|A(L)|L_0)\,(L_0'|A(L)|L_0')}} = \frac{(L_0|A(L)|L_0')}{\sqrt{(L_0|A(L)|L_0)\,(L_0'|A(L)|L_0')}}. \tag{13.40}$$

The orthogonal antisymmetric eigenfunctions are, in general, no longer characterized by quantum numbers L_0 but by different quantum numbers α.

A general antisymmetric eigenfunction has then the form

$$(123]\!]\,(nl)^3\alpha L\} = \Sigma_{L'}[(12]\!]\,(nl)^2L'\} \times (3|nl\}]^{[L]}(l^2L', l, L]\!]\,l^3\alpha L). \qquad (13.41)$$

Its coefficients obey the equation

$$\Sigma_{L'}(L_0|A(L)|L')\,(l^2L', l, L]\!]\,l^3\alpha L) = (l^2L_0, l, L]\!]\,l^3\alpha L) \qquad (13.42)$$

which identifies them as eigenvectors of the matrix A corresponding to the eigenvalue 1. Coefficients of an orthonormal set of eigenfunctions obey themselves the condition of orthonormalization

$$\Sigma_{L'}(l^3\alpha L[\![\,l^2L', l, L)\,(l^2L', l, L]\!]\,l^3\alpha' L) = \delta_{\alpha\alpha'}.$$

The states (13.31) have the well defined parent $(12|l^2L_0\}$ but are not antisymmetric, the states (13.39) and (13.41) are antisymmetric but have no well defined parent. Therefore the coefficients $(l^2L', l, L]\!]\,l^3\alpha L)$ of the expansion (13.41) are called "coefficients of fractional parentage."

The extension to antisymmetric eigenfunctions of r particles with the same quantum numbers (nl) is almost immediate. These eigenfunctions will be obtained by antisymmetrizing

$$[(12\ldots r-1]\!]\,(nl)^{r-1}\alpha_0L_0\} \times (r|nl\}]^{[L]} \qquad (13.43)$$

and will have a form analogous to (13.41)

$$(12\ldots r]\!]\,(nl)^r\alpha L\} \qquad (13.44)$$

$$= \Sigma_{\alpha' L'}[(12\ldots r-1]\!]\,(nl)^{r-1}\alpha' L'\} \times (r|nl\}]^{[L]}\,(l^{n-1}\alpha' L', lL]\!]\,l^n\alpha L)$$

The antisymmetrization operator is defined similarly to (13.32) by

$$A[(12\ldots r-1]\!]\,(nl)^{r-1}\alpha_0L_0\} \times (r|nl\}]^{[L]} \qquad (13.45)$$

$$= \frac{1}{r}\Big([(12\ldots r-1]\!]\,(nl)^{r-1}\alpha_0L_0\} \times (r|nl\}]^{[L]} -$$

$$\sum_{k}^{r-1}[(12\ldots k-1, r, k+1\ldots r-1]\!]\,(nl)^{r-1}\alpha_0L_0\} \times (k|nl\}]^{[L]}\Big)$$

and its matrix elements are (Redmond, 1954)

$$(\alpha' L' | A(L) | \alpha_0 L_0) = (\alpha_0 L_0 | A(L) | \alpha' L') \tag{13.46}$$

$$= \frac{1}{r}\,\delta_{\alpha'\alpha_0}\,\delta_{L'L_0} - \frac{r-1}{r}(-1)^{L'+L_0} \sum_{\alpha'' L''} \overline{W}\begin{pmatrix} l\,L''\,L' \\ l\,L\;\;L_0 \end{pmatrix} \times$$

$$(l^{r-1}\alpha' L' \{| l^{r-2}\alpha'' L'', l, L')\,(l^{r-2}\alpha'' L'', l, L_0 |\} l^{r-1}\alpha_0 L_0),$$

which is the extension of (13.35.)

The antisymmetrization of eigenfunctions of spinning particles, both in LS-coupling and in jj-coupling, and the introduction of the isotopic spin for nuclear states make the formulas more complicated, but do not introduce any new concept. These extensions will not be considered here.

14

Tensorial Sets of Operators. The Wigner-Eckart Theorem

The operators J_x, J_y, and J_z, which represent the components of the angular momentum in units of $\hbar$, constitute a tensorial set. The position coordinates of a particle, x, y, and z, are also represented in quantum mechanics by a tensorial set of operators. The most familiar sets of this kind are sets of order 3, i.e., vectorial sets. Examples of sets of higher order are the operators representing the electric quadrupole moment and higher multipoles of a system, and the components of second degree tensors which enter the representation of a nuclear tensor-force interaction $[3(\boldsymbol{\sigma}\cdot\mathbf{r})(\boldsymbol{\sigma}\cdot\mathbf{r})-(\boldsymbol{\sigma}\cdot\boldsymbol{\sigma})r^2]/r^2$.

Physical quantities are real and the operators that represent them are hermitian. This holds, for example, for the x, y, and z components of the angular momentum, which constitute a tensorial set, and for the corresponding set of operators J_x, J_y, J_z. However, a set of real physical quantities t_i may be replaced, through a complex linear substitution, with a set of complex quantities t_α. The same substitution replaces the hermitian operators T_i corresponding to the t_i with non-hermitian operators T_α. The transformation to complex conjugate quantities has been indicated in Section 4 by an operator K_0, such that $t_\alpha{}^* = K_0 t_\alpha$; the operator $T_\alpha^\dagger$, hermitian conjugate to T_α, which represents $t_\alpha{}^*$ will be accordingly indicated by $K_0 T_\alpha K_0{}^{-1}$ or by $(K_0 T_\alpha)$. The symbol $K_0{}^{-1}$ on the right of T_α or the notation $(K_0 T_\alpha)$ are introduced to indicate that K_0 does not operate on any quantity beyond, i.e., on the right of, T_α.

If the t_α and T_α constitute tensorial sets, we know that the sets $t_\alpha{}^* = K_0 t_\alpha$ and $T_\alpha^\dagger = (K_0 T_\alpha)$ are contragredient to them. The operation K_0 can also be combined with the unitary transformation U to yield the conjugation operation $K = K_0 U$ which changes the sets t_α and T_α into sets Kt_α and (KT_α) cogredient to t_α and T_α (see Section 4).

The vectors and tensors that are usually considered in atomic physics, like the angular momentum, the multipole moments of a system, etc., can be, and often are, represented by real components with real r-transformations. These sets of components are, therefore, self-conjugate, and will remain self-conjugate also under complex unitary substitutions. The sets of quantum mechanical operators which represent these quantities are self-conjugate too. Irreducible sets of these operators are of integral degree.

Following the practice which is usual in the treatment of tensorial sets of operators, we shall indicate the degree of the operator sets by k instead of j, and we shall consider sets that have been reduced to contrastandard form. Thus a generic tensorial set of operators will be indicated by $\mathfrak{T}^{[k]}$. A matrix element of an operator of this set, in a scheme of eigenstates with quantum numbers α, j, and m, will be indicated by

$$(\alpha jm|\mathfrak{T}^{[k]}{}_q|\alpha' j' m'). \tag{14.1}$$

We shall consider in particular, here and in the following sections, a class of tensorial sets of operators which has attracted most interest. Operators of this class have their matrix elements (14.1) *independent of the orientation* of coordinate axes to which all three sets $\{aj|$, $|\alpha' j'\}$, and $\mathfrak{T}^{[k]}$ are referred. These operators are functions of the position coordinates, velocities, and spin operators of the particles of the system. Their matrix elements are constant under coordinate rotations because they are determined by the very same calculation for any orientation of the coordinates. Operators that depend on a fixed direction of space, for example on the direction of an external magnetic field, do *not* belong to the class considered here. For example, the set of operators representing the components of the orbital angular momentum $\mathbf{l} = \mathbf{r} \times \mathbf{p}$ of a particle belongs to this class, whereas the set corresponding to the components of the Lorentz force $\mathbf{v} \times \mathbf{H}$ does not. The extent of this class of operator sets depends on the system being considered. For example, the operator $\mathbf{l}_1 \cdot \mathbf{l}_2$ belongs to this class, as the single element of a set of degree zero, if the eigenstates $|\alpha j\}$ are states of the system of both particles 1 and 2, but not if they are states of one particle only. The operator $-\gamma \mathbf{J} \cdot \mathbf{H}$ which represents the magnetic energy of an atom (γ = gyromagnetic ratio) is not ordinarily regarded as a scalar operator of this limited class, but would belong to it if the magnetic field were due to currents that are part of the system.

The tensorial sets of operators which are usually called vector or tensor operators (see e.g., Condon and Shortley, 1935; Wigner, 1931) are defined so as to belong to the special class considered here. In the following a tensorial set of operators $\mathfrak{T}^{[k]}$ will also be understood to belong to this class, unless otherwise noted.

Matrix elements (14.1) which are independent of coordinate orientation have a property known as the Wigner-Eckart theorem, namely, that the matrix elements with equal values of α, j, α', j', and k, but with different m, m', and q, bear fixed ratios to one another. These ratios depend on j, j' and on the degree k of the set of operators but do not depend on the nature of the operators or on the quantum numbers α, α'. To derive this theorem one may consider that, whereas on the one hand the matrix elements (14.1) are independent of the frame of reference, on the other hand they are linear functions of the eigenstates $(jm|$ and $|j'm')$ and of the operators $\mathfrak{T}^{[k]}{}_q$. From this point of view, the matrix elements with different m, m', and q constitute a tensorial set whose r-transformations coincide with those of a direct product $\mathfrak{a}^{(j)}\mathfrak{b}^{[j']}\mathfrak{c}^{[k]}$. Such a tensorial set, whose elements are actually invariant even though they have seemingly nontrivial r-transformations, may be called an isotropic set with reference to the definition of isotropic tensor (see Section 3).

The properties of an isotropic set of elements f_i are brought out by reducing the set as indicated by (5.8)

$$\mathfrak{g}^{(\beta J)}{}_M = \Sigma_i(\beta JM|i)f_i. \tag{14.2}$$

A rotation of the coordinate system leaves the f_i invariant and therefore should also leave invariant their linear combinations $\mathfrak{g}^{(\beta J)}{}_M$. On the other hand these combinations are elements of standard sets and have standard nontrivial r-transformations except for $J = 0$. These two requirements are consistent only if all $\mathfrak{g}^{(\beta J)}{}_M$ with $J \neq 0$ vanish and the elements of an isotropic tensorial set are linearly related by the homogeneous equations $\Sigma_i(\beta JM|i)f_i = 0$ for all $J \neq 0$. The inversion of the transformation (14.2), indicated by (5.9), reduces accordingly to

$$f_i = \Sigma_\beta(i|\beta 00)\,\mathfrak{g}^{(\beta 0)}{}_0. \tag{14.3}$$

The elements of an isotropic set are thereby expressed in terms of a limited number of invariants, as many invariants as there are columns of the matrix $(i|\beta JM)$ with $J = M = 0$.

The matrix $(i|\beta JM)$ which reduces the set of matrix elements (14.1) is the same which reduces the direct product $\mathfrak{a}^{(j)}\,\mathfrak{b}^{[j']}\mathfrak{c}^{[k]}$. It consists of the matrix $\mathfrak{U}^{(j)}$ which makes $\mathfrak{a}^{(j)}$ contrastandard, with elements $\mathfrak{a}^{[j]}{}_{-m} = (-1)^{j+m}\mathfrak{a}^{(j)}{}_m$, and then of a contrastandard transformation (8.4) for triple products, $(\beta JM|-mm'q)$. We know from Section 10 that this transformation has only one row with $J = M = 0$. Therefore no index β is needed here, and the expression corresponding to (14.3) contains only one invariant $\mathfrak{g}$. This invariant is called a *reduced matrix element* and is indicated by $(\alpha j||T^{[k]}||\alpha' j')$. The expression (14.3) of the $(2j+1)(2j'+1)(2k+1)$ matrix elements (14.1) with different m, m', and q is, then,

$$
\begin{aligned}
(\alpha jm|\mathfrak{T}^{[k]}_q|\alpha' j' m') &= (\alpha j||T^{[k]}||\alpha' j')\,(00|-mm'q)\,(-1)^{j+m} \\
&= (\alpha j||T^{[k]}||\alpha' j')\,\overline{V}\begin{pmatrix} j & j' & k \\ -m & m' & q \end{pmatrix}(-1)^{j-m} \qquad (14.4)\\
&= \frac{(\alpha j||T^{[k]}||\alpha' j')\,(j'kjm|j'm',kq)}{\sqrt{2j+1}}.
\end{aligned}
$$

Equations (10.11) and (10.13) have been utilized here, as well as the fact that $(-1)^{j-m} = (-1)^{j+m+2j'}$ because their product $(-1)^{2(j+j')}$ is always one. Equation (14.4) coincides with (29) of Racah (1942) when the connection (10.12) between $\overline{V}$ and V is taken into account. Notice that the matrix elements vanish unless $m = m'+q$ and unless k, j, and j' obey the triangular conditions (7.4).

The reduced matrix element $(\alpha j||T^{[k]}||\alpha' j')$ is given by (14.4) if one knows any particular matrix element $(\alpha jm|\mathfrak{T}^{[k]}_q|\alpha' j' m')$ with $m = m'+q$. In the special case of a scalar operator, $k = q = 0$, we have $(j'0jm|j'm',00) = \delta_{jj'}\,\delta_{mm'}$ and (14.4) reduces to

$$
(\alpha jm|\mathfrak{T}^{[0]}_0|\alpha' j' m') = (\alpha j||T^{[0]}||\alpha' j')\,\frac{\delta_{jj'}\,\delta_{mm'}}{\sqrt{2j+1}}, \qquad (14.5)
$$

which shows that the matrix element of a scalar operator must be diagonal in j and m and independent of m. (This property holds of course only for scalar operators of the special class considered here.)

The Wigner-Eckart theorem (14.4) also has the following application. The factor $\overline{V}(jj'k;-mm'q)$, which depends on m, m', and q, is the same for the matrices of all tensorial sets of operators of the same degree. That is, the matrix elements of any two sets of operators of the same degree are proportional to one another for different values of m, m', and q, with the proportionality factor expressed in terms of the reduced matrices. Thus we can write for two sets of operators $\mathfrak{T}^{[k]}$ and $\mathfrak{S}^{[k]}$

$$
(\alpha jm|\mathfrak{T}^{[k]}_q|\alpha' j' m') = \frac{(\alpha j||T^{[k]}||\alpha' j')}{(\beta j||S^{[k]}||\beta' j')}\,(\beta jm|\mathfrak{S}^{[k]}_q|\beta' j' m'). \qquad (14.6)
$$

This formula no longer contains the $\overline{V}$ coefficients and is convenient when one already knows the matrix of another operator $\mathfrak{S}^{[k]}_q$.

Calculation of the trace. The trace of an operator, that is, the sum of its diagonal elements, is an important quantity. Setting in (14.4) $m' = m$ and $j' = j$, the sum over m and j yields, owing to (10.21),

$$
Tr(\mathfrak{T}^{[k]}_q) = \delta_{k0}\,\Sigma_{\alpha j}\sqrt{2j+1}\,(\alpha j||\mathfrak{T}^{[k]}||\alpha j). \qquad (14.7)
$$

That is, the *trace* of operators belonging to tensorial sets *vanishes* except for operators of degree zero.

Conjugation property of reduced matrices. From the definition of conjugation of tensorial sets of operators, $(K\mathfrak{T})^{[k]} = \mathfrak{U}^{(k)}\mathfrak{T}^{[k]\dagger}$, it follows that

$$(\alpha jm|(K\mathfrak{T})^{[k]}_q|\alpha'j'm') = (-1)^{k-q}(\alpha jm|\mathfrak{T}^{[k]}{}_{-q}{}^{\dagger}|\alpha'j'm')$$
$$= (-1)^{k-q}(\alpha'j'm'|\mathfrak{T}^{[k]}{}_{-q}|\alpha jm)^*.$$

Expressing the ordinary matrix elements of this equation in terms of reduced matrix elements, and utilizing the symmetry of the $\overline{V}$, one finds

$$(\alpha j||(KT)^{[k]}||\alpha'j') = (-1)^{j-j'-k}(\alpha'j'||T^{[k]}||\alpha j)^*. \tag{14.8}$$

This equation shows that the diagonal elements of the reduced matrix of self-conjugate tensorial operator sets, for which $(K\mathfrak{T})^{[k]} = \mathfrak{T}^{[k]}$, are either real or imaginary, depending on whether k is even or odd.‡

Examples. The reduced matrices of a few sets of tensorial operators, pertaining to typical atomic systems, will be calculated here for purpose of illustration and later application.

The operator J_z has the matrix elements $(\alpha jm|J_z|\alpha'j'm') = m\delta_{\alpha\alpha'}\delta_{jj'}\delta_{mm'}$. Considering that the standardized operator $\mathfrak{J}^{[1]}_0$ equals iJ_z, and that, for $m = j$, we have $\overline{V}(jj1; -jj0) = [2j/(2j+1)(2j+2)]^{\frac{1}{2}}$, Eq. (14.4) yields

$$(\alpha j||J^{[1]}||\alpha'j') = i\sqrt{j(j+1)(2j+1)}\,\delta_{\alpha\alpha'}\delta_{jj'}. \tag{14.9}$$

Consider next the set of operators $\mathfrak{C}^{[k]}(\theta,\varphi)$ defined in (5.19), operating on the eigenfunctions $\mathfrak{Y}^{[l]}(\theta,\varphi)$ of a quantum mechanical rotator. Its matrix elements are

$$(lm|\mathfrak{C}^{[k]}_q|l'm') = \int_0^{\pi}\sin\theta\,d\theta\int_0^{2\pi}d\varphi\,\mathfrak{Y}^{[l]}{}_m{}^*(\theta\varphi)\,\mathfrak{C}^{[k]}_q(\theta\varphi)\,\mathfrak{Y}^{[l']}{}_{m'}(\theta\varphi). \tag{14.10}$$

This integral is given in terms of $\overline{V}$ coefficients by expressing the $\mathfrak{C}$ and $\mathfrak{Y}$ in terms of the functions $\mathfrak{D}^{(j)}$ by means of (5.18) and (5.19), and then applying (G.1). The matrix element (14.10) is thus shown to be equal to

‡ The definition of self-conjugate set of tensorial operators differs from the corresponding definition of "hermitian tensor operator" given in Eq. (25) of Racah (1942) by a factor $(-1)^k$ which derives from the phase standardization given in (5.12). Accordingly, (14.8) differs from the corresponding Eq. (31′) of the same paper.

$$i^{k+l'-l}\frac{\sqrt{(2l+1)(2l'+1)}}{4\pi}\frac{4\pi}{2l+1}(k0l'0|kl'l0)(kl'lm|kql'm')$$
$$= i^{k+l'+l}\sqrt{(2l+1)(2l'+1)}(-1)^{l-m}\,\overline{V}\begin{pmatrix}k & l' & l\\ 0 & 0 & 0\end{pmatrix}\overline{V}\begin{pmatrix}k & l' & l\\ q & m' & -m\end{pmatrix}. \qquad (14.11)$$

Comparison with (14.4) yields

$$(l||C^{[k]}||l') = (-1)^{\frac{1}{2}(l+l'+k)}\sqrt{(2l+1)(2l'+1)}\,\overline{V}\begin{pmatrix}l & l' & k\\ 0 & 0 & 0\end{pmatrix}, \qquad (14.12)$$

where the $\overline{V}$ is given by (10.16) and vanishes unless $l+l'+k$ is even; therefore the exponent of -1 is an integer.‡

The multipole moments of the density of a particle moving in a central field are easily expressed in terms of (14.12). Representing the eigenfunctions by $rR_{\alpha l}(r)\mathfrak{Y}^{[l]}(\theta,\varphi)$ and the 2^k-pole moment operator by $\mathfrak{M}^{[k]} = r^k\,\mathfrak{C}^{[k]}(\theta,\varphi)$, as in (6.14), we have §

$$(\alpha l||M^{[k]}||\alpha' l') = (l||C^{[k]}||l')\int_0^\infty r^k R_{\alpha l}^*(r)\,R_{\alpha' l'}(r)\,dr. \qquad (14.13)$$

The electric potential generated in the middle of an atom by an orbital electron may be characterized by sets of operators $\mathfrak{N}^{[k]}$ analogous to the $\mathfrak{A}^{[l]}$ of (6.13), whose reduced matrix elements are

$$(\alpha l||N^{[k]}||\alpha' l') = (l||C^{[k]}||l')\int_0^\infty r^{-(k+1)}\,R_{\alpha l}^*(r)\,R_{\alpha' l'}(r)\,dr. \qquad (14.14)$$

Operator representation in terms of reduced matrices. For a system with eigenstates $|\alpha jm)$, the reduced matrix elements of a set of tensorial operators characterize the set completely. The operators themselves can be expressed in terms of their reduced matrix and of the sets of eigenstates $|\alpha j\}$ and $\{\alpha' j'|$. This representation derives from the transformation theory formula

$$F = \Sigma_{ab}\,|a)\,(a|F|b)\,(b|, \qquad (14.15)$$

‡ Equation (14.11) differs from the corresponding Eq. (51) of Racah (1942) by a factor $(-1)^l$ because of the standardization conventions (5.18) and (5.19).

§ The numerical values of the electric and magnetic multipole moments $M^{[k]}$ of a nucleus or atom are usually given in the literature with the understanding that they represent the diagonal matrix elements $(\alpha jj|i^{-k}\mathfrak{M}^{[k]}|\alpha jj)$ and thus differ from the reduced matrix elements $(\alpha j||M^{[k]}||\alpha j)$ by a factor $i^k\,\overline{V}(jjk;-jj0) = i^{4j-k}(2j)!\,/\,\sqrt{(2j-k)!\,(2j+k+1)!}$.

which expresses an operator F in terms of its matrix and of state representatives $|a)$ and $(b|$, and which reads in our case

$$\mathfrak{T}^{[k]}_q = \sum_{\alpha j m \alpha' j' m'} |\alpha j m)\,(\alpha j m|\mathfrak{T}^{[k]}_q|\alpha' j' m')\,(\alpha' j' m'| \tag{14.16}$$

$$= \sum_{\alpha j \alpha' j'} (\alpha j||T^{[k]}||\alpha' j') \sum_{mm'} \overline{V}\begin{pmatrix} j & j' & k \\ -m & m' & q \end{pmatrix} (-1)^{j-m}\,|\alpha j m)\,(\alpha' j' m'|.$$

The expression $\Sigma_{mm'}\ldots$ can be recognized as an element of an irreducible product‡ of the sets $|\alpha j\}$ and $\{\alpha' j'|$, owing to the connection (10.13) between $\overline{V}$ and Wigner coefficients and to the symmetry of the $\overline{V}$. One finds

$$\mathfrak{T}^{[k]} = \sum_{\alpha j \alpha' j'} \frac{(-1)^{2j}}{\sqrt{2k+1}} (\alpha j||T^{[k]}||\alpha' j')\,[|\alpha j\} \times \mathfrak{U}^{(j')}\{\alpha' j'|)]^{[k]}$$

$$= \sum_{\alpha j \alpha' j'} \frac{(\alpha j||T^{[k]}||\alpha' j')}{\sqrt{2k+1}}\,[|\alpha j\} \times \widetilde{\mathfrak{U}}^{(j')}\{\alpha' j'|]^{[k]}. \tag{14.17}$$

‡ Notice that the product $|\alpha j m)\,(\alpha' j' m'|$ is an operator, whereas $(\alpha' j' m'||\alpha j m)$ is a number, namely $\delta_{\alpha\alpha'}\,\delta_{jj'}\,\delta_{mm'}$.

15

Products of Tensorial Sets of Operators

Because each tensorial set of operators is fully identified by its reduced matrix, the algebra of tensorial operators can be formulated in terms of their reduced matrices. The first and main problem of this kind is to relate the reduced matrix of an irreducible product of operator sets to the reduced matrices of the separate sets.

Each operator set is expressed according to (14.17) as a linear combination of products of two eigenstates. A product of two operator sets contains then quadruple products of eigenstates and its reduced matrix is obtained by recoupling the eigenstates. Two cases must be treated separately depending on whether the operators to be multiplied operate on different systems or on the same system. The difference between these cases is apparent in the formation of the product of two operators S_α and T_β. For operators of different systems, $S_\alpha T_\beta$ is represented by a matrix which is the direct (Kronecker) product of the matrices of S_α and T_β. For operators of the same system the matrix of $S_\alpha T_\beta$ is obtained by matrix multiplication of the matrices of S_α and T_β.

Consider first two tensorial sets of operators $\mathfrak{S}^{[k_1]}$ and $\mathfrak{T}^{[k_2]}$ operating on different systems with sets of eigenstates $|\alpha_1 j_1\}$ and $|\alpha_2 j_2\}$. If $\mathfrak{S}^{[k_1]}$ and $\mathfrak{T}^{[k_2]}$ are expressed according to (14.17) their irreducible product takes the form

$$[\mathfrak{S}^{[k_1]} \times \mathfrak{T}^{[k_2]}]^{[k]} = \sum_{\text{all } \alpha \text{ and } j} \frac{(\alpha_1 j_1 \| S^{[k_1]} \| \alpha_1' j_1')}{\sqrt{2k_1+1}} \frac{(\alpha_2 j_2 \| T^{[k_2]} \| \alpha_2' j_2')}{\sqrt{2k_2+1}} \times$$
$$[[|\alpha_1 j_1\} \times \tilde{\mathfrak{U}}^{(j_1')}\{\alpha_1' j_1'|]^{[k_1]} \times [|\alpha_2 j_2\} \times \tilde{\mathfrak{U}}^{(j_2')}\{\alpha_2' j_2'|]^{[k_2]}]^{[k]}. \tag{15.1}$$

The reduced matrix of the product set of operators is defined in a scheme of eigenstates of the combined system, which are represented by $[|\alpha_1 j_1\} \times |\alpha_2 j_2\}]^{[j]}$ as in Section 13. To express (15.1) in terms of these states, the quadruple product must be recoupled, that is, expanded in the form

$$\Sigma_{jj'} (k_1 k_2 | jj')^{(k)} [[|\alpha_1 j_1\} \times |\alpha_2 j_2\}]^{[j]} \times \tilde{\mathfrak{U}}^{(j')} [\{\alpha_1' j_1'| \times \{\alpha_2' j_2'|]^{(j')}]^{[k]}. \tag{15.2}$$

This expansion brings (15.1) to the required form

$$[\mathfrak{S}^{[k_1]} \times \mathfrak{T}^{[k_2]}]^{[k]}$$
$$= \sum_{\text{all } \alpha \text{ and } j} \frac{(\alpha_1 j_1 \alpha_2 j_2 j || [\mathfrak{S}^{[k_1]} \times \mathfrak{T}^{[k_2]}]^{[k]} || \alpha_1' j_1' \alpha_2' j_2' j')}{\sqrt{2k+1}} \times$$
$$[[|\alpha_1 j_1\} \times |\alpha_2 j_2\}]^{[j]} \times \widetilde{\mathfrak{U}}^{(j')} [\{\alpha_1' j_1'| \times \{\alpha_2' j_2'|]^{(j')}]^{[k]}, \tag{15.3}$$

where

$$(\alpha_1 j_1 \alpha_2 j_2 j || [\mathfrak{S}^{[k_1]} \times \mathfrak{T}^{[k_2]}]^{[k]} || \alpha_1' j_1' \alpha_2' j_2' j')$$
$$= (\alpha_1 j_1 || S^{[k_1]} || \alpha_1' j_1') (\alpha_2 j_2 || T^{[k_2]} || \alpha_2' j_2') \left[\frac{2k+1}{(2k_1+1)(2k_2+1)}\right]^{\frac{1}{2}} (k_1 k_2 | j j')^{[k]}$$
$$= (\alpha_1 j_1 || S^{[k_1]} || \alpha_1' j_1') (\alpha_2 j_2 || T^{[k_2]} || \alpha_2' j_2') \times$$
$$\sqrt{(2j+1)(2j'+1)(2k+1)}\; X \begin{pmatrix} j_1 & j_1' & k_1 \\ j_2 & j_2' & k_2 \\ j & j' & k \end{pmatrix} \tag{15.4}$$

owing to (12.11).

Two special cases of (15.4) are of interest for the problems of the following sections. One of them is the scalar product which is proportional to the irreducible product of degree zero,

$$\mathfrak{S}^{[k]}.\mathfrak{T}^{[k]} = \sqrt{2k+1}\, [\mathfrak{S}^{[k]} \times \mathfrak{T}^{[k]}]^{[0]}. \tag{15.5}$$

Its matrix elements are diagonal in j and are obtained by replacing in (15.4) k with 0, and k_1 and k_2 with k. Application of (12.14) and of (14.5), gives the matrix of $\mathfrak{S}^{[k]}.\mathfrak{T}^{[k]}$ in the form

$$(\alpha_1 j_1 \alpha_2 j_2 j m | \mathfrak{S}^{[k]}.\mathfrak{T}^{[k]} | \alpha_1' j_1' \alpha_2' j_2' j' m') \tag{15.6}$$
$$= (-1)^{j_1'+j_2+j+k} (\alpha_1 j_1 || S^{[k]} || \alpha_1' j_1') (\alpha_2 j_2 || T^{[k]} || \alpha_2' j_2')\, \overline{W} \begin{pmatrix} j_1 & j_1' & k \\ j_2' & j_2 & j \end{pmatrix} \delta_{jj'} \delta_{mm'}.$$

The other special case is that where one of the operator sets, say $\mathfrak{T}^{[k_2]}$, consists simply of the unit operator 1. Here the operation (15.4) amounts to transforming the reduced matrix of $\mathfrak{S}^{[k_1]}$ from the scheme of eigenstates $|\alpha_1 j_1\}$ to the scheme of combined eigenstates $[|\alpha_1 j_1\} \times |\alpha_2 j_2\}]^{[j]}$. We take in (15.4) $k_2 = 0$, $k_1 = k$, $[\mathfrak{S}^{[k]} \times 1]^{[k]} = \mathfrak{S}^{[k]}$. From (14.5) we find $(\alpha_2 j_2 || 1 || \alpha_2' j_2') = \sqrt{2j_2+1}\, \delta_{\alpha_2 \alpha_2'} \delta_{j_2 j_2'}$, and from (12.14) the X with one argument equal to zero, so that

$$(\alpha_1 j_1 \alpha_2 j_2 j || S^{[k]} || \alpha_1' j_1' \alpha_2 j_2 j') \tag{15.7}$$
$$= (-1)^{j_1+j_2+j'+k} (\alpha_1 j_1 || S^{[k]} || \alpha_1' j_1') \sqrt{(2j+1)(2j'+1)}\; \overline{W} \begin{pmatrix} j & j' & k \\ j_1' & j_1 & j_2 \end{pmatrix}.$$

The reduced matrix of $\mathfrak{T}^{[k_2]}$ is transformed by the analogous formula

$$(\alpha_1 j_1 \alpha_2 j_2 j||T^{[k]}||\alpha_1 j_1 \alpha_2' j_2' j') \tag{15.7'}$$

$$= (-1)^{j_1+j_2'+j+k}(\alpha_2 j_2||T^{[k]}||\alpha_2' j_2')\sqrt{(2j+1)(2j'+1)}\;\overline{W}\begin{pmatrix} j & j' & k \\ j_2' & j_2 & j_1 \end{pmatrix}.$$

The phase factors in the two formulas differ for off-diagonal elements, because the symmetry between the systems 1 and 2 in (15.4) is vitiated by the asymmetry of the factors in the products of eigenstates.

Consider now a product of two operator sets pertaining to the same system. This product can be expressed as in (15.1) except that there is only one kind of eigenstates $|\alpha j\}$ instead of $|\alpha_1 j_1\}$ and $|\alpha_2 j_2\}$,

$$[\mathfrak{S}^{[k_1]} \times \mathfrak{T}^{[k_2]}]^{[k]} = \sum_{\text{all } \alpha \text{ and } j} \frac{(\alpha j||T^{[k_1]}||\alpha'' j'')(\alpha''' j'''||S^{[k_2]}||\alpha' j')}{\sqrt{(2k_1+1)(2k_2+1)}} \times$$

$$[[|\alpha j\} \times \tilde{\mathfrak{U}}^{(j'')}\{\alpha'' j''|]^{[k_1]} \times [|\alpha''' j'''\} \times \mathfrak{U}^{(j''')}\{\alpha' j'|]^{[k_2]}]^{[k]}. \tag{15.8}$$

In the recoupling of the quadruple product in (15.8) one must take into account the orthogonality of the eigenstates

$$(\alpha'' j'' m''||\alpha''' j''' m''') = \delta_{\alpha''\alpha'''}\,\delta_{j''j'''}\,\delta_{m''m'''}, \tag{15.9}$$

from which follows

$$[\mathfrak{U}^{(j'')}\{\alpha'' j''| \times |\alpha''' j'''\}]^{[K]} = \sqrt{2j''+1}\;\delta_{\alpha''\alpha'''}\,\delta_{j''j'''}\,\delta_{K0}. \tag{15.10}$$

Therefore it is appropriate to transform the quadruple product to a coupling scheme in which the second and third factor are multiplied together, and the first with the fourth. We have then,

$$[[|\alpha j\} \times \tilde{\mathfrak{U}}^{(j'')}\{\alpha'' j''|]^{[k_1]} \times [|\alpha''' j'''\} \times \tilde{\mathfrak{U}}^{(j')}\{\alpha' j'|]^{[k_2]}]^{[k]}$$

$$= ((jj'')k_1, (j'''j')k_2|(jj')k, (j''j''')0)^{(k)}\,(-1)^{2j''}\,[|\alpha j\} \times \tilde{\mathfrak{U}}^{(j')}\{\alpha' j'|]^{[k]} \times$$

$$\sqrt{2j''+1}\;\delta_{\alpha''\alpha'''}\,\delta_{j''j'''}. \tag{15.11}$$

The recoupling coefficient in this equation is of the type (12.11), which gives

$$(k_1 k_2|k0)^{(k)} = (-1)^{j''+j'-k_2}\sqrt{(2k_1+1)(2k_2+1)(2k+1)}\;X\begin{pmatrix} j & j'' & k_1 \\ j' & j'' & k_2 \\ k & 0 & k \end{pmatrix}. \tag{15.12}$$

Application of (12.14) reduces this equation to

$$(k_1 k_2|k0)^{(k)} = (-1)^{j-j'+k}\sqrt{\frac{(2k_1+1)(2k_2+1)}{(2j''+1)}}\,\overline{W}\begin{pmatrix} j & j' & k \\ k_2 & k_1 & j'' \end{pmatrix}. \qquad (15.13)$$

Substituting (15.11) and (15.13) into (15.8) yields

$$[\mathfrak{S}^{[k_1]} \times \mathfrak{T}^{[k_2]}]^{[k]} = \sum_{\text{all } \alpha \text{ and } j} (-1)^{j+j'+k}\,\overline{W}\begin{pmatrix} j & j' & k \\ k_2 & k_1 & j'' \end{pmatrix} \times$$

$$(\alpha j||S^{[k_1]}||\alpha''j'')\,(\alpha''j''||T^{[k_2]}||\alpha'j')\,[|\alpha j\} \times \mathfrak{U}^{(j')}\{\alpha'j'|]^{[k]}. \qquad (15.14)$$

Comparison with (14.17) gives finally

$$(\alpha j||[\mathfrak{S}^{[k_1]} \times \mathfrak{T}^{[k_2]}]^{[k]}||\alpha'j') = (-1)^{j+j'+k}\sqrt{2k+1}\,\times$$

$$\sum_{\alpha''j''} (\alpha j||S^{[k_1]}||\alpha''j'')\,(\alpha''j''||T^{[k_2]}||\alpha'j')\,\overline{W}\begin{pmatrix} j & j' & k \\ k_2 & k_1 & j'' \end{pmatrix}. \qquad (15.15)$$

For the scalar product (15.5), $\overline{W}$ reduces to the simple expression (11.12) and the analog of (15.6) is

$$(\alpha jm|\mathfrak{S}^{[k]}.\mathfrak{T}^{[k]}|\alpha'j'm')$$

$$= \sum_{\alpha''j''} \frac{(-1)^{j-j''-k}}{2j+1}\,(\alpha j||S^{[k]}||\alpha''j'')\,(\alpha''j''||T^{[k]}||\alpha'j')\,\delta_{jj'}\,\delta_{mm'}$$

$$= \sum_{\alpha''j''} \frac{1}{2j+1}\,(\alpha''j''||(KS)^{[k]}||\alpha j)^*\,(\alpha''j''||T^{[k]}||\alpha'j')\,\delta_{jj'}\,\delta_{mm'}. \qquad (15.16)$$

16

Interaction Energy of Coupled Systems

The results of the last section, particularly (15.6) and also (15.7), have been derived originally for the purpose of calculating the interaction energy between atomic systems coupled with one another with a constant total angular momentum. Equation (15.6) applies whenever the interaction of two such systems can be represented as the scalar product of irreducible sets of operators, each operating on one system only, or as a sum of such products (see end of Section 6).

In special cases of practical importance, the $\overline{W}$ function of (15.6) reduces to very simple form, and the desired result can be obtained by well-known elementary procedures, without resorting to the method of Section 15. In other cases of intermediate complication the results have also been obtained prior to the development of tensorial techniques by elementary but laborious procedures. Still more complicated problems have been solved first with the method of Section 15. The situation is illustrated by the following familiar examples.

(a) The *spin-orbit interaction* of a particle depends on the scalar product of the magnetic moments of its spin and orbital motions, and may be expressed as $\zeta(\mathbf{s}\cdot\mathbf{l})$. Here $\mathbf{s}$ and $\mathbf{l}$ are the angular momenta of the spin and orbit and ζ is a factor, irrelevant for our purpose, which includes the gyromagnetic ratios of the two motions and an integral over radial eigenfunctions. For this simple coupling the value of the interaction energy is provided by the elementary formula

$$\zeta(sljm|\mathbf{s}\cdot\mathbf{l}|sljm) = \tfrac{1}{2}\zeta[j(j+1) - l(l+1) - s(s+1)], \tag{16.1}$$

which is an application of the identity $2\,\mathbf{s}\cdot\mathbf{l} = |\mathbf{s}+\mathbf{l}|^2 - \mathbf{s}^2 - \mathbf{l}^2$. This result is given by (15.6), since $\mathbf{s}\cdot\mathbf{l} = \mathfrak{s}^{[1]}\cdot\mathfrak{l}^{[1]}$, in the form

$$\zeta(-1)^{s+l+j+1}(s||s^{[1]}||s)\,(l||l^{[1]}||l)\,\overline{W}\begin{pmatrix} s & s & 1 \\ l & l & j \end{pmatrix}. \tag{16.2}$$

The reduced matrix elements in this formula are given by (14.9); considering also that $s = \frac{1}{2}$, (16.2) becomes

$$\zeta(-1)^{\frac{1}{2}+l+j}[\tfrac{3}{2}l(l+1)\,(2l+1)]^{\frac{1}{2}}\,\overline{W}\begin{pmatrix} \frac{1}{2} & \frac{1}{2} & 1 \\ l & l & j \end{pmatrix}. \tag{16.3}$$

In a two-particle system the spin-orbit interaction is $\zeta_1(\mathbf{s}_1\cdot\mathbf{l}_1)+\zeta_2(\mathbf{s}_2\cdot\mathbf{l}_2)$. The matrix of this interaction is not diagonal in the LS-coupling scheme and a formula analogous to (16.1) exists in this case only for the diagonal elements. All matrix elements, diagonal and non-diagonal, are instead given by (15.6) in a form analogous to (16.2)

$$(s_1l_1s_2l_2SLJM|\mathbf{s}_1\cdot\mathbf{l}_1|s_1l_1s_2l_2S'L'JM) \tag{16.4}$$
$$= (-1)^{S'+L+J+1}(s_1s_2S||s_1^{[1]}||s_1s_2S')\,(l_1l_2L||l_1^{[1]}||l_1l_2L')\,\overline{W}\begin{pmatrix} S & S' & 1 \\ L' & L & J \end{pmatrix}.$$

The reduced matrix elements in this formula may be obtained from (15.7),

$$(s_1s_2S||s_1^{[1]}||s_1s_2S')$$
$$= (-1)^{s_1+s_2+S'+1}(s_1||s_1^{[1]}||s_1)\sqrt{(2S+1)(2S'+1)}\,\overline{W}\begin{pmatrix} S & S' & 1 \\ s_1 & s_1 & s_2 \end{pmatrix}, \tag{16.5a}$$

$$(l_1l_2L||l_1^{[1]}||l_1l_2L')$$
$$= (-1)^{l_1+l_2+L'+1}(l_1||l_1^{[1]}||l_1)\sqrt{(2L+1)(2L'+1)}\,\overline{W}\begin{pmatrix} L & L' & 1 \\ l_1 & l_1 & l_2 \end{pmatrix}. \tag{16.5b}$$

Introducing (14.9) and (16.5) into (16.4), and eliminating from the exponent of (-1) terms that are obviously even, we get

$$(\tfrac{1}{2}l_1\tfrac{1}{2}l_2SLJM|\mathbf{s}_1\cdot\mathbf{l}_1|\tfrac{1}{2}l_1\tfrac{1}{2}l_2S'L'JM) \tag{16.6}$$
$$= (-1)^{l_1+l_2+L+L'+J+1}[\tfrac{3}{2}l_1(l_1+1)(2l_1+1)(2S+1)(2S'+1)\times$$
$$(2L+1)(2L'+1)]^{\frac{1}{2}}\,\overline{W}\begin{pmatrix} S & S' & 1 \\ \frac{1}{2} & \frac{1}{2} & \frac{1}{2} \end{pmatrix}\overline{W}\begin{pmatrix} L & L' & 1 \\ l_1 & l_1 & l_2 \end{pmatrix}\overline{W}\begin{pmatrix} S & S' & 1 \\ L' & L & J \end{pmatrix}.$$

The analogous expression for the matrix elements of $(\mathbf{s}_2\cdot\mathbf{l}_2)$ is

$$(\tfrac{1}{2}l_1\tfrac{1}{2}l_2SLJM|\mathbf{s}_2\cdot\mathbf{l}_2|\tfrac{1}{2}l_1\tfrac{1}{2}l_2S'L'JM) \tag{16.6'}$$
$$= (-1)^{l_1+l_2+S+S'+J+1}[\tfrac{3}{2}l_2(l_2+1)(2l_2+1)(2S+1)(2S'+1)\times$$
$$(2L+1)(2L'+1)]^{\frac{1}{2}}\,\overline{W}\begin{pmatrix} S & S' & 1 \\ \frac{1}{2} & \frac{1}{2} & \frac{1}{2} \end{pmatrix}\overline{W}\begin{pmatrix} L & L' & 1 \\ l_2 & l_2 & l_1 \end{pmatrix}\overline{W}\begin{pmatrix} S & S' & 1 \\ L' & L & J \end{pmatrix}.$$

The difference in the phase factors of (16.6) and (16.6′) follows from the difference between (15.7) and (15.7′). In the particular case $l_1 = l_2$, the expressions (16.6) and (16.6′) differ only by a factor ± 1, where the sign depends on whether $S+L$ and $S'+L'$ have equal or opposite parity. This should be so, because $(\mathbf{s}_1\cdot\mathbf{l}_1)+(\mathbf{s}_2\cdot\mathbf{l}_2)$ is a symmetric operator and its matrix elements connecting states of different symmetry must vanish.

Explicit expressions for the matrix elements of $\zeta_1(\mathbf{s}_1\cdot\mathbf{l}_1)+\zeta_2(\mathbf{s}_2\cdot\mathbf{l}_2)$, which may be obtained from (16.6) and (16.6′) by introducing the values of the $\overline{W}$ coefficients, have been given by Racah (1950).

(b) The *hyperfine splitting* of atomic and molecular energy levels is due to electric and magnetic interactions between the nucleus and the atomic electrons, which depend on the mutual orientation of these two systems. These interactions are conveniently expanded into series of invariant products of tensorial sets $\mathfrak{M}^{[k]}$ which represent nuclear moments and of sets $\mathfrak{N}^{[k]}$ which represent the fields generated by the electrons at the position of the nucleus and derivatives of these fields.

The interactions are usually weak enough for the nucleus and electrons to have "good" separate quantum numbers α_1, I, and α_2, J. Each level with these quantum numbers is merely split by the interaction into a number of levels with different values of the total angular momentum quantum number F, where $\mathbf{F}=\mathbf{I}+\mathbf{J}$ and F ranges from $|I-J|$ to $I+J$. The interaction energy for each level is therefore given, in first order approximation, by a diagonal matrix element which may be represented according to (15.6) in the form

$$(\alpha_1 I\,\alpha_2 JFM_F|\Sigma_k \mathfrak{M}^{[k]}\cdot\mathfrak{N}^{[k]}|\alpha_1 I\,\alpha_2 JFM_F)$$
$$= \sum_k (-1)^{I+J+F+k}(\alpha_1 I||M^{[k]}||\alpha_1 I)\,(\alpha_2 J||N^{[k]}||\alpha_2 J)\,\overline{W}\begin{pmatrix} I & I & k \\ J & J & F\end{pmatrix}. \quad (16.7)$$

There should actually be two sums over k, one for electric and one for magnetic interactions; however, the diagonal elements of the matrices of electric moments vanish for odd k, and those of magnetic moments vanish for even k. There is thus one term only for each value of k. The triangular conditions on (I,I,k) and (J,J,k) limit further the sum over k to a maximum value equal to $2I$ or $2J$, whichever is smaller. The number of interactions of different multipole orders k equals therefore the number of levels with different F. The strength of the interaction of any given order k' can be expressed in terms of experimental values of the matrix elements (16.7) utilizing the orthonormalization property (11.15) of the $\overline{W}$,

$$\sum_{F=|I-J|}^{I+J} (-1)^{I+J+F+k'}(2F+1)\,\overline{W}\begin{pmatrix} I & I & k' \\ J & J & F\end{pmatrix} \times$$
$$(\alpha_1 I\alpha_2 JFM_F|\Sigma_k \mathfrak{M}^{[k]}\cdot\mathfrak{N}^{[k]}|\alpha_1 I\,\alpha_2 JFM_F)$$
$$= \frac{1}{2k'+1}(\alpha_1 I||M^{[k']}||\alpha_1 I)\,(\alpha_2 J||N^{[k']}||\alpha_2 J). \quad (16.8)$$

Equation (16.7) may be compared with the corresponding expression provided by a classical vector model, which is $\Sigma_k M_k N_k P_k(\cos\langle\mathbf{IK}\rangle)$ according to (6.15). Here, because nucleus and electrons are regarded as spinning about their angular momenta **I** and **J**, each of the sets $\mathfrak{M}^{[k]}$ and $\mathfrak{N}^{[k]}$ consists of a single nonvanishing element M_k, and respectively N_k, and P_k is a Legendre function of the angle between **I** and **J**. The similarity with (16.7) is obvious, and indeed, for values of I and J large as compared to k, $\overline{W}$ approximates a semiclassical expression

$$\overline{W}\begin{pmatrix} I\ I\ K \\ J\ J\ F \end{pmatrix} \sim \frac{(-1)^{I+J+F}}{\sqrt{(2I+1)(2J+1)}} P_k\left(\frac{F(F+1)-I(I+1)-J(J+1)}{2\sqrt{I(I+1)J(J+1)}}\right). \tag{16.9}$$

In particular for the dipole interaction ($k = 1$), $\overline{W}(II1/JJF)$ has a simple form, seen by comparing (16.2) with (16.1), and the interaction energy may be calculated by the elementary method indicated for the spin-orbit coupling. The quadrupole interaction energy has also been calculated by an elementary, though laborious, method (Casimir, 1935).

The magnetic dipole interaction gives normally the major contribution to the hyperfine splitting. The electric quadrupole interaction has often a substantial effect. Higher multipole effects are quite minor.

In the present state of nuclear theory, the nuclear moments represented by the reduced matrix elements $(\alpha_1 I||M^{[k]}||\alpha_1 I)$ are not known from theory but have to be determined experimentally, often through (16.8) or equivalent expressions. The reduced matrices $(\alpha_2 J||N^{[k]}||\alpha_2 J)$ can generally be determined from theory.

The magnetic dipole operator set $\mathfrak{N}^{[1]}$, which represents the magnetic field generated at the nucleus by the electrons, may be represented as a sum of contributions of electron orbits and spins.‡ For a single electron with orbital quantum number $l \neq 0$, one has

$$\mathfrak{N}^{[1]} = 2\mu_0 \frac{1}{r^3}\{\mathfrak{l}^{[1]} + \sqrt{10}\,[\mathfrak{s}^{[1]} \times \mathfrak{C}^{[2]}]^{[1]}\}, \tag{16.10}$$

where μ_0 indicates the Bohr magneton $eh/4\pi mc$. The first term follows from elementary theory for an electron moving around the nucleus with angular momentum represented by $\hbar\mathfrak{l}^{[1]}$; the second term follows from (J.13) considering that the spin magnetic moment is represented by the operator set $2\mu_0\,\mathfrak{s}^{[1]}$. The reduced matrix of the operator in the

‡ These contributions need not be separated when the electrons are treated by Dirac's equation.

braces of (16.10), in a scheme with quantum numbers l, j, may be calculated from (15.7′) and (15.4),

$$(\tfrac{1}{2}lj||l^{[1]} + \sqrt{10}\,[\mathfrak{s}^{[1]} \times \mathfrak{C}^{[2]}]^{[1]}||\tfrac{1}{2}lj) \tag{16.11}$$

$$= (-1)^{\frac{1}{2}+l+j+1}(l||l^{[1]}||l)\,(2j+1)\,\overline{W}\begin{pmatrix} j\,j\,1 \\ l\,l\,\frac{1}{2} \end{pmatrix} +$$

$$(\tfrac{1}{2}||s^{[1]}||\tfrac{1}{2})\,(l||C^{[2]}||l)\,\sqrt{30}\,X\begin{pmatrix} \frac{1}{2}\,\frac{1}{2}\,1 \\ l\,l\,2 \\ j\,j\,1 \end{pmatrix}.$$

The reduced matrices in the last expression are given by (14.9) and (14.12) and the values of the $\overline{W}$ and X are simple functions of l and j only. One finds thus

$$(\tfrac{1}{2}lj||l^{[1]} + \sqrt{10}\,[\mathfrak{s}^{[1]} \times \mathfrak{C}^{[2]}]^{[1]}||\tfrac{1}{2}lj) = -\,il(l+1)\sqrt{\frac{2j+1}{j(j+1)}}. \tag{16.12}$$

The reduced matrix of $\mathfrak{N}^{[1]}$ is the product of (16.12), of $2\mu_0$, and of $\langle 1/r^3\rangle$, the mean value of $1/r^3$ over the radial distribution of electron density.

The nuclear magnetic moment is often expressed in terms of the nuclear magneton $\mu_n = \mu_0/1836$ and of an effective Landé factor g_I by setting $\mathfrak{M}^{[1]} = \mu_n g_I \mathfrak{J}^{[1]}$. The reduced matrix element of $\mathfrak{J}^{[1]}$ is given by (14.9). Considering also the explicit expression of $W(II1/JJF)$, the magnetic dipole interaction energy may be finally written in the form

$$\mu_0\mu_n g_I \left\langle \frac{1}{r^3} \right\rangle \frac{l(l+1)}{j(j+1)}\,[F(F+1) - j(j+1) - I(I+1)]. \tag{16.13}$$

For atoms with many electrons, additional applications of (15.7) are required, as in the problem of spin-orbit coupling, to obtain the reduced matrix elements of $\mathfrak{N}^{[1]}$ in the scheme $(\alpha_2 J)$ from one-electron matrix elements.

For the electric quadrupole interaction, the reduced matrix element of $\mathfrak{N}^{[2]}$ for a single electron is given by (14.14) and (14.12). For many-electron configurations, application of (15.7) is required as for previous problems.

(c) The *electrostatic interaction* among any two atomic electrons can be expanded in a series of spherical harmonics of the angle ω_{12} between vectors pointing from the nucleus to the electrons

$$\frac{e^2}{r_{12}} = e^2 \sum\nolimits_k \frac{r_<^{\,k}}{r_>^{\,k+1}}\,P_k(\cos\omega_{12}), \tag{16.14}$$

where $r_<$ indicates the distance from the nucleus to the nearer one of the two electrons, and $r_>$ indicates the distance to the electron farther away. Each Legendre polynomial P_k in this expansion can be expressed as the scalar product $\mathfrak{C}^{[k]}(1)\cdot\mathfrak{C}^{[k]}(2)$ of tensorial sets of spherical harmonics (5.19), where 1 and 2 indicate the polar coordinates θ and φ of each electron. The matrix elements of the interaction are then

$$(n_a l_a n_b l_b LM|e^2/r_{12}|n_c l_c n_d l_d LM) \\ = \Sigma_k R^k(n_a l_a n_b l_b, n_c l_c n_d l_d)\,(l_a l_b LM|\mathfrak{C}^{[k]}(1)\cdot\mathfrak{C}^{[k]}(2)|l_c l_d LM), \tag{16.15}$$

where R^k is the Slater integral

$$R^k(n_a l_a n_b l_b, n_c l_c n_d l_d) \\ = e^2 \int_0^\infty\int_0^\infty \frac{r_<^k}{r_>^{k+1}} R_{n_a l_a}(r_1)\, R_{n_b l_b}(r_2)\, R_{n_c l_c}(r_1)\, R_{n_d l_d}(r_2)\, dr_1\, dr_2. \tag{16.16}$$

The matrix elements of the scalar product $\mathfrak{C}^{[k]}(1)\cdot\mathfrak{C}^{[k]}(2)$ are, according to (15.6),

$$(l_a l_b LM|\mathfrak{C}^{[k]}(1)\cdot\mathfrak{C}^{[k]}(2)|l_c l_d LM) \\ = (-1)^{l_b+l_c+L+k}(l_a||C^{[k]}||l_c)\,(l_b||C^{[k]}||l_d)\,\overline{W}\begin{pmatrix} l_a l_c k \\ l_d l_b L \end{pmatrix}, \tag{16.17}$$

where the reduced matrix elements of $\mathfrak{C}^{[k]}$ are given by (14.12).

Because of the identity of the electrons, the actual eigenfunctions are in general not represented by (13.16) but by (13.20). Therefore the matrix elements connecting two symmetric or two antisymmetric states are given, not by (16.15), but respectively by

$$\tfrac{1}{2}[(n_a l_a n_b l_b LM|e^2/r_{12}|n_c l_c n_d l_d LM) \pm \\ (-1)^{l_a+l_b-L}(n_b l_b n_a l_a LM|e^2/r_{12}|n_c l_c n_d l_d LM) \pm \\ (-1)^{l_c+l_d-L}(n_a l_a n_b l_b LM|e^2/r_{12}|n_d l_d n_c l_c LM) + \\ (-1)^{l_a+l_b-l_c-l_d}(n_b l_b n_a l_a LM|e^2/r_{12}|n_d l_d n_c l_c LM)]. \tag{16.18}$$

Owing to the symmetry of e^2/r_{12}, the last term of this expression equals the first one, and the second equals the third, so that the whole expression reduces to

$$(n_a l_a n_b l_b LM|e^2/r_{12}|n_c l_c n_d l_d LM) \pm \\ (-1)^{l_c+l_d-L}(n_a l_a n_b l_b LM|e^2/r_{12}|n_d l_d n_c l_c LM). \tag{16.19}$$

For matrix elements connecting two states with different symmetry, some signs in (16.18) have to be changed and the four terms cancel in pairs, in agreement with the selection rule for matrix elements connecting states with different symmetry. According to the Pauli principle, the spacial eigenfunctions are symmetric for singlet states and antisymmetric for triplet states. Therefore the $\pm$ sign in (16.19) may be replaced with the spin exchange operator $-\frac{1}{2}[1+4\mathbf{s}_1\cdot\mathbf{s}_2]$.

In the particular case $(n_al_a) = (n_bl_b)$, $(n_cl_c) = (n_dl_d)$, the eigenfunctions have still the form (13.16) and the matrix elements the corresponding form (16.15). If $(n_al_a) = (n_bl_b)$, but $(n_cl_c) \neq (n_dl_d)$, the spin of the states of the configuration $(n_al_a)^2$ is fixed by the parity of L, but the spin of the states of the configuration $(n_cl_cn_dl_d)$ may assume both values, 0 and 1, for each allowed value of L. In this case the matrix element is

$$\sqrt{2}\,(n_al_an_al_aLM|e^2/r_{12}|n_cl_cn_dl_dLM) \tag{16.20}$$

if it connects states with the same spin, and it vanishes if it connects states with different spin.

For two electrons in different shells or subshells, the first order perturbation energy due to the electrostatic interaction is given by the diagonal elements of (16.19), with $(n_al_a) = (n_cl_c)$ and $(n_bl_b) = (n_dl_d)$. Defining as usual

$$\begin{aligned} F^k(n_al_a, n_bl_b) &= R^k(n_al_an_bl_b, n_al_an_bl_b) \\ G^k(n_al_a, n_bl_b) &= R^k(n_al_an_bl_b, n_bl_bn_al_a), \end{aligned} \tag{16.21}$$

the perturbation energy is

$$\Sigma_k f_k(l_al_bL)\,F^k(n_al_a, n_bl_b) - \tfrac{1}{2}[1+4\mathbf{s}_1\cdot\mathbf{s}_2]\;\Sigma_k g_k(l_al_bL)\,G^k(n_al_a, n_bl_b), \tag{16.22}$$

where

$$\begin{aligned} f_k(l_al_bL) &= (l_al_bLM|\mathfrak{C}^{[k]}(1)\cdot\mathfrak{C}^{[k]}(2)|l_al_bLM) \\ &= (-1)^{l_a+l_b+L+k}(l_a||C^{[k]}||l_a)\,(l_b||C^{[k]}||l_b)\,\overline{W}\begin{pmatrix} l_al_ak \\ l_bl_bL \end{pmatrix}, \end{aligned} \tag{16.23}$$

$$\begin{aligned} g_k(l_al_bL) &= (-1)^{l_a+l_b-L}(l_al_bLM|\mathfrak{C}^{[k]}(1)\cdot\mathfrak{C}^{[k]}(2)|l_bl_aLM) \\ &= (-1)^k(l_a||C^{[k]}||l_b)^2\,\overline{W}\begin{pmatrix} l_al_bk \\ l_al_bL \end{pmatrix}. \end{aligned} \tag{16.24}$$

The first term of (16.22) represents the direct interaction and the second term the exchange interaction.

The extension of these results to configurations with more than two electrons is straightforward for the direct interaction, because the matrix element of a scalar product like (16.23) may be obtained in any coupling scheme by calculating first in that coupling scheme the reduced matrices of $\mathfrak{C}^{[k]}$ by means of (15.7) and then applying (15.6).

For the exchange interaction the problem is more difficult because the expressions (16.24) are not matrices of scalar products of operator sets operating on different parts of a system. A convenient approach, followed by Racah (1942) for central forces and by Arima *et al.* (1954) for spin-dependent forces, is to expand the "exchange" interaction into a sum of "direct" interactions with the help of (11.16). According to that equation, we have

$$(-1)^k \overline{W}\begin{pmatrix} l_a l_b k \\ l_a l_b L \end{pmatrix} = \sum_r (-1)^{L+r}(2r+1)\, \overline{W}\begin{pmatrix} l_a l_a r \\ l_b l_b k \end{pmatrix} \overline{W}\begin{pmatrix} l_a l_a r \\ l_b l_b L \end{pmatrix} \tag{16.25}$$

and, therefore, $g_k(l_a l_b L)$ may be written in the form

$$g_k(l_a l_b L) = (-1)^{l_a+l_b} (l_a \| C^{[k]} \| l_b)^2 \times \\ \sum_r (2r+1)\, \overline{W}\begin{pmatrix} l_a l_a r \\ l_b l_b k \end{pmatrix} (l_a l_b LM | \mathbf{u}^{[k]} \cdot \mathbf{u}^{[k]} | l_a l_b LM), \tag{16.26}$$

where the tensorial set of operators $\mathbf{u}^{[k]}$ is defined by its reduced matrix

$$(nl \| u^{[k]} \| n'l') = \delta_{nn'}\, \delta_{ll'}. \tag{16.27}$$

The fact that this procedure is based on (11.16), which derives from the associative property (11.14) of recoupling transformations, provides a geometrical interpretation of (16.26) and explains why the coefficients of this expansion are themselves $\overline{W}$ coefficients. If (16.24) is derived following the procedure of Section 15 step by step, instead of applying the final result (15.6), the last factor of (15.1) is in this case

$$[[|n_a l_a\} \times \widetilde{\mathfrak{U}}^{(l_b)} \{n_b l_b|]^{[k]} \times [|n_b l_b\} \times \widetilde{\mathfrak{U}}^{(l_a)} \{n_a l_a|]^{[k]}]^{[0]}. \tag{16.28}$$

To expand this expression into a sum of "direct interactions" means to recouple its factors in the form

$$[[|n_a l_a\} \times \widetilde{\mathfrak{U}}^{(l_a)} \{n_a l_a|]^{[r]} \times [|n_b l_b\} \times \widetilde{\mathfrak{U}}^{(l_b)} \{n_b l_b|]^{[r]}]^{[0]}, \tag{16.29}$$

prior to transformation to the eventual coupling

$$[[|n_a l_a\} \times |n_b l_b\}]^{[L]} \times \widetilde{\mathfrak{U}}^{(L)} [\{n_b l_b| \times \{n_a l_a|]^{(L)}]^{[0]}. \tag{16.30}$$

Apart from normalization and phase factors, the sets of operators

$$[|n_a l_a\} \times \widetilde{\mathfrak{U}}^{(l_a)} \{n_a l_a|]^{[r]}$$

are essentially the sets $\mathbf{u}^{[r]}$ and the recoupling transformation from (16.28) to (16.29) is essentially given by $\overline{W}(l_a l_a r / l_b l_b L)$.

17

Interaction of Coupled Systems with External Fields

In a number of situations, where two or more atomic systems are tightly coupled together, one wants to calculate a multipole interaction between individual component systems and an external field. In this problem the angular momentum of each component system — and therefore its orientation — is not constant, but "precesses" about the total angular momentum. Accordingly the interaction must be averaged out over this precession. This type of problem is solved by Eq. (15.7), as shown by the discussion of the following examples.

(a) The theory of the *anomalous Zeeman effect* regards the spin and orbital motions in an atom as tightly coupled, but deals separately with their interactions with a magnetic field **H**, because these motions have different gyromagnetic ratios γ_S and γ_L. The magnetic energy can be written as

$$\hbar(\gamma_S \mathbf{S}\cdot\mathbf{H} + \gamma_L \mathbf{L}\cdot\mathbf{H}). \tag{17.1}$$

If the z-axis is laid along the magnetic field, and the field is sufficiently weak, a set of "good" quantum numbers includes S, L, J, and M. The quantum mechanical value of (17.1) depends on the matrix elements of the operators S_z and L_z in this scheme of quantum numbers. The elementary theory proceeds either from the matrices of these operators in the scheme SM_SLM_L, to be transformed to the other scheme, in essence, by means of Wigner coefficients, or from the proof (Condon and Shortley, 1935, § 8[3]) that the mean value $\langle S_z\rangle$ equals $\mathbf{S}\cdot\mathbf{J}\langle J_z\rangle/J(J+1)$ (which represents S_z as effectively equal to the z component of the projection of **S** along **J**). The value of $\langle J_z\rangle$ is the quantum number M and that of $\mathbf{S}\cdot\mathbf{J}$ is given by the elementary formula, analogous to (16.1),

$$\mathbf{S}\cdot\mathbf{J} = \tfrac{1}{2}[J(J+1) + S(S+1) - L(L+1)]. \tag{17.2}$$

On the other hand, considering that $S_z = -i\mathfrak{S}^{[1]}{}_0$, (14.4) and (15.7) give directly

$$\begin{aligned}(LSJM|S_z|LSJM) &= -i(LSJ||S^{[1]}||LSJ)\,(-1)^{J-M}\,\overline{V}(JJ1;\text{-}MM0)\\ &= -i(-1)^{L+S+J+1}(2J+1)\,(S||S^{[1]}||S)\,\overline{W}\begin{pmatrix}J\,J\,1\\ S\,S\,L\end{pmatrix}(-1)^{J-M}\,\overline{V}\begin{pmatrix}J\;\;J\;\;1\\ \text{-}M\,M\,0\end{pmatrix},\end{aligned} \tag{17.3}$$

and, considering the values of $(S||S^{[1]}||S)$ and of the $\overline{V}$,

$$(LSJM|S_z|LSJM) \tag{17.4}$$

$$= (-1)^{L+S+J+1} \sqrt{\frac{(2S+1)(2J+1)S(S+1)}{J(J+1)}}\, \overline{W}\begin{pmatrix} J\,J\,1 \\ S\,S\,L \end{pmatrix} M.$$

Here again, as in the theory of the spin-orbit interaction, the results of the elementary theory are simpler than those obtained from the recoupling formula (15.7). However, the recoupling method gives also the matrix elements non-diagonal in J by straightforward generalization and is quite easily applied to couplings of higher order.

(b) The *Stark effect* of the *hyperfine rotation* spectrum of a molecule, is due to the interaction of an electric field with the dipole of the rotating molecule. When the field is weak the rotation, with quantum number J, must be treated as strongly coupled to the nuclear spin, with quantum number I. Therefore the molecular rotation "precesses" about the total angular momentum $\mathbf{F} = \mathbf{J} + \mathbf{I}$, just as in preceding example $\mathbf{S}$ precesses about $\mathbf{J} = \mathbf{L} + \mathbf{S}$. What is wanted here is the matrix elements of the electric field interaction in the scheme of quantum numbers $(JIFM_F)$.

The electric dipole interaction vanishes in first approximation, for the very reason of parity which causes (14.11) to vanish for $l' = l$ and $k = 1$. The second order interaction, when calculated in detail (Brouwer, 1930), turns out to be represented by a tensorial polarization energy operator of second degree $\mathfrak{B}^{[2]}{}_0$, provided the z axis has been taken parallel to the field. The diagonal reduced matrix elements of this tensorial operator in the scheme of rotational quantum numbers are

$$(J||V^{[2]}||J) = -\frac{\mu^2 E^2 A}{\hbar^2} \sqrt{\frac{(2J+1)}{J(J+1)(2J-1)(2J+3)}}, \tag{17.5}$$

where μ is the magnitude of the dipole moment, E the field strength, and A the moment of inertia of the molecule. The desired splitting of the hyperfine levels is then given according to (14.4) and (15.7) by the effective polarization operator in the frame of reference of the total angular momentum, i.e., by the matrix element

$$(JIFM_F|\mathfrak{B}^{[2]}{}_0|JIF'M_F)$$

$$= (JIF||V^{[2]}||JIF')(-1)^{F-M_F}\, V(FF'2; -M_F M_F 0)$$

$$= (-1)^{J+I+F'+F-M_F} \sqrt{(2F+1)(2F'+1)} \times$$

$$(J||V^{[2]}||J)\, \overline{W}\begin{pmatrix} F\,F'\,2 \\ J\;J\;I \end{pmatrix} \overline{V}\begin{pmatrix} F & F' & 2 \\ -M_F & M_F & 0 \end{pmatrix}. \tag{17.6}$$

This matrix element has been previously calculated for $F' = F$ by a more laborious elementary method (Fano, 1948); it was noticed that the result could be expressed by a formula somewhat analogous to (17.1) and (17.2), but no justification of that formula was found.

(c) A classical problem of spectroscopy, which is approached conveniently by the method of recoupling transformations, is that of the relative *line strengths in a multiplet* or of the relative strengths of the multiplets in a supermultiplet. The strength of a spectral line depends on the electric dipole moment associated with the transition of an electron from one to another energy level. The *strength* is defined, according to Condon and Shortley (1935) §7[4], as

$$\mathsf{S}(\alpha j, \alpha' j') = \Sigma_{mm'} |(\alpha j m|\mathbf{P}|\alpha' j' m')|^2 = \Sigma_{mm'q} |(\alpha j m|\mathfrak{P}^{[1]}{}_q|\alpha' j' m')|^2, \tag{17.7}$$

where $\mathbf{P}$ is the electric dipole moment of the atomic electrons defined by

$$\mathbf{P} = -e\Sigma_i \mathbf{r}_i. \tag{17.8}$$

According to (14.4) and (10.20) we see that

$$\mathsf{S}(\alpha j, \alpha' j') = |(\alpha j||P^{[1]}||\alpha' j')|^2. \tag{17.9}$$

The strength of any line is then given by (15.7) for any system with a well-defined coupling scheme. In particular the different lines of a Russell-Saunders multiplet have strengths

$$\mathsf{S}(\alpha SLJ, \alpha' SL'J') = (2J+1)\,(2J'+1)\,\overline{W}\begin{pmatrix} J & J' & 1 \\ L' & L & S \end{pmatrix}^2 |(\alpha SL||P^{[1]}||\alpha' SL')|^2. \tag{17.10}$$

Since $(\alpha SL||P^{[1]}||\alpha' SL')$ is the same for all lines of a multiplet, this formula gives the relative strengths of the lines.

Summing (17.10) over J' by means of (11.15) one finds

$$\sum_{J'} \mathsf{S}(\alpha SLJ, \alpha' SL'J') = \frac{2J+1}{2L+1} |(\alpha SL||P^{[1]}||\alpha' SL')|^2, \tag{17.11}$$

which proves the well-known rule of Ornstein, Burger, and Dorgelo stating that the total strength of the lines having a given initial (final) level is proportional to the statistical weight of that initial (final) level.

Summing (17.11) over J, and recalling that the statistical weight of a whole term is $(2S+1)\,(2L+1)$, we find that the total strength of the multiplet is

$$\mathsf{S}(\alpha SL, \alpha' SL') = \Sigma_{JJ'} \mathsf{S}(\alpha SLJ, \alpha' SL'J') = (2S+1)|(\alpha SL||P^{[1]}||\alpha' SL')|^2. \tag{17.12}$$

The relative strengths of the multiplets in a supermultiplet and the relative strengths of the different supermultiplets in a transition array (Condon and Shortley, 1935, § 3[9]) may be obtained in a similar way, working out by means of (15.7) the dependence of $|(\alpha SL||P^{[1]}||\alpha' SL')|^2$ on L, L', and on other quantum numbers.

18

Reduced Form of Operator Matrices

This section extends to general operators much of the treatment of the special class of tensorial sets of operators which were discussed in Section 14. We shall be interested in operators that depend on the orientation of a system with respect to external frames of reference, whereas we were dealing previously with operators whose matrices (14.1) are independent of such external frames.

Physical quantities which depend on the mutual orientation of different systems are conveniently expressed in terms of tensorial sets of quantities of the separate systems, as pointed out in Section 6. Some applications of this approach in quantum mechanics have been given in Sections 16 and 17. The electrostatic interaction between atomic electrons has been represented by scalar products of multipole moments of different electrons. The magnetic energy of an atom in a magnetic field, $-\gamma\mathbf{J}\cdot\mathbf{H}$, is a linear combination of the operators J_x, J_y, J_z with coefficients $-\gamma H_x$, $-\gamma H_y$, and $-\gamma H_z$ which are not operators of the system.

Operators which represent for example the interaction of an atom with an approaching particle or the detection in a certain direction of a photon emitted by a nucleus often do not have a tensorial structure as obvious as that of the operator $-\gamma\mathbf{J}\cdot\mathbf{H}$. We shall show here how to bring a general operator to a form which is a generalization of $-\gamma\mathbf{J}\cdot\mathbf{H}$. As an application, the expectation value of an operator will be expressed in terms of the angles between the frame of reference of the operator and the frame of reference in which information is provided about the state of the system.

It will be sufficient to consider scalar operators F. The matrix elements $(i|F|k)$ of a scalar operator are not invariant, in general, because the eigenstates $(i|$, $|k)$, corresponding to the rows and columns of the matrix, experience r-transformations when the coordinate axes rotate. (Among the scalar operators only the $\mathfrak{T}^{[0]}{}_0$, which belong to the special class discussed in Section 14, have matrices invariant under coordinate rotations). It is convenient to choose, as usual, a scheme of states $(i|$ and $|k)$, which are eigenstates $(\alpha jm|$ and $|\alpha' j' m')$ of the angular momentum, so that their r-transformations are standard or contrastandard.

The matrix elements $(\alpha jm|F|\alpha' j' m')$ of a scalar F, with given α, j, α', j', are linear functions of the sets of eigenstates $\{\alpha j|$ and $|\alpha' j'\}$ and therefore constitute a reducible tensorial set with the same r-transformations as the elements of a direct product $\mathfrak{a}^{(j)}\,\mathfrak{b}^{[j']}$. This reducible set may then be replaced with irreducible sets of matrix elements, through a unitary substitution which reduces a direct product $\mathfrak{a}^{(j)}\mathfrak{b}^{[j']}$ and constructs irreducible products of $\mathfrak{a}^{(j)}$ and $\mathfrak{b}^{[j']}$. These products may be constructed so as to be standard or contrastandard as indicated in (7.18) and (7.19) and with the matrix $\mathfrak{U}$ or $\mathfrak{U}^{-1} = \tilde{\mathfrak{U}}$; the product construction appropriate to our problem is one similar to (14.17), namely $[\mathfrak{a}^{(j)} \times \tilde{\mathfrak{U}}^{[j']}\,\mathfrak{b}^{[j']}]^{(k)}$. We may thus define standard sets of matrix elements, whose elements are

$$[(\alpha j|F|\alpha' j')]^{(k)}_{q} = \Sigma_{mm'}(jj'kq|jm, j' -m')\,(\alpha jm|F|\alpha' j' m')\,(-1)^{j'-m'}. \qquad (18.1)$$

The sets of these elements‡ will also be indicated with the matrix symbol enclosed in square brackets, but with the brackets in bold face, $\mathbf{[}(\alpha j|F|\alpha' j')\mathbf{]}^{(k)}$. The aggregate of these sets for all values of α, j, α', j', and k is a set of matrix elements in reduced form.

If F is an operator $\mathfrak{T}^{[0]}_{0}$ with the matrix (14.5), Eq. (18.1) yields

$$[(\alpha j|\mathfrak{T}^{[0]}_{0}|\alpha' j')]^{(k)}_{q} = (\alpha j||T^{[0]}||\alpha' j)\,\delta_{jj'}\,\delta_{k0}\,\delta_{q0}. \qquad (18.2)$$

The ordinary matrix of F is expressed in terms of the irreducible sets of matrix elements by inverting the substitution (18.1),

$$(\alpha jm|F|\alpha' j' m') = (-1)^{j'-m'}\,\Sigma_{kq}(jm, j' -m'|jj'kq)\,[(\alpha j|F|\alpha' j')]^{(k)}_{q}. \qquad (18.3)$$

The matrices in ordinary form and in reduced form have, of course, equal numbers of elements.

The operator F may be expressed in terms of its irreducible sets of matrix elements and in terms of sets of eigenstates by a formula analogous to (14.16) and (14.17)

$$\begin{aligned} F &= \Sigma_{\alpha jm\,\alpha' j' m'}|\alpha jm)\,(\alpha jm|F|\alpha' j' m')\,(\alpha' j' m'| \qquad (18.4)\\ &= \Sigma_{\alpha jm\,\alpha' j' m' kq}|\alpha jm)\,(\alpha' j' m'|\,(-1)^{j'-m'}\,(m\,-m'|kq)\,[(\alpha j|F|\alpha' j')]^{(k)}_{q}\\ &= \Sigma_{\alpha j\,\alpha' j' k}\,[|\alpha j\} \times \tilde{\mathfrak{U}}^{(j')}\{\alpha' j'|]^{[k]}\,\mathbf{[}(\alpha j|F|\alpha' j')\mathbf{]}^{(k)}. \end{aligned}$$

The last expression is a sum of inner products; it will be agreed that irreducible contrastandard products of eigenstates are to be regarded

‡ Because j and j' are either both integral or both half-integral, k is integral and these sets can be replaced with irreducible sets having real r-transformations.

as row matrices without a specific notation corresponding to the tilde of (5.7) and (6.2). If the irreducible sets of matrix elements and the sets of eigenstates are referred to different coordinate axes, the inner products take the form (6.8) rather than (6.2), and (18.4) becomes

$$F = \Sigma_{\alpha j\, \alpha' j' k} [|\alpha j\} \times \tilde{\mathfrak{U}}^{(j')}\{\alpha' j'|]^{[k]} \mathfrak{D}^{(k)}(\psi, \theta, \varphi) [(\alpha j|F|\alpha' j')]^{(k)}. \tag{18.5}$$

Expansion of operators into invariant products. Equations (18.4) and (18.5) constitute expansions of F into invariant products of tensorial sets. However, these expansions are not completely analogous to the expansions (6.13) or (6.15) of an electric potential energy. Both the products of eigenstates and the sets $[(\alpha j|F|\alpha' j')]^{(k)}$ depend on quantum numbers, and therefore on variables of the system, whereas in the expansion (6.13) one set of each product depends only on variables of the system and the other only on field variables.

Suppose that the operator F can be expanded into tensorial sets of operators $\mathfrak{T}^{[k]}_q$ (of the class of Section 14), with coefficients $\mathfrak{A}^{(k)}_q$

$$F = \Sigma_k \mathfrak{T}^{[k]} \mathfrak{A}^{(k)}. \tag{18.6}$$

Entering in this formula the expression (14.17) of $\mathfrak{T}^{[k]}$ and comparing the result with (18.4) yields

$$[(\alpha j|F|\alpha' j']^{(k)}_q = (\alpha j||T^{[k]}||\alpha' j')\, \mathfrak{A}^{(k)}_q, \tag{18.7}$$

where each element of the matrix in reduced form is split into a factor independent of q and one independent of α, j, α', j'.

The expansion (18.6) is possible only for particular operators, such as the potential energy of a system of electric charges and the magnetic energy $-\gamma \mathbf{J}\cdot\mathbf{H}$. For a general operator we can expect only a multiple expansion

$$F = \Sigma_{\lambda k} \mathfrak{T}^{[\lambda,k]} \mathfrak{A}^{(\lambda,k)}, \tag{18.8}$$

where λ is a further summation index, and $[(\alpha j|F|\alpha' j')]^{(k)}_q$ does not split into factors but is given by a sum of products

$$[(\alpha j|F|\alpha' j')]^{(k)} = \Sigma_\lambda (\alpha j||T^{[\lambda,k]}||\alpha' j')\, \mathfrak{A}^{(\lambda,k)}. \tag{18.9}$$

Calculation of the trace. Equation (18.3) yields a simple expression of the trace of an operator F

$$\begin{aligned} TrF &= \Sigma_{\alpha jm}(\alpha jm|F|\alpha jm) = \Sigma_{\alpha jmkq}(-1)^{j-m}(m\ -m|kq)\,[(\alpha j|F|\alpha j)]^{(k)}_q \\ &= \Sigma_{\alpha jm} \sqrt{2j+1}\,(00|m\ -m)\,(m\ -m|kq)\,[(\alpha j|F|\alpha j)]^{(k)}_q \\ &= \Sigma_{\alpha j} \sqrt{2j+1}\,[(\alpha j|F|\alpha j)]^{(0)}_0. \end{aligned} \tag{18.10}$$

That is, the irreducible sets of matrix elements of degree $k \neq 0$ do not contribute to the trace. This result parallels (14.7).

Conjugation property. From the hermitian conjugation relationship of ordinary matrix elements, $(\alpha jm|F|\alpha' j' m')^* = (\alpha' j' m'|F^\dagger|\alpha jm)$, follows that the irreducible sets of matrix elements have conjugates given by

$$K[(\alpha j|F|\alpha' j')]^{(k)} = \mathfrak{U}^{[k]}\,[(\alpha j|F|\alpha' j')]^{(k)*} \tag{18.11}$$
$$= (-1)^{j-j'-k}\,[(\alpha' j'|F^\dagger|\alpha j)]^{(k)}.$$

For hermitian operators, $F = F^\dagger$, the diagonal elements of the reduced matrix constitute self-conjugate or anti-self-conjugate sets depending on whether k is even or odd. This result parallels (14.8).

Matrices of operator products. The irreducible sets of matrix elements of an operator product FG are related to the corresponding sets of F and G by formulas analogous to those of Section 15. If F and G operate on different systems, the product of their expansions (18.4) may be recoupled first in the simple form

$$(\tilde{\mathfrak{a}}^{[k_1]}\,\mathfrak{b}^{(k_1)})\,(\tilde{\mathfrak{c}}^{[k_2]}\,\mathfrak{d}^{(k_2)}) = \Sigma_k[\tilde{\mathfrak{a}}^{[k_1]} \times \tilde{\mathfrak{c}}^{[k_2]}]^{[k]}\,[\mathfrak{b}^{(k_1)} \times \mathfrak{d}^{(k_2)}]^{(k)}, \tag{18.12}$$

indicated at the end of Section 9 for the products of invariant products, which gives

$$FG = \Sigma_{\text{all }\alpha,j,k}[[\,|\alpha_1 j_1\} \times \tilde{\mathfrak{U}}^{(j')}\{\alpha_1' j_1'|\,]^{[k_1]} \times [\,|\alpha_2 j_2\} \times \tilde{\mathfrak{U}}^{(j_2')}\{\alpha_2' j_2'|\,]^{[k_2]}]^{[k]} \times$$
$$[[(\alpha_1 j_1|F|\alpha_1' j_1')]^{(k_1)} \times [(\alpha_2 j_2|G|\alpha_2' j_2')]^{(k_2)}]^{(k)}. \tag{18.13}$$

The quadruple product of eigenstates gets recoupled according to (15.2), and (18.13) takes then the form (18.4) with

$$[(\alpha_1 j_1 \alpha_2 j_2 j|FG|\alpha_1' j_1' \alpha_2' j_2' j')]^{(k)}$$
$$= \cdot \sum_{k_1 k_2} (jj'|k_1 k_2)^{(k)}[[(\alpha_1 j_1|F|\alpha_1' j_1')]^{(k_1)} \times [(\alpha_2 j_2|G|\alpha_2' j_2')]^{(k_2)}]^{(k)}$$
$$= \sum_{k_1 k_2} [(2j+1)\,(2j'+1)\,(2k_1+1)\,(2k_2+1)]^{\frac{1}{2}}\, X \begin{pmatrix} j_1 & j_2 & j \\ j_1' & j_2' & j' \\ k_1 & k_2 & k \end{pmatrix} \times \tag{18.14}$$
$$[[(\alpha_1 j_1|F|\alpha_1' j_1')]^{(k_1)} \times [(\alpha_2 j_2|G|\alpha_2' j_2')]^{(k_2)}]^{(k)}.$$

This formula is analogous to (15.4).

For $k = 0$, the X function reduces to a $\overline{W}$ and the irreducible product in (18.14) may be expressed as a scalar product,

$$[(\alpha_1 j_1 \alpha_2 j_2 j|FG|\alpha_1' j_1' \alpha_2' j_2' j)]^{(0)} \tag{18.15}$$
$$= \sqrt{(2j+1)} \sum_k (-1)^{j_1'+j_2+j+k} \overline{W}\begin{pmatrix} j_1 & j_2 & j \\ j_2' & j_1' & k \end{pmatrix} \times$$
$$[(\alpha_1 j_1|F|\alpha_1' j_1')]^{(k)} \cdot [(\alpha_2 j_2|G|\alpha_2' j_2')]^{(k)}.$$

The X function in (18.13) also reduces to a $\overline{W}$ when G is an operator $\mathfrak{T}^{[0]}{}_0$ as in (18.2); one finds then

$$[(\alpha_1 j_1 \alpha_2 j_2 j|F\mathfrak{T}^{[0]}{}_0|\alpha_1' j_1' \alpha_2' j_2' j')]^{(k)} \tag{18.16}$$
$$= (-1)^{j_1+j_2+j'+k} \sqrt{(2j+1)(2j'+1)}\, \overline{W}\begin{pmatrix} j & j' & k \\ j_1' & j_1 & j_2 \end{pmatrix} [(\alpha_1 j_1|F|\alpha_1' j_1')]^{(k)} \times$$
$$\frac{(\alpha_2 j_2||T^{[0]}||\alpha_2' j_2)}{\sqrt{2j_2+1}} \delta_{j_2 j_2'}.$$

If $\mathfrak{T}^{[0]}{}_0$ is the unit operator, (18.16) becomes

$$[(\alpha_1 j_1 \alpha_2 j_2 j|F|\alpha_1' j_1' \alpha_2 j_2 j')]^{(k)} \tag{18.17}$$
$$= (-1)^{j_1+j_2+j'+k} \sqrt{(2j+1)(2j'+1)}\, \overline{W}\begin{pmatrix} j & j' & k \\ j_1' & j_1 & j_2 \end{pmatrix} [(\alpha_1 j_1|F|\alpha_1' j_1')]^{(k)},$$

which corresponds to (15.7).

When F and G operate on the same system, (18.13) is replaced with an analogous formula and the recoupling is given by (15.11) and (15.13). One finds a formula corresponding to (15.14), namely,

$$[(\alpha j|FG|\alpha' j')]^{(k)}$$
$$= (-1)^{j+j'+k} \sum_{\alpha'' j'' k_1 k_2} \sqrt{(2k_1+1)(2k_2+1)}\, \overline{W}\begin{pmatrix} j & j' & k \\ k_2 & k_1 & j'' \end{pmatrix} \times \tag{18.18}$$
$$[[(\alpha j|F|\alpha'' j'')]^{(k_1)} \times [(\alpha'' j''|G|\alpha' j')]^{(k_2)}]^{(k)}.$$

For $k = 0$ the $\overline{W}$ in this formula reduces to the simple expression (11.12) and the irreducible product may be expressed as a scalar product, or as a hermitian product utilizing the conjugation property (18.11),

$$[(\alpha j|FG|\alpha' j')]^{(0)}$$
$$= \sum_{\alpha'' j'' k} \frac{(-1)^{j''-j-k}}{\sqrt{2j+1}} [(\alpha j|F|a'' j'')]^{(k)} \cdot [(\alpha'' j''|G|\alpha' j')]^{(k)} \delta_{jj'} \tag{18.19}$$
$$= \frac{1}{\sqrt{2j+1}} \sum_{\alpha'' j'' k} [(\alpha'' j''|F^{\dagger}|\alpha j)]^{(k)*} [(\alpha'' j''|G|a j)]^{(k)} \delta_{jj'}.$$

It will be agreed here that the complex conjugates of standard sets of matrix elements are to be regarded as row matrices without any specific notation corresponding to the tilde in the definition of hermitian product (6.7).

Mean value of operators. Given the state of an atomi c system represented in a form similar to (2.3),

$$\psi_a = \Sigma_{\alpha jm}\, \mathfrak{u}^{[\alpha j]}{}_m\, \mathfrak{a}^{(\alpha j)}{}_m = \Sigma_{\alpha jm} |\alpha jm)\,(\alpha jm|a), \tag{18.20}$$

the mean value of an operator F for the system in this state is

$$\langle F \rangle = (a|F|a) = \Sigma_{\alpha jm\alpha' j' m'}\, (a|\alpha jm)\,(\alpha jm|F|\alpha' j' m')\,(\alpha' j' m'|a). \tag{18.21}$$

In this expression the coefficients $(a|\alpha jm)$ and $(\alpha' j' m'|a)$ may be written together in pairs so that each pair is handled as a matrix element, by setting

$$(\alpha' j' m'|a)\,(a|\alpha jm) = (\alpha' j' m'|\rho_a|\alpha jm). \tag{18.22}$$

The matrix so constructed is called the density matrix of the state ψ_a. Its irreducible sets of elements are

$$[(\alpha' j'|\rho_a|\alpha j)]^{(k)} = [\{\alpha' j'|a) \times (a|\alpha j\}\, \mathfrak{U}^{[j]}]^{(k)}. \tag{18.23}$$

In terms of this matrix the expression (18.21) of the mean value $\langle F \rangle_a$ becomes

$$\begin{aligned} \langle F \rangle_a &= \Sigma_{\alpha jm\alpha' j' m'}\, (\alpha' j' m'|\rho_a|\alpha jm)\,(\alpha jm|F|\alpha' j' m') = Tr(\rho_a F) \\ &= \Sigma_{\alpha j} \sqrt{2j+1}\, [(\alpha j|\rho_a F|\alpha j)]^{(0)} \\ &= \Sigma_{\alpha j\alpha' j' k}\, [(\alpha j|\rho_a|\alpha' j']^{(k)*}\, [(\alpha j|F|\alpha' j')]^{(k)}, \end{aligned} \tag{18.24}$$

where (18.10) and (18.19) have been utilized as well as the fact that ρ_a is hermitian.

A density matrix serves also to describe states of a system which are not "pure" and therefore are not represented by a superposition ψ_a of eigenstates according to (18.20). This more general description was introduced by von Neumann (1927, see also Weyl, 1931, pp. 78-79). It amounts to defining the matrix ρ as the set of numbers which serve to calculate the mean values of all operators F by means of (18.24); (see also Fano, 1957). Two important properties of the density matrix are

$$Tr\rho = \Sigma_{\alpha j} \sqrt{2j+1}\, [(\alpha j|\rho|\alpha j)]^{(0)} = 1, \tag{18.25}$$

$$Tr(\rho^2) = \Sigma_{\alpha j\alpha' j' kq} |[(\alpha j|\rho|\alpha' j')]^{(k)}{}_q|^2 \leq 1. \tag{18.26}$$

If the irreducible sets of matrix elements of ρ_a and F in (18.24) are referred to different frames, the hermitian products take the form (6.10), and (18.24) becomes

$$\langle F \rangle_a = \Sigma_{\alpha j\alpha' j' k}\, [(\alpha j|\rho_a|\alpha' j')]^{(k)*}\, \mathfrak{D}^{(k)}(\psi, \theta, \varphi)\, [(\alpha j|F|\alpha' j')]^{(k)}. \tag{18.27}$$

The density matrix ρ_a represents information on the system provided by some tools of observation, and the irreducible sets of ρ_a are appropriately referred to a frame attached to these tools. The operator F represents a quantity observable by some other instruments which provide the frame of reference appropriate to the sets $[(\alpha j|F|\alpha' j')]^{(k)}$. Thus (18.27) gives explicitly the dependence of $\langle F\rangle_a$ on the mutual orientation of the instruments for the preparation and for the observation of the system.

Polarization of atomic systems. For an operator $\mathfrak{T}^{[k]}_q$ with the matrix (14.5) the mean value may be calculated by entering (14.5) in place of the matrix of F in (18.24). One finds

$$\langle \mathfrak{T}^{[k]}_q\rangle_a = \sum_{\alpha j \alpha' j'} \frac{(\alpha j||T^{[k]}||\alpha' j')}{\sqrt{2k+1}} [(\alpha j|\rho_a|\alpha' j')]^{(k)}_q{}^*. \tag{18.28}$$

Equation (18.28) establishes a close relationship between the mean values of tensorial sets of operators of the class of Section 14 and the irreducible sets of equal degree of the density matrix. This relationship is a simple proportionality for atomic systems which are in a given energy level with quantum numbers $\alpha_a j_a$, because the density matrix of such a state contains a factor $\delta_{\alpha\alpha_a}\,\delta_{jj_a}\,\delta_{\alpha'\alpha_a}\,\delta_{j'j_a}$ and (18.28) becomes

$$\langle \mathfrak{T}^{[k]}_q\rangle_a = \frac{(\alpha_a j_a||T^{[k]}||\alpha_a j_a)}{\sqrt{2k+1}} [(\alpha_a j_a|\rho_a|\alpha_a j_a)]^{(k)}_q{}^*. \tag{18.29}$$

In particular, each element of the set $[(\alpha_a j_a|\rho_a|\alpha_a j_a)]^{(k)*}$ is proportional to the corresponding component of the mean 2^k-pole moment $\langle \mathbf{M}^{[k]}\rangle$ of the system. As indicated in the note on page 81, the quantity which is usually called the magnitude of the 2^k-pole moment of a system coincides, to within a numerical factor, with the reduced matrix element $(\alpha_a j_a||M^{[k]}||\alpha_a j_a)$. Fluctuations of the orientation of the system smear out its multipole moments. The effect of this smearing out is measured in magnitude and shape by the density matrix. Therefore the irreducible sets of elements of $\rho_a{}^*$ are parameters that characterize the kind and degree of polarization of the system‡. There is a dipole polarization, a quadrupole polarization, etc., indeed a polarization of each 2^k-pole with $k \leq 2j_a$.

In states of random orientation every polarization parameter with $k \neq 0$ vanishes; in states with cylindrical symmetry every parameter with $q \neq 0$ vanishes.

‡ These parameters have been called "statistical tensors" and "state multipoles" in preliminary reports (Fano 1951, 1953).

19

Angular Distribution of Radiations

The radiations emitted by atomic systems (atoms, molecules, nuclei, or disintegrating particles) have directions and polarizations which are often correlated to directions of other radiations or fields. This occurs, specifically, when the radiation emission is induced by a bombarding radiation, or is preceded by another emission process, or when the radiation source is exposed to orienting influences by external fields. The correlations we consider here are functions of the Euler angles between the frame of reference in which the radiation is observed and a frame of reference attached to the orienting radiation or field. These correlations can be expressed by a straightforward application of the equations of Section 18.

The response of a radiation detector with a given orientation is represented quantum mechanically by an operator F whose mean value in the state of the radiation equals the intensity to be measured. This operator is identified by its eigenstates and eigenvalues. An eigenstate of a radiation detector is usually a plane wave and the corresponding eigenvalue is the cross section of the detector for the radiation wave. For detectors sensitive to polarization, the eigenstates are plane waves with particular polarizations. For electromagnetic radiation and spin-$\frac{1}{2}$ particles the detector operator has two polarization eigenstates, one corresponding to maximum and one to minimum response.

The operator matrix is thus constructed initially in a scheme of plane waves but can be transformed to a scheme of eigenstates $|\alpha_r j_r m_r)$ of the radiation which are spherical waves. The matrix elements of this transformation are the coefficients of the expansion of plane into spherical waves. From the matrix $(\alpha_r j_r m_r|F|\alpha_r' j_r' m_r')$ irreducible sets $[(\alpha_r j_r|F|\alpha_r' j_r')]^{(k)}$ are constructed according to (18.1). This procedure is such that the irreducible sets are naturally referred to a polar axis in the direction of propagation of the plane waves, that is, along the axis of collimation of the detector. The directional distribution of the radiation and its polarization analysis, if any is performed, are given by the probability of response of the detector in different orientations (ψ, θ, φ). For a radiation characterized by a density matrix ρ_r, this probability is $\langle F\rangle_r$ where, according to (18.27),

$$\langle F \rangle_r = \Sigma_{\text{all } \alpha,j,k} [(\alpha_r j_r | \rho_r | \alpha_r' j_r')]^{(k)*} \mathfrak{D}^{(k)-1}(\psi, \theta, \varphi) \, [(\alpha_r j_r | F | \alpha_r' j_r')]^{(k)}. \quad (19.1)$$

The r-transformation matrix is indicated here as $\mathfrak{D}^{(k)-1}$ because the Euler angles usually refer to the rotation from the frame of reference in which ρ_r is given to the frame of the detector, rather than vice versa. The sum over k constitutes the harmonic analysis of the radiation distribution. The sum over j_r constitutes an analysis according to multipolarity (angular momentum quantum numbers) of the radiation. Terms of the sum with $j_r \neq j_r'$ represent interference of different multipole orders. Terms with lowest j_r usually give by far the largest contribution to $\langle F \rangle_r$, because elements of $[(\alpha_r j_r | \rho_r | \alpha_r' j_r')]^{[k]}$ with any but the lowest j_r are negligible in practice. The additional quantum numbers, α_r, α_r' relate usually to spin orientation or parity or magnetic *vs* electric character of the radiation and have only a few possible values.

Because only small values of j_r and j_r' are, in practice, significant, and because the values of k, j_r, j_r' obey the triangular conditions (7.4), the probability of response (19.1) depends in practice on the Euler angles only through harmonic functions $\mathfrak{D}^{(k)}$ of low degree k. Eisner and Sachs (1947) and Yang (1948) have formulated theorems that give the maximum value of k in specific cases, taking into account this limitation and similar ones that will be apparent below.

A detector with a cylindrical collimator (or with a sufficiently narrow collimator of any shape) and which performs no polarization analysis has sets of elements $[(\alpha_r j_r | F | \alpha_r' j_r')]^{(k)}{}_q$ which vanish for $q \neq 0$. In this case (19.1) contains only functions $\mathfrak{D}^{(k)-1}{}_{q'0}$ which reduce to spherical harmonics $Y_{kq'}(\theta, \varphi)$ independent of ψ. Similarly, if the state of the radiation has cylindrical symmetry the set elements $[(\alpha_r j_r | \rho_r | \alpha_r' j_r')]^{(k)}{}_{q'}$ vanish for $q' \neq 0$. Here again only functions $\mathfrak{D}^{(k)-1}{}_{0q}$ appear which reduce to $Y_{kq}(\theta, \psi)$ independent of φ. If both the detector and the radiation state have cylindrical symmetry, the distribution (19.1) involves only functions $\mathfrak{D}^{(k)-1}{}_{00}$ which are Legendre polynomials $P_k(\cos\theta)$.

The irreducible sets $[(\alpha_r j_r | \rho_r | \alpha_r' j_r')]^{(k)}$ to be entered in (19.1) must be determined on the basis of information available on the emission process. This process may well be complicated and involve several radiations emitted or absorbed. However it can be broken down into a succession of elementary steps of emission or absorption of one radiation at a time. The formulas required to deal with the various elementary steps may differ, but only superficially, depending on what specific information is available and what information is required. A few elementary problems of this nature will be considered in the following paragraphs, to illustrate their relationships. The formula which describes a complex process is to be obtained by combining the formulas pertaining to its successive elementary steps.

Problem I. Given an initial atomic system (atom, molecule, or nucleus) in a state a with quantum numbers α_a and j_a and with polarization specified by a density matrix ρ_a, and assuming that the system radiates and ends into an energy level b, with quantum numbers α_b and j_b, determine the distribution of the radiation.

This problem may be considered from the start in a somewhat more general form, in which the observation of the radiation is contingent to observation of the atomic system after the emission with a polarization analyzer. This analysis may be done by a Stern-Gerlach magnetic deflector, or, more simply, by observing a subsequent radiation emitted by the same system. The analyzer will be represented by an operator G.

The initial data on the process are specified by a density matrix ρ_a. Knowledge of the energy level implies that every element of ρ_a vanishes if one of its indices α or j differs from α_a and j_a. In the absence of any orienting influence on the system, all the irreducible sets $[(\alpha_a j_a|\rho_a|\alpha_a j_a)]^{(k)}$ with $k \neq 0$ vanish, and the element with $k = 0$ equals $1/\sqrt{2j_a+1}$ owing to (18.25). An orienting influence may consist of external fields, as when nuclear spins are oriented by crystal fields or by paramagnetic polarization, or when atoms have been filtered through a Stern-Gerlach analyzer. In each case the theory of the orienting effect determines the matrix ρ_a. Alternately the orienting influence may be provided by prior absorption or emission of another radiation; ρ_a is then determined by the solution of Problems *II* and *III*.

The physical process of radiation emission is represented by a transition matrix R which changes the density matrix ρ_a into $R\rho_a R^\dagger$. We are not interested here in the construction of R; for somewhat greater definiteness one can write $R = \exp(-iHt/\hbar)$, where H is the complete hamiltonian of matter and radiation and t is a time interval. More properly, R represents that part of the matrix of $\exp(-iHt/\hbar)$, which transforms the initial state of the atomic system into a joint state of radiation plus atomic system. That is, the columns of the matrix R are labeled with the quantum numbers of the initial state a, its rows with quantum numbers of the combined state $r+b$.

The hamiltonian H is an operator $\mathfrak{T}^{[0]}_0$ of the type (14.5) for the complete system of atom and radiation. Therefore the matrix of R is independent of magnetic quantum numbers and is diagonal in the total angular momentum quantum numbers j, that is, the elements that do not belong to a row with $j = j_a$ vanish. Accordingly the relevant matrix elements of R are

$$(\alpha_r j_r \alpha_b j_b j_a|R|\alpha_a j_a) \tag{19.2}$$

where the magnetic quantum number is omitted because it is immaterial. The values of α_a, j_a, α_b, j_b are fixed by the statement of the problem. The values of j_r, which are quantum numbers of spherical radiation waves, are limited by the triangular condition $j_a+j_b \geq j_r \geq |j_a-j_b|$. Moreover, the matrix element (19.2) with the smallest value of j_r is usually much larger than the others. Similarly one value of the additional quantum number α_r may give a much larger contribution than the others.

The matrix $R\rho_a R^\dagger$ is in effect the joint density matrix ρ_{rb} of the radiation and of the final atomic system b, as they arise from the emission process. If one constructs the irreducible sets of matrix elements of ρ_{rb} according to (18.1), starting from ordinary elements with quantum numbers m_a, m_a', the matrix elements of R and $R^\dagger$ factor out because they are independent of m_a and m_a'. Therefore we have

$$\begin{aligned}&[(\alpha_r j_r \alpha_b j_b j_a|\rho_{rb}|\alpha_r' j_r' \alpha_b j_b j_a)]^{(k)} \\ &\quad = (\alpha_r j_r \alpha_b j_b j_a|R|\alpha_a j_a)\,[(\alpha_a j_a|\rho_a|\alpha_a j_a)]^{(k)}\,(\alpha_a j_a|R^\dagger|\alpha_r' j_r' \alpha_b j_b j_a),\end{aligned} \tag{19.3}$$

stating that each irreducible set of matrix elements of ρ_{rb} is proportional to a corresponding set of elements of ρ_a. That is, the geometrical pattern of orientation and polarization of the radiation plus the residual atomic system equals the pattern of polarization of the initial nucleus; indeed this pattern could not have been modified by the emission process, since the interaction is invariant under coordinate rotations.

The probability of observing the radiation with a detector represented by an operator F and the residual atomic system with a detector represented by G is the mean value of FG calculated with the density matrix (19.3). The operator FG is given, in the scheme of quantum numbers of (19.3), by (18.14). If F and G are constructed in frames of reference attached to the respective detectors, they must be entered in (18.14) in combination with the transformation matrices to the frame of reference of ρ_{rb} which is the same as that of ρ_a. We have then

$$\langle FG\rangle_{rb} = \sum_{\alpha_r j_r \alpha_r' j_r' k} [(\alpha_r j_r \alpha_b j_b j_a|\rho_{rb}|\alpha_r' j_r' \alpha_b j_b j_a)]^{(k)*} \times \quad (19.4)$$
$$[(\alpha_r j_r \alpha_b j_b j_a|FG|\alpha_r' j_r' \alpha_b j_b j_a)]^{(k)}$$
$$= \sum_{\alpha_r j_r \alpha_r' j_r'} (\alpha_r' j_r' \alpha_b j_b j_a|R|\alpha_a j_a)\,(\alpha_a j_a|R^\dagger|\alpha_r j_r \alpha_b j_b j_a) \times$$
$$\sum_{k_a k_r k_b} (2j_a+1)\sqrt{(2k_r+1)\,(2k_b+1)}\; X\begin{pmatrix} j_r j_r' k_r \\ j_b j_b k_b \\ j_a j_a k_a \end{pmatrix} \times$$
$$[(\alpha_a j_a|\rho_a|\alpha_a j_a)]^{(k_a)*}\big[\mathfrak{D}^{(k_r)-1}(\psi_r,\theta_r,\varphi_r)\,[(\alpha_r j_r|F|\alpha_r' j_r')]^{(k_r)} \times$$
$$\mathfrak{D}^{(k_b)-1}(\psi_b,\theta_b,\varphi_b)\,[(\alpha_b j_b|G|\alpha_b j_b)]^{(k_b)}\big]^{(k_a)}.$$

This formula embodies the highest complication in a single emission (or absorption) process. Before discussing the complete formula we shall consider simpler particular cases. If no observation is made on the atomic system after the emission, the operator G is the unit operator for states with quantum numbers $\alpha_b j_b$ and (18.2) gives

$$[(\alpha_b j_b|G|\alpha_b j_b)]^{(k_b)} = \sqrt{2j_b+1}\;\delta_{k_b 0}. \quad (19.5)$$

The function X in (19.4) reduces then to a $\overline{W}$, corresponding to the application of (18.16) instead of (18.14), and (19.4) becomes

$$\langle F\rangle_r = \sum_{\alpha_r j_r \alpha_r' j_r'} (\alpha_r' j_r' \alpha_b j_b j_a|R|\alpha_a j_a)\,(\alpha_a j_a|R^\dagger|\alpha_r j_r \alpha_b j_b j_a) \times \quad (19.6)$$
$$\sum_k (-1)^{j_a+j_b+j_r+k}(2j_a+1)\,\overline{W}\begin{pmatrix} j_a & j_a & k \\ j_r' & j_r & j_b \end{pmatrix} \times$$
$$[(\alpha_a j_a|\rho_a|\alpha_a j_a)]^{(k)*}\,\mathfrak{D}^{(k)-1}(\psi_r,\theta_r,\varphi_r)\,[(\alpha_r j_r|F|\alpha_r' j_r')]^{(k)}.$$

Comparison of (19.6) with (19.1) shows that the emitted radiation may be described by irreducible sets of matrix elements $[(\alpha_r j_r|\rho_r|\alpha_r' j_r')]^{(k)}$ proportional to those of the initial atomic state and thus that the radiation pattern reflects the polarization pattern of the initial state a. However, the proportionality constant differs in general for each value of k, depending on the value of $\overline{W}(j_a j_a k/j_r' j_r j_b)$, whereas no such difference was exhibited in the relationship (19.4) between ρ_{rb} and ρ_a. This value of $\overline{W}$ depends on the spin j_b of the residual atomic system and is largest and independent of k for $j_b = 0$, in which case $(-1)^{j_a+j_b+j_r+k}(2j_a+1) \times \overline{W}(j_a j_a k/j_r' j_r j_b) = 1$. The coefficient $(2j_a+1)\overline{W}$ may be regarded as a *depolarization coefficient*, which decreases the value of the parameters $[(\alpha_a j_a|\rho_a|a_a j_a)]^{(k)}$ of the initial system, in connection with the lack of information about the orientation of the final system ("averaging over the spin direction of b").

The initial state a may not have unique values of the quantum numbers α_a and j_a, in which case the matrix ρ_a has elements $[(\alpha_a j_a|\rho_a|\alpha_a' j_a')]^{(k)}$ with different values of these quantum numbers. Similarly, the quantum numbers of the final state b may not have fixed values of α_b and j_b. In such cases one arrives at the same result (19.6) except that there are indexes α_a' and j_a' different from α_a and j_a and that the summations extend over all values of these quantum numbers and of $\alpha_b j_b$ as well.

A result similar to (19.6) is also obtained if the nucleus is observed after the radiation emission, but the radiation itself is not observed. One finds

$$\langle G\rangle_b = \sum_{\alpha_r j_r} (\alpha_r j_r \alpha_b j_b j_a|R|\alpha_a j_a)\,(\alpha_a j_a|R^\dagger|\alpha_r j_r \alpha_b j_b j_a) \times \quad (19.7)$$
$$\sum{}'_k (-1)^{j_a+j_b+j_r+k}(2j_a+1)\,\overline{W}\begin{pmatrix} j_a\, j_a\, k \\ j_b\, j_b\, j_r\end{pmatrix} \times$$
$$[(\alpha_a j_a|\rho_a|\alpha_a j_a)]^{(k)*}\,\mathfrak{D}^{(k)-1}(\psi_b,\theta_b,\varphi_b)\,[(\alpha_b j_b|G|\alpha_b j_b)]^{(k)}.$$

The X function in (19.4) also reduces to a $\overline{W}$ when the initial state a is one of random spin orientation. One finds

$$\langle FG\rangle_{rb} = \sum_{\alpha_r j_r \alpha_r' j_r'} (\alpha_r' j_r' \alpha_b j_b j_a|R|\alpha_a j_a)\,(\alpha_a j_a|R^\dagger|\alpha_r j_r \alpha_b j_b j_a) \times \quad (19.8)$$
$$\sum_k (-1)^{j_a+j_b+j_r+k}\,\overline{W}\begin{pmatrix} j_b\, j_b\, k \\ j_r'\, j_r\, j_a\end{pmatrix} \times$$
$$[(\alpha_r j_r|F|\alpha_r' j_r')]^{(k)}\cdot\mathfrak{D}^{(k)-1}(\psi_b,\theta_b,\varphi_b)\,[(\alpha_b j_b|G|\alpha_b j_b)]^{(k)},$$

where the Euler angles relate the frame attached to the detector G to that of the detector F. This formula establishes a correlation between the emission of a radiation and the polarization of the residual nucleus.

Whereas each of (19.6), (19.7), and (19.8) contains an invariant product of two irreducible sets and a function $\mathfrak{D}^{(k)}$ between two frames of reference, (19.4) contains a product of three sets and two functions $\mathfrak{D}^{(k)}$ relating three frames of reference. Equation (19.4) also contains a function X instead of $\overline{W}$.

Multiple radiation processes may involve relationships between more than three separate elements of information, to be described by quadruple or higher products. However, each step of absorption or emission requires at most an X coefficient.

Problem II. Given an atomic system in an initial state with quantum numbers α_a and j_a and with polarization specified by a density matrix ρ_a, and assuming that the system absorbs radiation from an incident beam and ends in an energy level b with quantum numbers α_b and j_b, determine the density matrix of the state b. This problem constitutes the first step in the analysis of radiation distributions from artificial disintegration or fluorescence, in which cases the initial system is usually unpolarized. The density matrix ρ_r of the incident radiation is determined by the characteristics of the beam. A well-collimated beam is represented adequately by a plane wave which may be polarized. The calculation of the irreducible sets $[(\alpha_r j_r|\rho_r|\alpha_r' j_r')]^{(k)}$ from the information about the beam is quite similar to the calculation of $[(\alpha_r' j_r'|F|\alpha_r j_r)]^{(k)}$ for a specified detector.

The combination of the radiation and of the initial atomic system has a joint density matrix $\rho_{ar} = \rho_a \rho_r$. The irreducible sets of elements of $\rho_a \rho_r$ are given by (18.14). The density matrix of the final atomic system results from the joint matrix $\rho_a \rho_r$ through a transformation matrix R similar to that of the preceding problem, $\rho_b = R\rho_a\rho_r R^\dagger$. In (19.3) the matrix products $R\rho_a R^\dagger$ did not involve any summation because the quantum numbers $\alpha_a j_a$ had fixed values. Here α_r, j_r, α_r', j_r' have many values and a sum over these values must be made. This sum is limited by the triangular conditions on $(j_a j_r j_b)$ and $(j_a j_r' j_b)$; moreover the matrix elements of R are usually negligible except for the lowest values of j_r and j_r'. The result is

$$[(\alpha_b j_b|\rho_b|\alpha_b j_b)]^{(k_b)} = \sum_{\alpha_r' j_r' \alpha_r j_r} (a_b j_b|R|\alpha_a j_a \alpha_r' j_r' j_b)\,(\alpha_a j_a \alpha_r j_r j_b|R^\dagger|\alpha_b j_b) \times$$

$$\sum_{k_r k_a} (2j_b + 1)\sqrt{(2k_r + 1)(2k_a + 1)}\, X\begin{pmatrix} j_a & j_a & k_a \\ j_r' & j_r & k_r \\ j_b & j_b & k_b \end{pmatrix} \times \tag{19.9}$$

$$[[(a_a j_a|\rho_a|\alpha_a j_a)]^{(k_a)} \times \mathfrak{D}^{(k_r)-1}(\psi_r, \theta_r, \varphi_r)\,[(\alpha_r' j_r'|\rho_r|\alpha_r j_r)]^{(k_r)}]^{(k_b)},$$

where the irreducible sets of ρ_a and ρ_b are referred to the frame in which information is provided about ρ_a and where $(\psi_r, \theta_r, \varphi_r)$ are the Euler angles of the radiation beam in that frame.

In the usual case that the initial state of the atomic system is unpolarized, (19.9) becomes

$$[(\alpha_b j_b|\rho_b|\alpha_b j_b)]^{(k)} \tag{19.10}$$

$$= \sum\nolimits_{\alpha_r' j_r' \alpha_r j_r} (\alpha_b j_b|R|\alpha_a j_a \alpha_r' j_r' j_b)(\alpha_a j_a \alpha_r j_r j_b|R^\dagger|\alpha_b j_b) \times$$

$$(-1)^{j_r'+j_a+j_b+k} \frac{2j_b+1}{2j_a+1} \overline{W}\begin{pmatrix} j_b j_b k \\ j_r j_r' j_a \end{pmatrix} [(\alpha_r' j_r'|\rho_r|\alpha_r j_r)]^{(k)},$$

where both sets are now referred to a frame attached to the radiation source. This formula shows that the parameters $[(\alpha_b j_b|\rho_b|\alpha_b j_b)]^{(k)}$ of the polarization of the final atomic system are proportional to the parameters $[(\alpha_r' j_r'|\rho_r|\alpha_r j_r)]^{(k)}$ which may be regarded as coefficients of a harmonic analysis of the incident radiation beam. The proportionality constant depends on k through the depolarization coefficient $(2j_b+1)\overline{W}$. Absorption of radiation from the incident beam causes the atomic system to be polarized; the polarization is strongest when the initial spin j_a vanishes and $\overline{W}$ takes its largest value.

The depolarization coefficients in (19.10) and in (19.6) differ only in the interchange of the initial and final quantum numbers j_a and j_b. The same holds for the matrix elements of R.

A typical process of artificial nuclear disintegration consists of two steps, absorption of a radiation No. 1 and emission of a radiation No. 2. Equation (19.10) describes the state of the intermediate ("compound") nucleus in terms of data on the incident radiation. To obtain the distribution of disintegration products one must then take the solution (19.6) of Problem I and enter into it, in place of $[(\alpha_a j_a|\rho_a|\alpha_a j_a)]^{(k)}$ the result (19.10) of Problem II. The final result is

$$\langle F\rangle = \sum\nolimits_{\text{all } \alpha_r \text{ and } j_r} (\alpha_b j_b|R|\alpha_a j_a \alpha_{r1}' j_{r1}' j_b)\,(\alpha_a j_a \alpha_{r1} j_{r1} j_b|R^\dagger|\alpha_b j_b) \times \tag{19.11}$$

$$(\alpha_{r2}' j_{r2}' \alpha_c j_c j_b|R|\alpha_b j_b)\,(\alpha_b j_b|R^\dagger|\alpha_{r2} j_{r2} \alpha_c j_c j_b) \times$$

$$\sum\nolimits_k (-1)^{j_{r1}'+j_a+2j_b+j_{r2}+j_c} \frac{(2j_b+1)^2}{2j_a+1} \overline{W}\begin{pmatrix} j_b & j_b & k \\ j_{r1} & j_{r1}' & j_a \end{pmatrix} \overline{W}\begin{pmatrix} j_b & j_b & k \\ j_{r2}' & j_{r2} & j_c \end{pmatrix} \times$$

$$[(\alpha_{r1} j_{r1}|\rho_{r1}|\alpha_{r1}' j_{r1}')]^{(k)*}\, \mathfrak{D}^{(k)-1}(\psi_{12}, \theta_{12}, \varphi_{12})\, [(\alpha_{r2} j_{r2}|F|\alpha_{r2}' j_{r2}')]^{(k)}.$$

The core of this formula consists of the hermitian products of the type (6.10) which depend on the Euler angles of the detector of the emitted radiation in the frame of reference of the source of the incident radiation. Each of these products is multiplied by *two* depolarization coefficients $(2j_b+1)\overline{W}$, one pertaining to the absorption process and the other to the emission process. Additional factors are four matrix elements $R, R^\dagger$, two from each process, which, however, do not depend on the degree k of the harmonics $\mathfrak{D}^{(k)}$, but only on the quantum numbers α and j. The values of the matrix elements of R decrease very rapidly as the j_r increase; this fact, together with the triangular conditions, eliminates the terms with large values of k. Anyhow k cannot exceed $2j_b$.

The depolarization factor of the angular distribution formula (19.11) may be analyzed according to the net angular momentum transferred from the radiation to the nucleus, i.e., according to eigenvalues of the operator $\mathbf{J}_t^2 = (\mathbf{J}_{r1} - \mathbf{J}_{r2})^2 = (\mathbf{J}_a - \mathbf{J}_c)^2$.

The Biedenharn identity (I.3) yields

$$(-1)^{j_{r1}'+j_a+2j_b+j_{r2}+j_c}(2j_b+1)\,\overline{W}\begin{pmatrix} j_b & j_b & k \\ j_{r1} & j_{r1}' & j_a \end{pmatrix}\overline{W}\begin{pmatrix} j_b & j_b & k \\ j_{r2} & j_{r2}' & j_c \end{pmatrix} \tag{19.12}$$

$$= \sum_{j_t}\left\{(2j_b+1)(2j_t+1)\,\overline{W}\begin{pmatrix} j_a & j_c & j_t \\ j_{r2}' & j_{r1}' & j_b \end{pmatrix}\overline{W}\begin{pmatrix} j_a & j_c & j_t \\ j_{r2} & j_{r1} & j_b \end{pmatrix}\right\}\times$$

$$\left\{(-1)^{j_{r1}+j_{r2}'+j_t+k}\,\overline{W}\begin{pmatrix} j_{r1} & j_{r1}' & k \\ j_{r2}' & j_{r2} & j_t \end{pmatrix}\right\}.$$

The expression in the second braces depends on the degree k of the function $\mathfrak{D}^{(k)}$ and on the j-numbers of the radiation, but is independent of the j-numbers of the nucleus. The expression in the first braces depends on the j-numbers of the nucleus but is independent of k.

For each value of j_t the summation over k yields then a distribution function

$$\sum_k (-1)^{j_{r1}+j_{r2}'+j_t+k}\,\overline{W}\begin{pmatrix} j_{r1} & j_{r1}' & k \\ j_{r2}' & j_{r2} & j_t \end{pmatrix}\times \tag{19.13}$$

$$[(\alpha_{r1}j_{r1}|\rho_{r1}|\alpha_{r1}'j_{r1}')]^{(k)*}\,\mathfrak{D}^{(k)^{-1}}(\psi_{12},\theta_{12},\varphi_{12})\,[(\alpha_{r2}j_{r2}|F|\alpha_{r2}'j_{r2}')]^{(k)},$$

which is independent of the nuclear j-numbers. The depolarization factor in this formula is quite similar to the depolarization factor in the single-process formula (19.8). The distribution function (19.13) is subsequently averaged through the summation over j_t. The expression in the first braces of (19.12) may be regarded as the weight factor in the averaging, i. e., as the probability of each value of j_t, since it is the product of two matrix elements of recoupling from the scheme $((j_{r1}j_a)j_b(j_{r2}j_c)j_b)$ to the scheme $((j_{r1}j_{r2})j_t(j_aj_c)j_t)$.

The transformation (19.12) of the depolarization factor of (19.11) proves convenient when there is only one value of j_t consistent with the triangular conditions on the triads $(j_{r1}j_{r2}j_t)$, $(j_{r1}'j_{r2}'j_t)$, and $(j_aj_cj_t)$. This special, but important, case occurs whenever the vectors $\mathbf{J}_a$, $\mathbf{J}_b$, $\mathbf{J}_c$, $\mathbf{J}_{r1}$, and $\mathbf{J}_{r2}$ are "parallel" or "anti-parallel" in the classical model of addition of angular momenta (Fano, 1957a); this condition also implies that $j_{r1}' = j_{r1}$ and $j_{r2}' = j_{r2}$. In this special case the summation in (19.12) reduces of course to a single term, and the expression in the first braces reduces to 1 owing to (11.15). It follows then that the distribution of disintegration products is proportional to (19.13) and thereby *independent of the nuclear quantum numbers.*

Problem III. Given an initial atomic system in a state a, with quantum numbers α_a and j_a and with polarization specified by a density matrix ρ_a, and assuming: (1) that the system radiates and ends in an energy level b, with quantum numbers α_b and j_b, and (2) that the radiation has been observed with a detector represented by an operator F, determine the density matrix ρ_b which specifies the polarization of the final state.

This problem arises in the first step of an angular correlation process, in which information on the polarization of an intermediate state of the nucleus derives from the observation of a prior radiation, and the initial nucleus is usually unpolarized. It also concerns the intermediate steps of a process where several radiations are emitted in succession; if the intermediate radiation is not actually observed, F becomes the unit operator.

The solution of this problem need not be worked out separately but may be derived from the solution (19.4) of Problem I. For this purpose the mean value of the operator FG given by (19.4) may be regarded as the mean value of G conditional upon the observation F. Therefore comparison with (18.27) shows that $[(\alpha_b j_b|\rho_b|\alpha_b j_b)]^{(k)*}$ conditional upon the observation F is that part of (19.4) which multiplies $\mathfrak{D}^{(k)-1}(\psi_b, \theta_b, \varphi_b)$ $[(\alpha_b j_b|G|\alpha_b j_b)]^{(k)}$. To isolate this part, we recouple the product in (19.4) according to

$$\tilde{\mathfrak{A}}^{(k_a)*}\,[\mathfrak{B}^{(k_r)}\times\mathfrak{C}^{(k_b)}]^{(k_a)} = \sqrt{\frac{2k_a+1}{2k_b+1}}\,[\tilde{\mathfrak{A}}^{(k_a)*}\times\overline{\mathfrak{U}^{(k_r)}\,\mathfrak{B}^{(k_r)}}]^{[k_b]}\,\mathfrak{C}^{(k_b)} \tag{19.14}$$

and utilize the conjugation property (18.11) of the hermitian operator F. We find

$$[(\alpha_b j_b|\rho_b|\alpha_b j_b)]^{(k_b)} = \sum\nolimits_{\alpha_r j_r \alpha_r' j_r'} (\alpha_r j_r \alpha_b j_b j_a|R|\alpha_a j_a)\,(\alpha_a j_a|R^\dagger|\alpha_r' j_r' \alpha_b j_b j_a)\,\times$$
$$\sum\nolimits_{k_a k_r} (2j_a+1)\sqrt{(2k_r+1)\,(2k_a+1)}\;X\begin{pmatrix} j_a & j_a & k_a \\ j_r' & j_r & k_r \\ j_b & j_b & k_b \end{pmatrix}\times$$
$$[[(\alpha_a j_a|\rho_a|\alpha_a j_a)]^{(k_a)}\times\mathfrak{D}^{(k_r)-1}(\psi_r, \theta_r, \varphi_r)\,[(\alpha_r' j_r'|F|\alpha_r j_r)]^{(k_r)*}]^{(k_b)}, \tag{19.15}$$

in the frame of reference in which information is provided about the initial states.

This expression is quite similar to (19.9), which gives ρ_b for the case where the radiation is absorbed rather than emitted. The role of the density matrix ρ_r in (19.9) is filled in (19.15) by the matrix of detector F

showing that emission and absorption are equivalent for the theory of angular correlations.

This explicit formulation of ρ_b can actually be by-passed in practical problems. The matrix ρ_b would be used anyhow to determine the probability of further processes, which follow the formation of the state b. This probability is represented by the mean value of a suitable operator. The operator can be represented by a matrix in the scheme of eigenstates of b, and can then be entered in the place of G in (19.4) or in (19.8). Thereby one determines directly the joint probability of events pertaining to different steps in the chain of processes.

This procedure will be illustrated by writing down the formula for the angular correlation of two successive nuclear radiations, i.e., for the probability of joint response of two detectors, F_1 and F_2. Radiation 1 is emitted in a transition where the nuclear quantum numbers change from $(\alpha_a j_a)$ to $(\alpha_b j_b)$, radiation 2 in a transition from $(\alpha_b j_b)$ to $(\alpha_c j_c)$. To obtain the angular correlation one might take the solution (19.6) of Problem I for radiation 2 and enter into it in place of $[(\alpha_a j_a|\rho_a|\alpha_a j_a)]^{(k)}$ the result (19.13) of Problem III for radiation 1. Instead we take the solution (19.8) of Problem I for radiation 1 and enter into it, in place of $\mathfrak{D}^{(k)-1}(\psi_b, \theta_b, \varphi_b)\,[(\alpha_b j_b|G|\alpha_b j_b)]^{(k)}$, a modified form of the solution (19.6) of Problem I for radiation 2. The modification consists simply of grouping every factor on the right of (19.6), except $[(\alpha_a j_a|\rho_a|\alpha_a j_a)]^{(k)*}$, with $\mathfrak{D}^{(k)-1}[(\alpha_r j_r|F|\alpha_r' j_r')]^{(k)}$. Thereby the matrix of F is transformed to the scheme $(\alpha_a j_a)$ and can be handled like the matrix of G in (19.8), after changing, of course, the indices a into b and b into c. One finds

$$\langle F_1 F_2\rangle = \sum\nolimits_{\text{all } \alpha_r \text{ and } j_r} (-1)^{j_{r1}+j_{r2}+j_a+2j_b+j_c} (\alpha_{r1} j_{r1} \alpha_b j_b j_a|R|\alpha_a j_a) \times$$
$$(\alpha_a j_a|R^\dagger|\alpha_{r1}' j_{r1}' \alpha_b j_b j_a)\,(\alpha_b j_b|R^\dagger|\alpha_{r2} j_{r2} \alpha_c j_c j_b)\,(\alpha_{r2}' j_{r2}' \alpha_c j_c j_b|R|\alpha_b j_b) \times$$
$$\sum\nolimits_k (2j_b+1)\,\overline{W}\begin{pmatrix} j_b & j_b & k \\ j_{r1} & j_{r1}' & j_a \end{pmatrix} \overline{W}\begin{pmatrix} j_b & j_b & k \\ j_{r2} & j_{r2}' & j_c \end{pmatrix} \times$$
$$[(\alpha_{r1} j_{r1}|F_1|\alpha_{r1}' j_{r1}')]^{(k)} \cdot \mathfrak{D}^{(k)-1}(\psi, \theta, \varphi)\,[(\alpha_{r2} j_{r2}|F_2|\alpha_{r2}' j_{r2}')]^{(k)}, \qquad (19.16)$$

where ψ, θ, φ are now the Euler angles of the frame attached to F_2 with respect to the frame attached to F_1. This formula has a structure quite similar to that of (19.11) and therefore requires no further discussion.

The formula (19.16) for the angular correlation of two successive nuclear radiations may be transformed, like (19.11), by means of the Biedenharn identity; the results thus obtained are analogous to those obtained by the transformation of (19.11).

Summary of problems. Problem III has been brought back to the solution of Problem I. It has also been shown that the solution of III thus obtained is symmetric to the solution of II, because of the equivalence of information on incident and on emitted radiation. Therefore every one of the problems considered in this section is equivalent, in essence, to Problem I, and every solution may be regarded as a particular application of (19.4). Other problems such as the electron-neutrino correlation and the angular distribution of the disintegration products of τ mesons do not quite fit in the classes of problems treated in this section, but may be treated by adapting the same procedures.

The equations of this section are constructed with the following building blocks: (1) the standard r-transformation matrices $\mathfrak{D}^{(k)}(\psi, \theta, \varphi)$, and the spherical harmonics which are special cases of them; (2) the X functions and the $\overline{W}$ functions which are special cases of the X; (3) the transition matrices R; (4) the irreducible sets of elements of density matrices and of radiation detector operators.

The matrices $\mathfrak{D}^{(k)}$ and the X and $\overline{W}$ are universal functions. The transition matrices depend on the interaction terms of the hamiltonian operator, which can generally be expressed as scalar products of tensorial sets and, therefore, may be calculated as in the examples of Section 16. Such a calculation will give the matrices R in terms of the reduced matrices of Section 14, which are more elementary building blocks, and of additional $\overline{W}$ coefficients. Some of these more elementary building blocks will be of standard types, as e.g., the reduced matrix of $\mathfrak{C}^{[k]}$ given by (14.12), others will depend on radial wave functions and on other quantities related to the detailed structure of the system under consideration.

The calculation of the irreducible sets $[(\alpha'j'|\rho|\alpha j)]^{(k)}$ and $[(\alpha j|F|\alpha'j')]^{(k)}$ constitutes a problem of the same general nature as that of the calculation of the matrices R. However, neither for these sets nor for the R has there been any systematic effort with the object of constructing these quantities with tensorial notations and techniques and of tabulating them for the numerous cases of interest.

On the other hand many calculations have been made for special purposes and with various notations and techniques. The most extensive studies in this direction have been made by Biedenharn and Rose (1953) and Blatt and Biedenharn (1953).

APPENDICES

A

Group Properties of *r*-transformations

a. Reduction to Unitary Form. Given a tensorial set of quantities a_i, which transforms under coordinate rotations into $b_r = \Sigma_i D_{ri} a_i$, we seek to replace this set with a new set $a_k' = \Sigma_i A_{ki} a_i$, such that its r-transformations be unitary. According to (2.11), these transformations have matrices ADA^{-1}; they will be unitary if

$$(ADA^{-1})^{-1} = (ADA^{-1})^{\dagger}. \tag{A.1}$$

Notice that

$$(ADA^{-1})^{-1} = AD^{-1}A^{-1} \tag{A.2}$$

and

$$(ADA^{-1})^{\dagger} = A^{\dagger -1}D^{\dagger}A^{\dagger}. \tag{A.3}$$

Multiply (A.1) from the left by DA^{-1} and from the right by $A^{\dagger -1}$, which yields

$$A^{-1}A^{\dagger -1} = DA^{-1}A^{\dagger -1}D^{\dagger}. \tag{A.4}$$

The product $A^{-1}A^{\dagger -1}$ is a hermitian matrix with positive eigenvalues and will be called G. Our problem consists then of finding a hermitian matrix G with positive eigenvalues, which satisfies the equation

$$G = DGD^{\dagger} \tag{A.5}$$

for every D. Once G is known, the determination of A from the equation $A^{-1}A^{\dagger -1} = G$ is equivalent to the standard problem of diagonalizing G. Indeed, if V is the unitary matrix which diagonalizes G, and

$$d = VGV^{-1}, \tag{A.6}$$

then

$$A = d^{-\frac{1}{2}}V, \tag{A.7}$$

where $d^{-\frac{1}{2}}$ is the diagonal matrix whose elements are reciprocal to the positive square roots of the elements of d.

To find G, consider D as a function of the rotation R of the coordinate system, which can be identified by three Euler angles ψ, θ, φ (see Section 5), $D = D(R) = D(\psi, \theta, \varphi)$. We propose to show that

$$G = \int D(R)\, D^{\dagger}(R)\, dR \tag{A.8}$$

is a solution of (A.5). The differential dR represents a volume element of the space of Euler angles, $f(\psi, \theta, \varphi)\, d\psi\, d\theta\, d\varphi$, where f is suitably chosen below.

To this end we utilize the following "group property" of $D(R)$. The combined effect of two rotations R and R_0 is given by the two matrices $D(R)$ and $D(R_0)$ applied in succession. On the other hand, the combined rotations constitute a single rotation $R' = R_0 R$. Therefore D must obey the equations

$$D(R') = D(R_0)\, D(R) \tag{A.9}$$

and

$$D^\dagger(R') = D^\dagger(R)\, D^\dagger(R_0). \tag{A.10}$$

Enter now in (A.5) $D = D(R_0)$, where R_0 is a general rotation and G is given by (A.8). The right side of (A.5) equals

$$D(R_0) \int D(R)\, D^\dagger(R)\, dR\, D^\dagger(R_0) = \int D(R')\, D^\dagger(R')\, dR'. \tag{A.11}$$

To complete the proof that (A.8) satisfies (A.5), it must be shown that the right side of (A.11) is identical with G as given by (A.8). This identity holds provided $dR = dR' = d(R_0 R)$, and indeed the volume element dR must be so defined that it remains invariant when R is replaced with $R' = R_0 R$. The analytical relationship between dR and dR' is

$$\begin{aligned} dR &= f(\psi, \theta, \varphi)\, d\psi\, d\theta\, d\varphi = f(\psi, \theta, \varphi)\, \frac{\partial(\psi, \theta, \varphi)}{\partial(\psi', \theta', \varphi')}\, d\psi'\, d\theta'\, d\varphi' \\ &= \frac{f(\psi, \theta, \varphi)}{f(\psi', \theta', \varphi')}\, \frac{\partial(\psi, \theta, \varphi)}{\partial(\psi', \theta', \varphi')}\, dR'. \end{aligned} \tag{A.12}$$

It can be verified, from the definition of R, R_0, and R' in terms of Euler angles, that the Jacobian $\partial(\psi, \theta, \varphi)/\partial(\psi', \theta', \varphi')$ equals $\sin\theta'/\sin\theta$. Therefore (A.12) reduces to $dR = dR'$ provided $f(\psi, \theta, \varphi)$ equals $\sin\theta$ to within a constant. We set this constant equal to 1 and write

$$f(\psi, \theta, \varphi) = \sin\theta, \qquad dR = \sin\theta\, d\psi\, d\theta\, d\varphi. \tag{A.13}$$

In the expression of dR, the element $d\varphi$ corresponds to the choice of the azimuth of the new coordinate axis z' with respect to the old axes, $\sin\theta\, d\theta$ corresponds to the obliquity of z' with respect to z, and $d\psi$ to the orientation of x' and y' about z'.

b. Invariance under irreducible *r*-transformations. A matrix M which commutes with every irreducible $D(R)$ is a multiple of the unit matrix, that is,

$$MD(R) = D(R)M \tag{A.14}$$

entails

$$M = c\mathbf{1} \tag{A.15}$$

If M is hermitian, this theorem follows from an argument given in Section 3. When M is brought to its diagonal form $M' = BMB^{-1}$, all off-diagonal elements of $D' = BDB^{-1}$ which connect different diagonal elements of M' must vanish. The r-transformations D' would thereby be further reduced, contrary to the assumption of irreducibility. It follows that all the diagonal elements of M', i.e., all eigenvalues of M, must be equal, which proves (A.15).

If M is not hermitian, hermitian conjugation of (A.14) shows that $M^\dagger$ also commutes with $D(R)$, because $D^\dagger = D^{-1}$. Therefore the two hermitian matrices $M+M^\dagger$ and $i(M-M^\dagger)$ commute with $D(R)$. Both of them are then multiples of the unit matrix, and M itself must satisfy (A.15).

c. The Schur Lemma. If $D(R)$ and $D'(R)$ are two unitary irreducible r-transformations of dimensions n and n', and there exists a matrix M with n columns and n' rows such that

$$MD(R) = D'(R)\, M \tag{A.16}$$

for every R, then either $M = 0$ or $n = n'$ and $\det M \neq 0$; in the latter case D and D' are equivalent (Schur, 1905).

The hermitian conjugate of (A.16) is

$$M^\dagger D'^\dagger(R) = D^\dagger(R) M^\dagger. \tag{A.17}$$

Multiply this equation from the left by $D(R)$ and from the right by $D'(R)$, which yields, because the r-transformations are unitary,

$$D(R)M^\dagger = M^\dagger D'(R). \tag{A.18}$$

From (A.18) and (A.16) follows

$$MM^\dagger D'(R) = MD(R)\, M^\dagger = D'(R)MM^\dagger, \tag{A.19}$$

so that, according to (A.15) $MM^\dagger$ is a multiple of the unit matrix,

$$MM^\dagger = c\mathbf{1}. \tag{A.20}$$

If $n = n'$ and $c \neq 0$, $\det(MM^\dagger) \neq 0$ and therefore also $\det M \neq 0$. In this case M^{-1} does exist, and it follows from (A.16) that $D'(R) = M\,D(R)M^{-1}$ for all R, i.e., that $D(R)$ and $D'(R)$ are equivalent.

If $n = n'$ and $c = 0$, (A.20) may be written explicitly in the form

$$\Sigma_k M_{ik} M_{jk}^* = 0, \tag{A.21}$$

and for $i = j$

$$\Sigma_k |M_{ik}|^2 = 0, \tag{A.22}$$

from which follows that every M_{ik} vanishes.

If $n < n'$, the matrix M may be completed to a square matrix N by adding $n' - n$ columns of zeros. In this case $NN^\dagger = MM^\dagger$, but since $\det N = 0$ also c vanishes and (A.21) and (A.22) hold. If $n > n'$, the whole reasoning may be repeated after interchanging D with D' and M with $M^\dagger$.

d. Orthogonality of irreducible r-transformations. If X is an arbitrary matrix with n columns and n' rows, the matrix

$$M = \int D'(R)\, X\, D^{-1}(R)\, dR \tag{A.23}$$

satisfies (A.16). We have indeed

$$D'(S)M = \int D'(S)\, D'(R)\, X\, D^{-1}(R)\, dR = M'D(S), \tag{A.24}$$

with

$$M' = \int D'(SR)\, X\, D^{-1}(SR)\, dR, \tag{A.25}$$

and the equality

$$M = M' \tag{A.26}$$

follows from the argument utilized in (A.11).

If $D(R)$ and $D'(R)$ are not equivalent, it follows from the lemma that the matrix M vanishes for every choice of the matrix X; for the particular choice

$$X_{pq} = \delta_{kp}\, \delta_{mq} \tag{A.27}$$

we have

$$M_{il} = \int D_{ik}'(R)\, D^{-1}{}_{ml}(R)\, dR = \int D_{ik}'(R)\, D_{lm}^*(R)\, dR = 0 \tag{A.28}$$

stating that matrix elements of non-equivalent irreducible r-transformations are orthogonal functions of R, i.e., of the Euler angles ψ, θ, φ.

If $D(R) = D'(R)$, M must be a multiple of the unit matrix, and if we choose again X according to (A.27), we have

$$M_{il} = \int D_{ik}(R)\, D_{ml}(R^{-1})\, dR = c\delta_{il}, \tag{A.29}$$

where c is independent of i and l, but still depends on k and m. In order to evaluate c, we take the trace of (A.29). The left side gives

$$\Sigma_i M_{ii} = \Sigma_i \int D_{ik}(R) D_{mi}(R^{-1})\, dR = \int \Sigma_i D_{mi}(R^{-1}) D_{ik}(R)\, dR$$
$$= \int \delta_{mk}\, dR = \delta_{mk} \int\int\int \sin\theta\, d\psi\, d\theta\, d\varphi = 8\pi^2 \delta_{mk}. \tag{A.30}$$

The trace of the right side of (A.29) is simply cn, where n is the dimension (order) of D. Therefore

$$c = \delta_{mk} 8\pi^2/n \tag{A.31}$$

and (A.29) becomes

$$\int D_{ik}(R) D_{ml}(R^{-1})\, dR = \int D_{ik}(R) D_{lm}^{*}(R)\, dR = \delta_{il}\delta_{km} 8\pi^2/n. \tag{A.32}$$

which also provides the normalization of the functions $D_{ik}(R)$.

e. Character. The trace of an r-transformation,

$$\chi(R) = \Sigma_k D_{kk}(R), \tag{A.33}$$

considered as a function of R, is called the *character* of the r-transformation. If a tensorial set undergoes a linear substitution (2.3), the character of its r-transformation is not changed, because (2.11) does not change the trace of the matrix. This means that the characters of two equivalent r-transformations are equal.

If we decompose an r-transformation into its irreducible components, the character of the transformation will be equal to the sum of the characters of the components. On the other hand it follows from (A.28) that the characters of two irreducible non-equivalent r-transformations are orthogonal, and therefore the character of an r-transformation determines uniquely, apart from equivalence, the irreducible components into which it decomposes. In conclusion the equality of the characters is a necessary and sufficient condition for the equivalence of two r-transformations, i.e., for the existence of a matrix A which transforms one into the other according to (2.11).

B

Infinitesimal *r*-transformations and Angular Momentum

The transformations of tensorial sets induced by infinitesimal rotations of the coordinate system are of particular interest. As emphasized by Lie, a knowledge of all infinitesimal transformations amounts implicitly to a knowledge of all transformations. Moreover, infinitesimal *r*-transformations are closely related to the angular momentum operators of quantum mechanics, and it is of interest to identify this relationship.

Consider rotations of the coordinate system about a particular axis, say rotations $R_z(\varphi)$ of φ radians about the z axis, and the corresponding *r*-transformations of a tensorial set, $D_z(\varphi)$. When φ is very small, $\varphi = \varepsilon \ll 1$, the matrix D_z is approximately equal to the unit matrix and may be expressed as

$$D_z(\varepsilon) = \mathbf{1} + \varepsilon I_z + O(\varepsilon^2) \tag{B.1}$$

where

$$I_z = [dD_z(\varphi)/d\varphi]_{\varphi=0} \tag{B.2}$$

and $O(\varepsilon^2)$ indicates, as usual, terms of order ε^2.

A rotation by a finite φ may be generated as a succession of a large number n of rotations of φ/n radians, so that

$$D_z(\varphi) = [D_z(\varphi/n)]^n = [\mathbf{1} + (\varphi/n)I_z]^n + O(1/n), \tag{B.3}$$

and, in the limit $n = \infty$,

$$D_z(\varphi) = \lim_{n=\infty} [\mathbf{1} + (\varphi/n)I_z]^n = e^{\varphi I_z} = \mathbf{1} + \varphi I_z + \tfrac{1}{2}\varphi^2 I_z{}^2 + \dots. \tag{B.4}$$

To treat rotations about an arbitrary axis $\mathbf{u}$, we introduce besides I_z analogous matrices I_x and I_y pertaining to rotations about the axes x and y, and we have

$$\begin{aligned} D_{\mathbf{u}}(\varepsilon) &= \mathbf{1} + \varepsilon[u_x I_x + u_y I_y + u_z I_z] + O(\varepsilon^2) \\ &= \mathbf{1} + \varepsilon\, \mathbf{u}\cdot\mathbf{I} + O(\varepsilon^2) \end{aligned} \tag{B.5}$$

and

$$D_{\mathbf{u}}(\varphi) = e^{\varphi \mathbf{u}\cdot\mathbf{I}}, \tag{B.6}$$

where $\mathbf{I}$ indicates the set of three matrices I_x, I_y, and I_z in vector notation.

A relationship between the matrices I_x, I_y, and I_z is established by the fact that the combined effects of coordinate rotations $R_1, R_2 \ldots$ about different axes depends on the order in which the rotations are applied, i.e., $R_1R_2 \neq R_2R_1$. To work out the relationship between the matrices

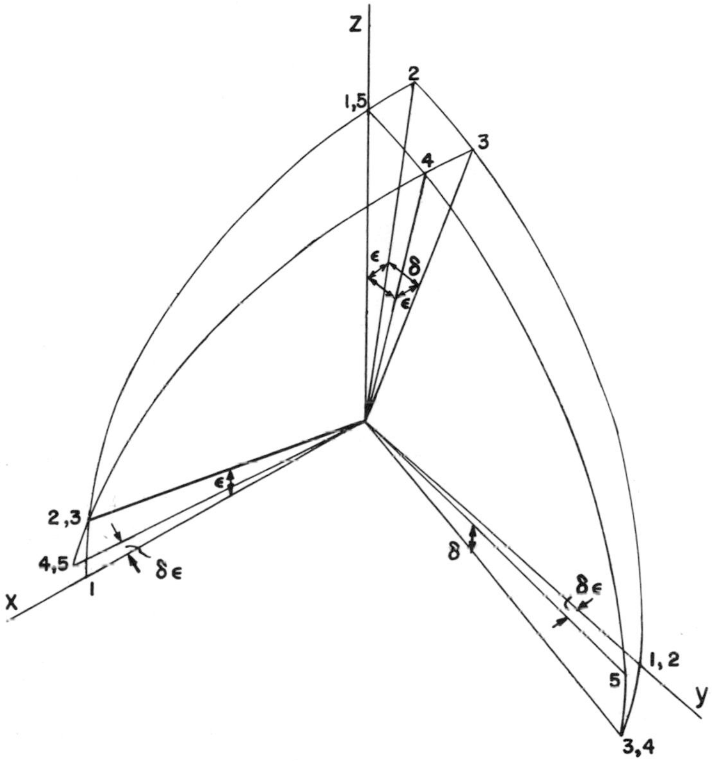

FIG. 5. Graphical demonstration of the commutation rule $I_xI_y - I_yI_x = -I_z$.

I_k (with $k = x, y, z$) consider the succession of four infinitesimal rotations indicated by

$$R_x(\delta)\, R_y(\varepsilon)\, R_x(-\delta)\, R_y(-\varepsilon), \tag{B.7}$$

which would yield no net rotation if the order of application were irrelevant. (The formula means that $R_y(-\varepsilon)$ is applied first, then $R_x(-\delta)$, etc.) The corresponding r-transformation formula, obtained from (B.6) by expansion to second order in the angles, is

$$e^{\delta I_x}\, e^{\varepsilon I_y}\, e^{-\delta I_x}\, e^{-\varepsilon I_y} = 1 + \delta\varepsilon(I_x I_y - I_y I_x). \tag{B.8}$$

The resultant of the four rotations is, in the same approximation, a single rotation of $-\delta\varepsilon$ radians about the z axis, $R_z(-\delta\varepsilon)$. This is shown by a geometrical construction, as in Fig. 5 where the numbers mark the five successive positions of the tips of unit vectors along the coordinate axes. Analytically, the result of the four rotations (B.7) may be derived by calculating explicitly (B.8) for the set of coordinates (xyz) of a point. The r-transformations of this set are given by elementary formulas, such as

$$x' = x \cos\varphi + y \sin\varphi, \quad y' = -x \sin\varphi + y \cos\varphi, \quad z' = z, \tag{B.9}$$

for $D_z(\varphi)$. The corresponding matrices I_k are

$$I_x = \begin{vmatrix} 0 & 0 & 0 \\ 0 & 0 & 1 \\ 0 & -1 & 0 \end{vmatrix}, \quad I_y = \begin{vmatrix} 0 & 0 & -1 \\ 0 & 0 & 0 \\ 1 & 0 & 0 \end{vmatrix}, \quad I_z = \begin{vmatrix} 0 & 1 & 0 \\ -1 & 0 & 0 \\ 0 & 0 & 0 \end{vmatrix}, \tag{B.10}$$

and matrix multiplication yields

$$I_x I_y - I_y I_x = -I_z \tag{B.11}$$

Replacing then in (B.8) $I_x I_y - I_y I_z$ with $-I_z$, we see that the result is $D_z(-\delta\varepsilon)$.

Because (B.7) equals $R_z(-\delta\varepsilon)$, it follows that (B.8) must equal $1 - \delta\varepsilon I_z$ in general, that is not only for the matrices (B.10) but for the matrices I_k of every r-transformation. Therefore (B.11) has general validity, and similarly one finds

$$I_y I_z - I_z I_y = -I_x, \quad I_z I_x - I_x I_z = -I_y, \tag{B.12}$$

The matrices I_k are not hermitian and are conveniently replaced with hermitian ones. Because we deal with tensorial sets with unitary r-transformations, the eigenvalues of $D_z(\varphi)$ in (B.4) must have the form $\exp(i\alpha)$ with α real. That is, the eigenvalues of I_z and of I_x, I_y must be imaginary and the matrices

$$J_x = -iI_x, \quad J_y = -iI_y, \quad J_z = -iI_z, \tag{B.13}$$

must be hermitian. We replace then (B.6) with

$$D_{\mathbf{u}}(\varphi) = e^{i\varphi\mathbf{u}\cdot\mathbf{J}}, \tag{B.14}$$

and the commutation rules (B.11) and (B.12) become

$$J_x J_y - J_y J_x = iJ_z, \quad J_y J_z - J_z J_y = iJ_x, \quad J_z J_x - J_x J_z = iJ_y. \tag{B.15}$$

The equations (B.15) are the well-known commutation rules of the components of the angular momentum of a quantum mechanical system, measured in units of $\hbar$. Actually, in the special case of the tensorial set consisting of the coefficients $a^{(j)}{}_m$ which identify the state ψ_a of an atomic system, the matrices defined by (B.13) coincide with the quantum-mechanical representation of the components of the angular momentum. For the sets of eigenstates $u^{(j)}{}_m$ there is no such straightforward coincidence, because the matrices of angular momentum operators are applied to the sets of $u^{(j)}{}_m$ from the right, whereas in general the r-transformation matrices D operate from the left according to (2.4). However, if the r-transformations of the $u^{(j)}{}_m$ are indicated as $D^{-1} = \exp(-i\varphi\mathbf{u}\cdot\mathbf{J})$ to be applied on the right, as in (2.3), to emphasize the contragredience of the $u^{(j)}{}_{m}$, then this $\mathbf{J}$ coincides again with the angular momentum divided by $\hbar$.

The properties of the set of matrices J_x, J_y, and J_z, which follow from their commutation rules (B.15), are well known but will be summarized here for the sake of completeness. These properties are important because they lead independently not only to the concept of irreducible sets but also to a procedure for actually resolving any set into irreducible sets with standardized r-transformations.

Firstly one can construct from the matrices J_x, J_y, and J_z of a given set the matrix

$$\mathbf{J}^2 = J_x{}^2 + J_y{}^2 + J_z{}^2. \tag{B.16}$$

One verifies, by applying (B.15), that $\mathbf{J}^2$ commutes with each of J_x, J_y, and J_z and, therefore, with the general r transformation (B.14). When two matrices commute and one of them is reduced to diagonal form, the other matrix resolves into a number of submatrices, each corresponding to one eigenvalue of the first matrix. In our case if $\mathbf{J}^2$ is reduced to diagonal form, each off-diagonal element of the matrix $D_{\mathbf{u}}(\varphi)$ vanishes when it belongs to a row and a column pertaining to different eigenvalues of $\mathbf{J}^2$, as indicated in Fig. 1. Suppose, then, that a tensorial set is given, with a unitary transformation law $D(R)$. One can obtain from $D(R)$ the matrix $\mathbf{J}^2$, and then find a unitary substitution of the set which diagonalizes $\mathbf{J}^2$. After the substitution the transformation $D(R)$ intermixes only elements that correspond to the same eigenvalue of $\mathbf{J}^2$. Thus the substitution has resolved the set into invariant subsets, that is, it has reduced it. By the same token, the matrix $\mathbf{J}^2$ of an irreducible set must be diagonal and have all its eigenvalues equal to one another, otherwise the set could be reduced further.

Consider now a set for which $\mathbf{J}^2$ is diagonal with its eigenvalues equal to one another and indicated by β, and consider one among the matrices J_k, say J_z. The matrix J_z can be diagonalized by a unitary substitution of the set. Its eigenvalues will be indicated by m, and its eigenvectors, which are elements of the set, by $v_{m\alpha}$, where α is introduced if there is more than one eigenvector corresponding to the same eigenvalue m.

As a next step we begin to examine the limitations placed by the commutation formulas upon the matrix elements of the J_k. From (B.15) we have

$$J_z(J_x+iJ_y)-(J_x+iJ_y)J_z = J_x+iJ_y, \tag{B.17}$$
$$J_z(J_x-iJ_y)-(J_x-iJ_y)J_z = -(J_x-iJ_y).$$

The elements of these matrix equations connecting the set elements $v_{m\alpha}$ and $v_{m'\alpha'}$ yield

$$(m'-m-1)\,(J_x+iJ_y)_{m'\alpha',m\alpha} = 0, \tag{B.18}$$
$$(m'-m+1)\,(J_x-iJ_y)_{m'\alpha',m\alpha} = 0,$$

showing that non-vanishing elements of $J_x \pm iJ_y$ connect only set elements with $m' = m\pm 1$.

Owing to (B.16) and (B.15), the matrices

$$(J_x-iJ_y)\,(J_x+iJ_y) = J_x^{\,2}+J_y^{\,2}+i(J_xJ_y-J_yJ_x) = \mathbf{J}^2-J_z^{\,2}-J_z,$$

and

$$(J_x+iJ_y)\,(J_x-iJ_y) = J_x^{\,2}+J_y^{\,2}-i(J_xJ_y-J_yJ_x) = \mathbf{J}^2-J_z^{\,2}+J_z$$

are diagonal in the scheme of eigenvectors $v_{m\alpha}$, and their diagonal elements are

$$\Sigma_{\alpha'}(J_x-iJ_y)_{m\alpha,m+1\alpha'}(J_x+iJ_y)_{m+1\alpha',m\alpha}$$
$$= \Sigma_{\alpha'}|(J_x+iJ_y)_{m+1\alpha',m\alpha}|^2 = \beta-m(m+1), \tag{B.19a}$$

$$\Sigma_{\alpha'}(J_x+iJ_y)_{m\alpha,m-1\alpha'}(J_x-iJ_y)_{m-1\alpha',m\alpha}$$
$$= \Sigma_{\alpha'}|(J_x-iJ_y)_{m-1\alpha',m\alpha}|^2 = \beta-m(m-1). \tag{B.19b}$$

Because the middle part of these equations is non-negative, we have here two relationships between the eigenvalues of $\mathbf{J}^2$ and J_z, namely

$$\beta-m(m+1)\geq 0, \qquad \beta-m(m-1)\geq 0. \tag{B.20}$$

Therefore the sequence of eigenvalues of $J_z, \ldots m+2, m+1, m, m-1 \ldots$, derived from (B.18) cannot extend indefinitely either toward $m=\infty$ or $m=-\infty$. This sequence terminates, according to (B.18), on the side of the highest m only where the matrix elements of J_x+iJ_y vanishes, that is, in view of (B.19a), only if and when $\beta-m(m+1)=0$; on the side of the lowest m, the sequence stops similarly only if and when $\beta - m(m-1) = 0$. We call j the largest value of m, at which the sequence stops, and we must then have

$$\beta = j(j+1). \tag{B.21}$$

The sequence will also stop at a lowest m which obeys the equation $m(m-1) = \beta = j(j+1)$. This equation has the solutions $m = j+1$ and $m = -j$, of which $j+1$ is not acceptable because the lowest j cannot exceed the largest one; the solution $-j$ is acceptable as a lowest m provided j is *not negative.* Moreover the two limiting values of m, namely $\pm j$, are part of the same sequence of values of m, with intervals one, only if the number j is either *integral* or *half-integral.* To the eigenvalue (B.21) of $\mathbf{J}^2$, there correspond then the eigenvalues of J_z

$$m = j, j-1, j-2 \ldots -j+1, -j. \tag{B.22}$$

We examine now the possible degeneracy of the eigenvalues of J_z, i.e., the possible number g_m of set elements $v_{m\alpha}$ with different α, which are eigenvectors of J_z pertaining to the same eigenvalue m. For this purpose we write (B.19b) replacing m with $m+1$,

$$\Sigma_{\alpha'}(J_x+iJ_y)_{m+1\alpha,m\alpha'}\,(J_x-iJ_y)_{m\alpha',m+1\alpha} = \beta - m(m+1), \tag{B.19c}$$

and then sum (B.19a) over the g_m values of α corresponding to the eigenvalue m, and sum (B.19c) over the g_{m+1} values of α corresponding to $m+1$. The sums give

$$\Sigma_{\alpha\alpha'}(J_x-iJ_y)_{m\alpha,m+1\alpha'}\,(J_x+iJ_y)_{m+1\alpha',m\alpha} = g_m[\beta - m(m+1)] \tag{B.23}$$

$$\Sigma_{\alpha\alpha'}(J_x+iJ_y)_{m+1\alpha,m\alpha'}\,(J_x-iJ_y)_{m\alpha',m+1\alpha} = g_{m+1}[\beta - m(m+1)].$$

The left sides of the two equations are equal, and therefore the multiplicity g_{m+1} must be equal to g_m. Proceeding chainwise from one m to the next we see that the multiplicity has the same value for all m. The set of elements $v_{m\alpha}$ consists therefore of g elements for each of the $2j+1$ values of m, i.e., of $g(2j+1)$ elements in all.

For $g > 1$, it will be shown that the set can be further reduced, namely split into g sets of $2j+1$ elements each. Taking into account that $J_x - iJ_y = (J_x + iJ_y)^\dagger$, it follows from (B.19) and (B.21) that

$$(J_x+iJ_y)_{m+1\alpha,m\alpha'} = [j(j+1)-m(m+1)]^{\frac{1}{2}}\, U^{(m)}_{\alpha\alpha'}, \tag{B.24}$$

$$(J_x-iJ_y)_{m\alpha',m+1\alpha} = [j(j+1)-m(m+1)]^{\frac{1}{2}}\, U^{(m)\dagger}_{\alpha'\alpha},$$

where $U^{(m)}$ is a unitary matrix of order g. One can then apply a unitary substitution to the set $v_{m\alpha}$ as indicated by

$$v'_{m\alpha} = \Sigma_{\alpha'} V^{(m)}_{\alpha\alpha'} v_{m\alpha'}, \tag{B.25}$$

where $V^{(m)}$ is also a unitary matrix of order g, namely,

$$V^{(m)} = 1\, U^{(j-1)}\, U^{(j-2)} \ldots U^{(m)}. \tag{B.26}$$

The matrix elements (B.24) are then replaced, according to (2.8), with

$$\begin{aligned}(J_x + iJ_y)_{m+1\alpha, m\alpha'} &= [j(j+1) - m(m+1)]^{\frac{1}{2}} (V^{(m+1)} U^{(m)} V^{(m)-1})_{\alpha\alpha'} \\ &= [j(j+1) - m(m+1)]^{\frac{1}{2}} \delta_{\alpha\alpha'}, \\ (J_x - iJ_y)_{m\alpha', m+1\alpha} &= [j(j+1) - m(m+1)]^{\frac{1}{2}} (V^{(m)} U^{(m)\dagger} V^{(m+1)-1})_{\alpha'\alpha} \\ &= [j(j+1) - m(m+1)]^{\frac{1}{2}} \delta_{\alpha'\alpha}.\end{aligned} \tag{B.27}$$

Because $J_x \pm iJ_y$ is now diagonal in α, and J_z is diagonal too, the subsets of $2j+1$ elements $v'_{m\alpha}$ with equal α and different m have separate matrices J_k and therefore separate r-transformations. These new subsets constitute *irreducible* sets because the matrix J_z must have all the $2j+1$ eigenvalues (B.22) and none of these eigenvalues is now degenerate.

The irreducible sets with integral j and those with half-integral j differ characteristically in their r-transformations corresponding to coordinate rotations of 360°. Calling z the direction of the axis of rotation, the r-transformation (B.14) takes the form $\exp(i2\pi J_z)$ when $\varphi = 2\pi$ and $\mathbf{u}\cdot\mathbf{J} = J_z$. The elements of a set for which J_z is diagonal are therefore eigenvectors of this r-transformation and each of them is simply multiplied by the corresponding eigenvalue $\exp(i2\pi m)$. According to (B.22) these eigenvalues are all equal to 1 if j is an integer and to -1 if it is a half-integer, so that an irreducible set is left unchanged by a rotation of 360°, if its j value is integral, but it is multiplied by -1 if its j value is half-integral.

C

Properties of the Matrix U

a. Existence of U. The equation

$$D^*(R) = UD(R)U^{-1} \tag{4.2}$$

indicates that the r-transformations $D(R)$ and $D^*(R)$ can be transformed into one another by a unitary U which is the same for all coordinate rotations R; that is, U exists if D and D^* are equivalent. It is shown at the end of Appendix A that $D(R)$ and $D^*(R)$ are equivalent if they have equal characters. Therefore a solution of (4.2) exists if, and only if, $Tr[D^*(R)] = Tr[D(R)]$. Since $D^*(R)$ is the transposed of $D^{-1}(R) = D(R^{-1})$, it is sufficient to show that $Tr[D(R^{-1})] = Tr[D(R)]$.

Now a rotation R of space coordinates about an axis $\mathbf{u}$ and its inverse R^{-1} have the property that R^{-1} is a rotation of equal magnitude as R about the inverted axis $-\mathbf{u}$, and that the axis $-\mathbf{u}$ is obtained from $\mathbf{u}$ by a rotation S of 180° about any axis orthogonal to $\mathbf{u}$. This relationship is indicated by the equation

$$R^{-1} = SRS^{-1}, \tag{C.1}$$

from which follows the relationship among r-transformations

$$D(R^{-1}) = D(S)\,D(R)\,D^{-1}(S), \tag{C.2}$$

and hence $Tr[D(R^{-1})] = Tr[D(R)]$.

b. Degree of indeterminacy of U. Suppose that (4.2) holds, and also $D^* = U'DU'^{-1}$, with $U' \neq U$. We have then

$$D = U^{-1}D^*U = U^{-1}U'DU'^{-1}U = (U^{-1}U')D(U^{-1}U')^{-1}, \tag{C.3}$$

showing that $U^{-1}U'$ must commute with $D(R)$ for all R. That is, U is identified by (4.2) to within multiplication by any matrix $V = U^{-1}U'$ which commutes with all $D(R)$. It follows then from (A.15) that

$$V = U^{-1}U' = c\,\mathbf{1}, \qquad \text{for } D \text{ irreducible}, \tag{C.4}$$

where $|c| = 1$ in order that V be unitary.

c. Transformations of U. The effect of substitutions upon a general transformation T is represented by the formula (2.8), $T' = BTA^{-1}$. In the case of the transformation U, which changes a set into one contragredient to it, we have

$$B = A^* \tag{C.5}$$

and therefore

$$U' = A^*UA^{-1} \tag{C.6}$$

That is, U' is not equivalent to U unless A is real.

U is invariant under r-transformations because

$$U' = D^*UD^{-1} = UDU^{-1}UD^{-1} = U \tag{C.7}$$

d. The matrix U*U. If the linear transformation U changes a tensorial set of elements a_r into a set contragredient to a_r, successive application of U and U^* changes a_r into a new set cogredient to itself. Indeed the complex conjugate of (4.2) is $D = U^*D^*U^{*-1}$ and substitution of (4.2) in this equation yields

$$D = U^*UD(U^*U)^{-1}. \tag{C.8}$$

That is, the matrix U^*U must commute with D. If D is irreducible, it follows again from (A.15) that U^*U must have the form $c\mathbf{1}$, with $|c| = 1$. The constant c is also seen to be real, because $c^*\mathbf{1} = UU^* = UU^*UU^{-1} = UcU^{-1} = c\mathbf{1}$, and we write

$$U^*U = \pm\mathbf{1}, \qquad \text{for } D \text{ irreducible.} \tag{C.9}$$

Even though the matrix U does not transform according to (2.10), as shown by (C.6), U^*U does, because it follows from (C.6) that

$$U'^*U' = AU^*A^{-1*}A^*UA^{-1} = AU^*UA^{-1} \tag{C.10}$$

for reducible as for irreducible sets.

e. Real r-transformations; sets with symmetric U. For a set of quantities a_i whose r-transformations D are real ($D = D^*$) there is no distinction of contragredience, so that U may be taken equal to $\mathbf{1}$. It follows then from (C.10) that $U'^*U' = \mathbf{1}$ and $U' = U'^{*-1} = \widetilde{U}'$ for all A, that is, all sets whose r-transformations are equivalent to real ones have a symmetric U.

Conversely any set with a symmetric U may be transformed into a set with real r-transformations and $U = \mathbf{1}$.‡ Any unitary symmetric matrix U can be factored in the form §

‡ A lengthy proof of this theorem was given by Frobenius and Schur (1906). The proof given here originates from unpublished notes of E. P. Wigner.

§ To prove (C.11), one shows first that, for any symmetric unitary U, if there is a complex eigenvector its complex conjugate is also an eigenvector corresponding to the same eigenvalue. Therefore the eigenvectors can all be made real and U takes the form $R\exp(i\Delta)\widetilde{R}$, with R unitary and real and Δ real and diagonal. We have then $U = \widetilde{Q}Q$ with $Q = \exp(i\Delta/2)\widetilde{R}$.

$$U = \widetilde{Q}Q, \tag{C.11}$$

with Q unitary. Therefore, given a set of quantities a_i, which is changed into a contragredient set by a symmetric U, the set of quantities $a_k' = \Sigma_i Q_{ki} a_i$ has real r-transformations, because, according to (C.6),

$$U' = Q^* U Q^{-1} = Q^* \widetilde{Q} Q Q^{-1} = 1. \tag{C.12}$$

f. Application of U to infinitesimal *r*-transformations. When the r-transformation D is expressed in the form (B.14), as $\exp(i\varphi \mathbf{u}\cdot\mathbf{J})$, Eq. (4.2) becomes

$$e^{-i\varphi \mathbf{u}\cdot\mathbf{J}^*} = U\, e^{i\varphi \mathbf{u}\cdot\mathbf{J}}\, U^{-1} = e^{i\varphi \mathbf{u}\cdot U\mathbf{J}U^{-1}}. \tag{C.13}$$

This equation is equivalent to

$$-\mathbf{J}^* = U\mathbf{J}U^{-1} \tag{C.14}$$

or

$$U\mathbf{J} + \mathbf{J}^* U = 0, \tag{C.15}$$

which are understood to hold for each of the matrices J_x, J_y, and J_z. If any of these matrices is real ($J_k^* = J_k$), (C.15) shows that it anti-commutes with U; if it is imaginary ($J_k^* = -J_k$), it commutes with U.

It is of interest to consider the possibility of choosing the matrices J_k either real or imaginary, i.e., of classifying them according to parity under complex conjugation and commutability with U. The choice is limited by the commutation rules (B.15) among the J, which are seen on inspection to exclude the possibility of having all J real or one real and two imaginary. There remains two possibilities consistent with (B.15): (1) All three J_k are made imaginary, which implies D real owing to (B.14) and therefore $U = 1$. This can be achieved by unitary substitution of a set only if the set has initially a symmetric U, as seen in Section (e) above. (2) Two of the J_k are made real and one imaginary. This can always be achieved, for example by the procedure of Appendix B. The set is brought to reduced form and one of the J_k, say J_z, is made diagonal and hence real. Equation (B.17) shows that, when J_z is diagonal, the matrices of J_x and J_y have non-zero elements connecting only those elements of each irreducible subset for which the eigenvalues m and m' of J_z differ by one. The complex phases of these matrix elements depend on the phase differences of the corresponding pairs of elements of the subset. It is possible to multiply each element of the subset for which $J_z = m$ by a suitable factor $\exp(i\gamma_m)$ with the γ_m so chosen as to make the matrix J_x real. The matrix J_y is then imaginary, owing to $J_zJ_x - J_xJ_z = iJ_y$.

When the choice (2) is made and J_x, J_z are brought to real form,

$$J_x = J_x^*, \quad J_y = -J_y^*, \quad J_z = J_z^*, \tag{C.16}$$

we have

$$\begin{aligned} D_x(\varphi)^* &= e^{-i\varphi J_x^*} = e^{-i\varphi J_x} = D_x(-\varphi) \\ D_y(\varphi)^* &= e^{-i\varphi J_y^*} = e^{i\varphi J_y} \;\, = D_y(\varphi) \\ D_z(\varphi)^* &= e^{-i\varphi J_z^*} = e^{-i\varphi J_z} = D_z(-\varphi). \end{aligned} \tag{C.17}$$

Equation (C.16) gives then

$$J_x = -UJ_xU^{-1}, \quad J_y = UJ_yU^{-1}, \quad J_z = -UJ_zU^{-1}. \tag{C.18}$$

The equations (C.18) are clearly fulfilled when U represents a rotation of 180° about the y axis because this rotation inverts the directions of x and z, and therefore we may take

$$U = D_y(\pi) = e^{i\pi J_y}. \tag{C.19}$$

It should be clearly understood that the choice of U made here in conformity to general practice depends on the convention (C.16) and is altered by any non-real substitution of the set.

g. Symmetry of U for irreducible sets. If the r-transformations D of a set are irreducible, it follows from (C.9) that

$$\tilde{U} = \pm U, \tag{C.20}$$

showing that U is either symmetric or antisymmetric. Owing to (C.10) this result is invariant under unitary transformations A. Therefore the symmetry of U is a characteristic property of each irreducible set.

This symmetry depends only on the order $2j+1$ of the set. For irreducible sets of odd order (integral j), U must be symmetric because antisymmetric matrices of odd order have vanishing determinants and cannot be unitary. For irreducible sets of even order (half-integral j), U must be antisymmetric, as shown by the following argument.

When the matrix J_z is reduced to diagonal form, the $(\frac{1}{2}, \frac{1}{2})$ element of the equation (C.15), $U(J_x - iJ_y) + (J_x^* - iJ_y^*)\,U = 0$, is, owing to (B.18),

$$\begin{aligned} &U_{\frac{1}{2}\,-\frac{1}{2}}\,(J_x - iJ_y)_{-\frac{1}{2}\frac{1}{2}} + (J_x^* - iJ_y^*)_{\frac{1}{2}\,-\frac{1}{2}}\,U_{-\frac{1}{2}\frac{1}{2}} \\ &\qquad = (U_{\frac{1}{2}\,-\frac{1}{2}} + U_{-\frac{1}{2}\frac{1}{2}})\,(J_x - iJ_y)_{-\frac{1}{2}\frac{1}{2}} = 0, \end{aligned} \tag{C.21}$$

with $(J_x - iJ_y)_{-\frac{1}{2}\frac{1}{2}} \neq 0$. Therefore either U is antisymmetric or its elements $U_{\frac{1}{2}\,-\frac{1}{2}}$ and $U_{-\frac{1}{2}\frac{1}{2}}$ vanish. The latter possibility is excluded by the other component of (C.15), $UJ_z+J_z{}^*U = 0$, whose matrix elements are, when J_z is diagonal, $(m+m')\, U_{m'm} = 0$; $U_{m'm}$ must vanish for $m' \neq -m$ and therefore cannot vanish for $m' = -m$, otherwise the determinant of U would vanish and U would not have a reciprocal matrix.

h. Symmetry of U for reducible sets. This symmetry depends on the indeterminacy of U discussed in Section (b). The indeterminacy will be discussed assuming a set to be initially in reduced form, and for various cases separately.

(1) The reduced set consists of irreducible subsets with j values all integral (or all half-integral) and all different. The matrix U may consist of separate submatrices, one for each subset, with symmetry $(-1)^{2j}$. This whole matrix has symmetry $(-1)^{2j}$, but it may be replaced, according to (b), with any $U' = UV$ where V is any matrix which commutes with the whole D. This V has no elements which intermix the subsets, whose j are different (see Appendix A), i.e., it consists of separate submatrices, one for each subset. According to (C.4) each of these submatrices of V has the form $c_j\mathbf{1}$, so that V does not alter the symmetry $(-1)^{2j}$ of the complete matrix U. From $U' = (-1)^{2j}\, \widetilde{U}'$ follows $U'^*U' = (-1)^{2j}$ and (C.10) shows that this symmetry property is unaffected by any transformation A, so that the matrix U_A of the reducible set remains symmetric or antisymmetric even when the set is in a non-reduced form.

(2) The reduced set consists of subsets with j values all integral (or all half-integral) some of which are equal. The r-transformations $D^{(j)}$ may be assumed to have the same form for all subsets with the same j. The matrix U may again consist of separate submatrices, one for each subset, with the common symmetry $(-1)^{2j}$, and these submatrices may also be assumed equal for equal j. The entire matrix U thus constructed has symmetry $(-1)^{2j}$ but it may be replaced, according to Section (b), with $U' = UV$ where V is any matrix which commutes with the whole D. This V has no elements which intermix subsets with different j (see Appendix A), i.e., it consists of separate submatrices, one for each value of j. Each of these submatrices may be still represented in the form analogous to (C.4), $c_j \times \mathbf{1}$, where c_j indicates now a unitary matrix with as many rows and columns as there are subsets of degree j, and $\mathbf{1}$ is the unit matrix of order $2j+1$. That is, V intermixes subsets with equal j, in block, without transforming any of them. The matrices c_j need not have a definite symmetry. However, if the c_j are all *symmetric*, the whole matrix $U' = UV$ will have the symmetry $(-1)^{2j}$, and this symmetry will be maintained under any unitary transformation A. In particular,

since a symmetric unitary c_j may be diagonalized by a *real* unitary transformation, U' can be itself reduced to a form similar to U, consisting of a string of submatrices of order j, one for each irreducible subset, provided it has the correct symmetry $(-1)^{2j}$. This symmetry requirement on U' is necessary and sufficient to insure that U' can be reduced to a string of submatrices of order $(2j+1)$ at the same time as the r-transformation D is reduced to a string of submatrices $D^{(j)}$. This requirement restricts, of course, the indeterminacy of U' below the limit indicated in Section (b).

(3) The reduced set consists of subsets with j values partly integral and partly half-integral. In this case a reduced U, consisting of submatrices U_j, cannot have a definite symmetry. The same holds, therefore, for any U which can be reduced simultaneously with D. In the following we shall have no occasion to deal with sets of this class.‡

i. The conjugation relationship. Conjugation of a tensorial set has been defined in Section 4 as an operation represented by K_0U. This operation is reciprocal for tensorial sets with a symmetric U, i.e., the conjugate of the conjugate coincides with the initial set, because

$$K^2 = K_0UK_0U = U^*U \tag{C.22}$$

equals $\mathbf{1}$ for a symmetric unitary U. For tensorial sets with antisymmetric U, U^*U equals $-\mathbf{1}$, that is, double conjugation brings a set back to the original form with the sign changed. As seen in Section (h), an antisymmetric U usually belongs, either by necessity or by a requirement of reducibility, to sets which, upon reduction, resolve into subsets with half-integral j. These sets are multiplied by -1 by any r-transformation corresponding to a rotation of 360° and thus are inherently defined to within a factor ± 1. Indeed, if U is chosen as $D_y(\pi)$ on the basis of (C.18) and (C.19), it follows from these equations that $U^*U = D_y(2\pi)$.

---

‡ In quantum mechanics a set of class 3 would occur in the representation of a state resulting from the superposition of boson and fermion states. Wick *et al.* (1952) have emphasized that interference resulting from this superposition would be inconsistent with the expected behavior of quantum mechanical states under time reversal. The time reversal considerations appear equivalent to considerations of the behavior of the set when transformed by the matrix U^*U. If the set is in reduced form, the portion of it consisting of subsets with integral j is usually assumed to have a partial U which is symmetric, so that this portion is unaffected by U^*U, whereas the portion with half-integral j is assumed to have a partial U antisymmetric and therefore $U^*U = -\mathbf{1}$. Thus the transformation U^*U changes the initial set into a new one, which is inconsistent with the assumptions of these authors.

Because conjugate sets are defined so as to be cogredient, conjugation must be invariant under r-transformations. Indeed it follows from (4.2) that

$$DK = DK_0U = K_0D^*U = K_0UDU^{-1}U = KD. \tag{C.23}$$

From (C. 15) it follows that K anticommutes with J,

$$KJ + JK = 0. \tag{C.24}$$

Conjugation is changed by unitary substitution into the equivalent operation, as defined by (2.10), because

$$K' = K_0U' = K_0A^*UA^{-1} = AK_0UA^{-1} = AKA^{-1} \tag{C.25}$$

whereas U' is not equivalent to U.

For a set whose r-transformations are real and $U = \mathsf{1}$, K reduces to K_0. If the elements of the set are themselves real, they are unaffected by K_0 and the set is *self-conjugate*. However, the property of being self-conjugate is invariant under unitary transformations whereas the reality of the set elements is not. The components of real tensors constitute self-conjugate sets. There are no self-conjugate sets with antisymmetric U because $K = \mathsf{1}$ is inconsistent with $K^2 = U^*U = -\mathsf{1}$. The operations K_0 and U are equivalent for self-conjugate sets and for these sets only, since $K_0 = U$ implies $\mathsf{1} = K_0{}^2 = K_0U = K$.

D

Calculation of the Standard *r*-transformations

a. Factorization. When a rotation of coordinates is identified by its magnitude φ and axis $\mathbf{u}$, the corresponding standard r-transformation is given by $\exp(i\varphi\mathbf{u}\cdot\mathbf{J}) = \exp[i\varphi(u_xJ_x+u_yJ_y+u_zJ_z)]$, according to (B.14) and can be calculated, at least in principle, from the matrices of J_x, J_y, and J_z. More commonly, a rotation is resolved into a succession of rotations identified by Euler angles ψ, θ, and φ (see Fig. 2) and the corresponding standard r-transformation is

$$\mathfrak{D}^{(j)}(\psi, \theta, \varphi) = e^{i\psi J_z}\, e^{i\theta J_y}\, e^{i\varphi J_z}. \tag{D.1}$$

Owing to (5.1) the matrix elements of $\mathfrak{D}^{(j)}$ reduce to

$$\mathfrak{D}^{(j)}{}_{m'm}(\psi, \theta, \varphi) = e^{i\psi m'}\, (e^{i\theta J_y})_{m'm}\, e^{i\varphi m}, \tag{D.2}$$

where iJ_y is real and $[\exp(i\theta J_y)]_{m'm}$ is real too. We utilize the notation

$$\mathfrak{d}^{(j)}(\theta) = e^{i\theta J_y}\,, \tag{D.3}$$

so that

$$\mathfrak{D}^{(j)}{}_{m'm}(\psi, \theta, \varphi) = e^{i\psi m'}\, \mathfrak{d}^{(j)}{}_{m'm}(\theta)\, e^{i\varphi m}. \tag{D.4}$$

The matrix $\mathfrak{d}^{(j)}(\theta)$ can be calculated from the matrix of J_y. For $j = \frac{1}{2}$ we have $J_y = \frac{1}{2}\sigma_y$, where σ_y is the Pauli matrix

$$\sigma_y = \begin{Vmatrix} 0 & -i \\ i & 0 \end{Vmatrix}, \tag{D.5}$$

for which $\sigma_y{}^2 = \mathbf{1}$. We have, then, by power expansion

$$\mathfrak{d}^{(\frac{1}{2})}(\theta) = e^{i\theta J_y} = e^{i(\frac{1}{2}\theta)\sigma_y} = \mathbf{1}\sum_{n=0}^{\infty}\frac{(i\frac{1}{2}\theta)^{2n}}{(2n)!} + \sigma_y\sum_{n=0}^{\infty}\frac{(i\frac{1}{2}\theta)^{2n+1}}{(2n+1)!}$$

$$= \mathbf{1}\cos\tfrac{1}{2}\theta + i\sigma_y\sin\tfrac{1}{2}\theta = \begin{Vmatrix} \cos\frac{1}{2}\theta & \sin\frac{1}{2}\theta \\ -\sin\frac{1}{2}\theta & \cos\frac{1}{2}\theta \end{Vmatrix} \tag{D.6}$$

and

$$\mathfrak{D}^{(\frac{1}{2})}(\psi, \theta, \varphi) = \begin{Vmatrix} \cos\frac{1}{2}\theta\, e^{i(\psi+\varphi)/2} & \sin\frac{1}{2}\theta\, e^{i(\psi-\varphi)/2} \\ -\sin\frac{1}{2}\theta\, e^{-i(\psi-\varphi)/2} & \cos\frac{1}{2}\theta\, e^{-i(\psi+\varphi)/2} \end{Vmatrix}. \tag{D.7}$$

This direct procedure becomes laborious and hardly feasible as j increases.

The best known procedure for calculating $\mathfrak{d}^{(j)}(\theta)$ for any j derives this matrix from the matrix (D.6) for $j = \frac{1}{2}$; this procedure will be indicated in Appendix F. Here we give a derivation of the $\mathfrak{d}^{(j)}(\theta)$ from recursion formulas.

b. Recursion formulas. Consider an infinitesimal r-transformation about an axis $\mathbf{u}$ to which corresponds the matrix $\mathbf{J}\cdot\mathbf{u}$. Consider also a finite rotation of coordinate axes R which changes the components u_x, u_y, and u_z of $\mathbf{u}$ into u_x', u_y', and u_z', and thus changes $\mathbf{J}\cdot\mathbf{u}$ into $\mathbf{J}\cdot\mathbf{u}'$. The relationship between $\mathbf{J}\cdot\mathbf{u}$ and $\mathbf{J}\cdot\mathbf{u}'$ is given by (2.10), where we enter in the place of A the r-transformation matrix D corresponding to R, namely

$$\mathbf{J}\cdot\mathbf{u}' = D\,\mathbf{J}\cdot\mathbf{u}\,D^{-1} \tag{D.8}$$

or

$$\mathbf{J}\cdot\mathbf{u}'D = D\,\mathbf{J}\cdot\mathbf{u}. \tag{D.9}$$

Because we are interested in the matrix $\mathfrak{d}^{(j)}(\theta)$ we take a rotation R about the axis y, and choose three directions $\mathbf{u}$ which coincide with the coordinate axes after the rotation R. Thus we have for the three directions, respectively,

$$\begin{aligned} J_x\,\mathfrak{d}(\theta) &= \mathfrak{d}(\theta)\,(J_x\cos\theta - J_z\sin\theta), \\ J_y\,\mathfrak{d}(\theta) &= \mathfrak{d}(\theta)\,J_y, \\ J_z\,\mathfrak{d}(\theta) &= \mathfrak{d}(\theta)\,(J_x\sin\theta + J_z\cos\theta). \end{aligned} \tag{D.10}$$

Entering in these equations explicitly the matrix elements of J_x, J_y, and J_z, one obtains recursion formulas for the functions $\mathfrak{d}^{(j)}{}_{m'm}(\theta)$ with different values of m' and m. These formulas are particularly simple when J_x and J_y are combined in the form $J_x \pm iJ_y$, because of the simplicity of the standard form (B.27) of these matrices. Linear combinations of the equations (D.10) yields the useful formulas

$$[(J_x - iJ_y)\,(1+\cos\theta) + J_z\sin\theta]\mathfrak{d} = \mathfrak{d}[(J_x - iJ_y)\,(1+\cos\theta) - J_z\sin\theta], \tag{D.11}$$

$$[(J_x + iJ_y)\,(1-\cos\theta) - J_z\sin\theta]\mathfrak{d} = \mathfrak{d}[-(J_x - iJ_y)\,(1-\cos\theta) - J_z\sin\theta], \tag{D.12}$$

whose explicit form is

$$\begin{aligned} \sqrt{j(j+1) - m'(m'+1)}\,(1+\cos\theta)\,\mathfrak{d}^{(j)}{}_{m'+1\,m} &+ (m'+m)\sin\theta\,\mathfrak{d}^{(j)}{}_{m'm} \\ &= \sqrt{j(j+1) - m(m-1)}\,(1+\cos\theta)\,\mathfrak{d}^{(j)}{}_{m'm-1}, \end{aligned} \tag{D.13}$$

$$\begin{aligned} &\sqrt{j(j+1) - m'(m'-1)}\,(1-\cos\theta)\,\mathfrak{d}^{(j)}{}_{m'-1\,m} \\ &= (m'-m)\sin\theta\,\mathfrak{d}^{(j)}{}_{m'm} - \sqrt{j(j+1) - m(m-1)}\,(1-\cos\theta)\,\mathfrak{d}^{(j)}{}_{m'm-1}. \end{aligned} \tag{D.14}$$

c. Calculation of $\mathfrak{d}^{(j)}(\theta)$. Equation (D.13) gives on the right a function $\mathfrak{d}^{(j)}$ with the index $m-1$ in terms of $\mathfrak{d}^{(j)}$ with the index m on the left. On the left, however, there is a function with $m'+1$ instead of m', but the coefficient of the function vanishes for $m' = j$. We write then

$$(j+m)\sin\theta\, \mathfrak{d}^{(j)}{}_{jm}(\theta) = \sqrt{j(j+1)-m(m-1)}\,(1+\cos\theta)\, \mathfrak{d}^{(j)}{}_{jm-1}, \tag{D.15}$$

that is

$$\sqrt{j+m}\,\sin\tfrac{1}{2}\theta\, \mathfrak{d}^{(j)}{}_{jm}(\theta) = \sqrt{j-m+1}\,\cos\tfrac{1}{2}\theta\, \mathfrak{d}^{(j)}{}_{jm-1}(\theta), \tag{D.15$'$}$$

which gives the ratios between the functions $\mathfrak{d}^{(j)}{}_{jm}$ with different m. It follows that

$$\mathfrak{d}^{(j)}{}_{jm}(\theta) = Q\binom{2j}{j-m}^{\frac{1}{2}}\cos^{j+m}\tfrac{1}{2}\theta\,\sin^{j-m}\tfrac{1}{2}\theta, \tag{D.16}$$

where Q is a factor independent of m but which might still depend on θ. However, writing out explicitly the condition that $\boldsymbol{\mathfrak{d}}^{(j)}$ is unitary, $\Sigma_m|\mathfrak{d}^{(j)}{}_{jm}(\theta)|^2 = 1$, shows that $|Q|^2 = 1$. The conditions that a standard $\boldsymbol{\mathfrak{d}}^{(j)}$ is real and that $\mathfrak{d}^{(j)}{}_{jj}(0) = 1$ show further that $Q = 1$ and

$$\mathfrak{d}^{(j)}{}_{jm}(\theta) = \binom{2j}{j-m}^{\frac{1}{2}}\cos^{j+m}\tfrac{1}{2}\theta\,\sin^{j-m}\tfrac{1}{2}\theta. \tag{D.16$'$}$$

The functions $\mathfrak{d}^{(j)}{}_{m'm}(\theta)$ with $m' < j$ can now be obtained by recursion from (D.14) which has on the left one function with the index $m'-1$ and on the right functions with m'. The formulas are simplified by setting

$$\mathfrak{d}^{(j)}{}_{m'm} = \sqrt{(j+m')!\,(j-m')!\,(j+m)!\,(j-m)!}\, f^{(j)}{}_{m'm}, \tag{D.17}$$

after which (D.14) reduces to

$$f^{(j)}{}_{m'-1m} = \frac{m'-m}{j-m'+1}\operatorname{cotg}\tfrac{1}{2}\theta\, f^{(j)}{}_{m'm} - \frac{j-m+1}{j-m'+1} f^{(j)}{}_{m'm-1} \tag{D.18}$$

and (D.16$'$) takes the form

$$f^{(j)}{}_{jm} = \frac{\cos^{j+m}\frac{1}{2}\theta\,\sin^{j-m}\frac{1}{2}\theta}{(j+m)!\,(j-m)!}. \tag{D.19}$$

For $m' = j$, (D.18) gives

$$f^{(j)}{}_{j-1m} = \frac{\cos^{j+m+1}\frac{1}{2}\theta\,\sin^{j-m-1}\frac{1}{2}\theta}{(j+m)!\,(j-m-1)!\,1!} - \frac{\cos^{j+m-1}\frac{1}{2}\theta\,\sin^{j-m+1}\frac{1}{2}\theta}{(j+m-1)!\,(j-m)!\,1!}, \tag{D.20}$$

and proceeding in succession to lower m' one finds that

$$f^{(j)}{}_{m'm} = \sum_r (-1)^r \frac{(\cos\frac{1}{2}\theta)^{2j-m'+m-2r} (\sin\frac{1}{2}\theta)^{2r+m'-m}}{(j-m'-r)!(j+m-r)!r!(r+m'-m)!}. \tag{D.21}$$

Equation (D.17) gives then the matrix elements

$$\mathfrak{d}^{(j)}{}_{m'm}(\theta) = \sum_r (-1)^r \frac{\sqrt{(j+m')!(j-m')!(j+m)!(j-m)!}}{(j-m'-r)!(j+m-r)!r!(r+m'-m)!} \times$$
$$(\cos\tfrac{1}{2}\theta)^{2j-m'+m-2r} (\sin\tfrac{1}{2}\theta)^{2r+m'-m} \tag{D.22}$$

which, combined with (D.4), constitute the elements (5.2) of the standard r-transformation.

Three important symmetry properties follow from (D.22), namely

$$\mathfrak{d}^{(j)}{}_{mm'}(\theta) = (-1)^{m'-m} \mathfrak{d}^{(j)}{}_{m'm}(\theta), \tag{D.23}$$

$$\mathfrak{d}^{(j)}{}_{-m'-m}(\theta) = (-1)^{m'-m} \mathfrak{d}^{(j)}{}_{m'm}(\theta), \tag{D.24}$$

$$\mathfrak{d}^{(j)}{}_{m'-m}(\theta) = (-1)^{j-m'} \mathfrak{d}^{(j)}{}_{m'm}(\pi-\theta). \tag{D.25}$$

E

Differential Properties of *r*-transformations

The elements of *r*-transformation matrices D obey two systems of first order differential equations constructed by combining a finite coordinate rotation R with infinitesimal rotations applied after or before R. Indicating angles of rotation about the new and old coordinate axes, respectively, by $(\varepsilon_x', \varepsilon_y', \varepsilon_z')$ and $(\varepsilon_x, \varepsilon_y, \varepsilon_z)$, the combined *r*-transformations are respectively

$$e^{i(\varepsilon_x' J_x + \varepsilon_y' J_y + \varepsilon_z' J_z)} D(R) = D(R_a), \tag{E.1a}$$

$$D(R)\, e^{i(\varepsilon_x J_x + \varepsilon_y J_y + \varepsilon_z J_z)} = D(R_b). \tag{E.1b}$$

On the left side we have the products of the separate *r*-transformation matrices and on the right a single *r*-transformation corresponding to the combined rotation of axes called R_a or respectively R_b.

We take now the derivatives of (E.1) with respect to each of the ε_k' or ε_k, at $\varepsilon = 0$, that is, at $R_a = R_b = R$. A derivative of (E.1a) is

$$iJ_k D(\psi,\theta,\varphi) = \frac{\partial\psi}{\partial\varepsilon_k'}\frac{\partial D}{\partial\psi} + \frac{\partial\theta}{\partial\varepsilon_k'}\frac{\partial D}{\partial\theta} + \frac{\partial\varphi}{\partial\varepsilon_k'}\frac{\partial D}{\partial\varphi} = A_k D, \tag{E.2a}$$

where A_k indicates the differential operator $(\partial\psi/\partial\varepsilon_k')(\partial/\partial\psi) + \dots$ Once the standard form of the infinitesimal matrices J_k is adopted, the left side of (E.2a) is a linear combination of matrix elements $\mathfrak{D}^{(j)}{}_{m'm}(\psi,\theta,\varphi)$, whereas the right side is a linear combination of derivatives of one matrix element.

The coefficients $\partial\psi/\partial\varepsilon_k'$ must be entered in (E.2a) as explicit functions of ψ, θ and φ. We begin with the special case $\psi = 0$, for which the positions of the "old" and "new" axes is shown in Fig. 6. It is seen that a rotation ε_z' about the new axis z' increases ψ by ε_z' but does not change θ or φ, and similarly a rotation about y' increases θ by ε_y' but does not change ψ or φ. We have then

$$\frac{\partial\psi}{\partial\varepsilon_z'} = 1, \qquad \frac{\partial\theta}{\partial\varepsilon_z'} = 0, \qquad \frac{\partial\varphi}{\partial\varepsilon_z'} = 0, \qquad (\psi = 0) \tag{E.3}$$

$$\frac{\partial\psi}{\partial\varepsilon_y'} = 0, \qquad \frac{\partial\theta}{\partial\varepsilon_y'} = 1, \qquad \frac{\partial\varphi}{\partial\varepsilon_y'} = 0, \qquad (\psi = 0). \tag{E.4}$$

A rotation about x' changes both φ and ψ. Figure 6 indicates the position z'' of the z axis following a small rotation $\delta\varepsilon_x'$ about x'. The spherical triangle identified by the axes z, z'', and x' has its sides equal to θ, $\pi/2$, and $\pi/2+\theta$ and angles $\delta\varepsilon_x'$, $-\delta\varphi$, and $\pi-\delta\psi$. The sine theorem yields, for this triangle,

$$\frac{\sin\theta}{\sin(\delta\varepsilon_x')} = \frac{\sin(\frac{1}{2}\pi)}{\sin(-\delta\varphi)} = \frac{\sin(\frac{1}{2}\pi+\theta)}{\sin(\delta\psi)}, \tag{E.5}$$

from which we have

$$\frac{\partial\psi}{\partial\varepsilon_x'} = \frac{\cos\theta}{\sin\theta}, \qquad \frac{\partial\theta}{\partial\varepsilon_x'} = 0, \qquad \frac{\partial\varphi}{\partial\varepsilon_y'} = -\frac{1}{\sin\theta}, \qquad (\psi = 0). \tag{E.6}$$

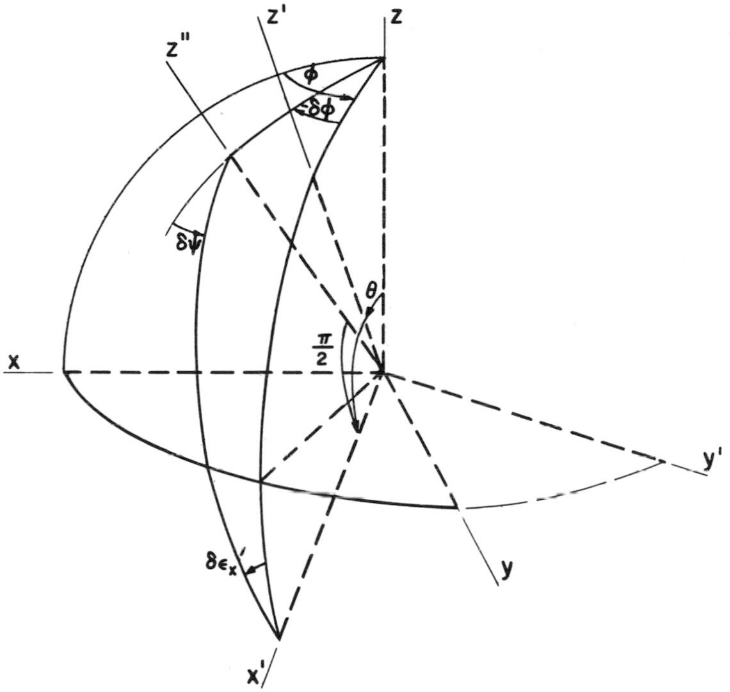

FIG. 6. Relationship between the angles $-\delta\varphi$, $\delta\psi$ and $\delta\varepsilon_x'$.

For $\psi \neq 0$, the axis z' remains the same but the axes x' and y' occupy new positions in the plane of the axes x' and y' shown in the figure. An infinitesimal rotation $\delta\varepsilon_x'$ about the axis x' for $\psi \neq 0$ can be resolved into two rotations $\delta\varepsilon_x' \cos\psi$ and $\delta\varepsilon_x' \sin\psi$ about the axes x' and y' for $\psi = 0$ and a rotation $\delta\varepsilon_y'$ is similarly resolved. Therefore (E.3) remains unchanged for $\psi \neq 0$, but (E.4) and (E.6) are replaced with linear combinations

$$\frac{\partial\psi}{\partial\varepsilon_y'} = -\sin\psi\frac{\cos\theta}{\sin\theta}, \qquad \frac{\partial\theta}{\partial\varepsilon_y'} = \cos\psi, \qquad \frac{\partial\varphi}{\partial\varepsilon_y'} = -\sin\psi\left(-\frac{1}{\sin\theta}\right), \tag{E.4$'$}$$

$$\frac{\partial\psi}{\partial\varepsilon_x'} = \cos\psi\frac{\cos\theta}{\sin\theta}, \qquad \frac{\partial\theta}{\partial\varepsilon_x'} = \sin\psi, \qquad \frac{\partial\varphi}{\partial\varepsilon_x'} = \cos\psi\left(-\frac{1}{\sin\theta}\right). \tag{E.6$'$}$$

The formulas (E.3), (E.4′), and (E.6′) can also be derived analytically, without reference to Fig. 6, by writing (E.2a) explicitly for the known r-transformation matrix of the set of cartesian coordinates x, y, z,

$$D = \left\| \begin{matrix} \cos\theta\cos\varphi\cos\psi - \sin\varphi\sin\psi & \cos\theta\sin\varphi\cos\psi + \cos\varphi\sin\psi & -\sin\theta\cos\psi \\ -\sin\varphi\cos\psi - \cos\theta\cos\varphi\sin\psi & \cos\varphi\cos\psi - \cos\theta\sin\varphi\sin\psi & \sin\theta\sin\psi \\ \sin\theta\cos\varphi & \sin\theta\sin\varphi & \cos\theta \end{matrix} \right\|. \tag{E.7}$$

The corresponding expression of the matrices $iJ_k = I_k$ is given in (B.10); the elements of these matrices are all ± 1 or 0 and no more than one element of each row is $\neq 0$. Therefore, indicating the rows and columns of the matrices by x, y, and z, we have for example $(I_x D)_{zz} = -D_{yz}$.

To determine the nine derivatives in (E.2a) it is sufficient to write out three elements of the matrix equation, each of them for $k = x$, y, and z. The zz elements of the equation, $(I_k D)_{zz} = \partial D_{zz}/\partial\varepsilon_k'$, are

$$\begin{aligned} -\sin\theta\sin\psi &= -\sin\theta\,\partial\theta/\partial\varepsilon_x', \\ -\sin\theta\cos\psi &= -\sin\theta\,\partial\theta/\partial\varepsilon_y', \\ 0 &= -\sin\theta\,\partial\theta/\partial\varepsilon_z', \end{aligned} \tag{E.8}$$

and determine the three derivatives $\partial\theta/\partial\varepsilon_k'$. Similarly, the yz elements are

$$\begin{aligned} \cos\theta &= \sin\theta\cos\psi\,(\partial\psi/\partial\varepsilon_x') + \cos\theta\sin\psi\,(\partial\theta/\partial\varepsilon_x'), \\ 0 &= \sin\theta\cos\psi\,(\partial\psi/\partial\varepsilon_y') + \cos\theta\sin\psi\,(\partial\theta/\partial\varepsilon_y'), \\ \sin\theta\cos\psi &= \sin\theta\cos\psi\,(\partial\psi/\partial\varepsilon_z') + \cos\theta\sin\psi\,(\partial\theta/\partial\varepsilon_z'), \end{aligned} \tag{E.9}$$

and determine the derivatives $\partial\psi/\partial\varepsilon_k'$ since the $\partial\theta/\partial\varepsilon_k'$ have already been found. The zy elements

$$\begin{aligned} -\cos\varphi\cos\psi + \cos\theta\sin\varphi\sin\psi &= \cos\theta\sin\varphi\,(\partial\theta/\partial\varepsilon_x') + \sin\theta\cos\varphi\,(\partial\varphi/\partial\varepsilon_x'), \\ \cos\theta\sin\varphi\cos\psi + \cos\varphi\sin\psi &= \cos\theta\sin\varphi\,(\partial\theta/\partial\varepsilon_y') + \sin\theta\cos\varphi\,(\partial\varphi/\partial\varepsilon_y'), \\ 0 &= \cos\theta\sin\varphi\,(\partial\theta/\partial\varepsilon_z') + \sin\theta\cos\varphi\,(\partial\varphi/\partial\varepsilon_z'), \end{aligned} \tag{E.10}$$

determine the derivatives $\partial\varphi/\partial\varepsilon_k'$, which completes the analytical derivation of (E.3), (E.4′), and (E.6′).

Entering (E.3), (E.4′), and (E.6′) into (E.2a), the operators A_k are seen to have the explicit form

$$\begin{aligned} A_x &= \frac{\cos\psi}{\sin\theta}\left(\cos\theta\frac{\partial}{\partial\psi} - \frac{\partial}{\partial\varphi}\right) + \sin\psi\frac{\partial}{\partial\theta}, \\ A_y &= -\frac{\sin\psi}{\sin\theta}\left(\cos\theta\frac{\partial}{\partial\psi} - \frac{\partial}{\partial\varphi}\right) + \cos\psi\frac{\partial}{\partial\theta}, \\ A_z &= \frac{\partial}{\partial\psi}. \end{aligned} \tag{E.11}$$

It will actually be convenient to utilize the complex operators $A_x \pm iA_y$, corresponding to $J_x \pm iJ_y$, and we write

$$A_x \pm iA_y = e^{\mp i\psi}\left[\frac{1}{\sin\theta}\left(\cos\theta\frac{\partial}{\partial\psi} - \frac{\partial}{\partial\varphi}\right) \pm i\frac{\partial}{\partial\theta}\right], \tag{E.12a}$$

$$A_z = \frac{\partial}{\partial\psi}.$$

Formulas analogous to (E.2a) and (E.12a) are obtained starting from (E.1b). They are

$$D(\psi,\theta,\varphi)\, iJ_k = B_k D(\psi,\theta,\varphi), \tag{E.2b}$$

$$B_x \pm iB_y = e^{\pm i\varphi}\left[\frac{1}{\sin\theta}\left(\frac{\partial}{\partial\psi} - \cos\theta\frac{\partial}{\partial\varphi}\right) \pm i\frac{\partial}{\partial\theta}\right],$$

$$B_z = \frac{\partial}{\partial\varphi}. \tag{E.12b}$$

When the standard form (5.1) of the matrices J_k for a particular value of j is entered in (E.2), these equations constitute a system sufficient to determine the entire r-transformation matrix $\mathfrak{D}^{(j)}{}_{m'm}(\psi, \theta, \varphi)$. In the equations for $k = z$ the standardization gives $(J_z\mathfrak{D}^{(j)})_{m'm} = m'\mathfrak{D}^{(j)}{}_{m'm}$ and $(\mathfrak{D}^{(j)}J_z)_{m'm} = m\mathfrak{D}^{(j)}{}_{m'm}$. Therefore (E.2a) and (E.2b) become

$$\frac{\partial\mathfrak{D}^{(j)}{}_{m'm}}{\partial\psi} = im'\mathfrak{D}^{(j)}{}_{m'm}, \qquad \frac{\partial\mathfrak{D}^{(j)}{}_{m'm}}{\partial\varphi} = im\mathfrak{D}^{(j)}{}_{m'm}, \tag{E.13}$$

from which follows

$$\mathfrak{D}^{(j)}{}_{m'm}(\psi,\theta,\varphi) = e^{i(m'\psi+m\varphi)}\mathfrak{d}^{(j)}{}_{m'm}(\theta), \tag{E.14}$$

namely (D.2). Similarly in the equations with $J_x \pm iJ_y$ the standardization gives $([J_x \pm iJ_y]\mathfrak{D}^{(j)})_{m'm} = (J_x \pm iJ_y)_{m'\, m'\mp 1}\mathfrak{D}^{(j)}{}_{m'\mp 1\, m}$ and $(\mathfrak{D}^{(j)}[J_x \pm iJ_y])_{m'm} = \mathfrak{D}^{(j)}{}_{m'\, m\pm 1}(J_x \pm iJ_y)_{m\pm 1\, m}$. The equations are

$$i\sqrt{j(j+1)-m'(m'\mp 1)}\,\mathfrak{D}^{(j)}{}_{m'\mp 1\, m} = e^{\mp i\psi}\left[\frac{1}{\sin\theta}\left(\cos\theta\frac{\partial}{\partial\psi} - \frac{\partial}{\partial\varphi}\right) \pm i\frac{\partial}{\partial\theta}\right]\mathfrak{D}^{(j)}{}_{m'm}, \tag{E.15a}$$

$$i\sqrt{j(j+1)-m'(m'\pm 1)}\,\mathfrak{D}^{(j)}{}_{m'\, m\pm 1} = e^{\pm i\varphi}\left[\frac{1}{\sin\theta}\left(\frac{\partial}{\partial\psi} - \cos\theta\frac{\partial}{\partial\varphi}\right) \pm i\frac{\partial}{\partial\theta}\right]\mathfrak{D}^{(j)}{}_{m'm}. \tag{E.15b}$$

Introducing (E.14) into (E.15) gives

$$\sqrt{j(j+1)-m'(m'\mp 1)}\,\mathfrak{d}^{(j)}{}_{m'\mp 1\, m} = \frac{m'\cos\theta - m}{\sin\theta}\mathfrak{d}^{(j)}{}_{m'm} \pm \frac{d\mathfrak{d}^{(j)}{}_{m'm}}{d\theta}, \tag{E.16a}$$

$$\sqrt{j(j+1)-m(m\pm 1)}\,\mathfrak{d}^{(j)}{}_{m'\, m\pm 1} = \frac{m' - m\cos\theta}{\sin\theta}\mathfrak{d}^{(j)}{}_{m'm} \pm \frac{d\mathfrak{d}^{(j)}{}_{m'm}}{d\theta}. \tag{E.16b}$$

Equation (E.16b) with the upper sign and $m' = m = j$ is

$$0 = j\,\frac{1-\cos\theta}{\sin\theta}\,\mathfrak{d}^{(j)}{}_{jj} + \frac{d\mathfrak{d}^{(j)}{}_{jj}}{d\theta}, \tag{E.17}$$

which is equivalent to

$$\frac{d\mathfrak{d}^{(j)}{}_{jj}}{d(\cos\theta)} = \frac{j}{1+\cos\theta}\,\mathfrak{d}^{(j)}{}_{jj} \tag{E.18}$$

and has the general integral

$$\mathfrak{d}^{(j)}{}_{jj}(\theta) = K(1+\cos\theta)^{j} \tag{E.19}$$

The value of the constant K is fixed by the condition $\mathfrak{d}^{(j)}{}_{jj}(0) = 1$, so that

$$\mathfrak{d}^{(j)}{}_{jj}(\theta) = \left(\frac{1+\cos\theta}{2}\right)^{j} = \left(\cos\frac{\theta}{2}\right)^{2j}. \tag{E.20}$$

Equation (E.16a) with the upper sign and (E.16b) with the lower sign may now be used as recursion formulas to obtain all $\mathfrak{d}^{(j)}{}_{m'm}$ from $\mathfrak{d}^{(j)}{}_{jj}$. This explicit calculation is very similar to that of Appendix D and will not be carried out here.

It is of interest to relate the construction of the functions $\mathfrak{D}^{(j)}{}_{m'm}(\psi,\theta,\varphi)$ to the solution of familiar problems of mathematical physics. Systems of first order differential equations obeyed by the components of a field are often replaced with higher order differential equations obeyed by each field component separately. For example Maxwell's equations for vacuum are so replaced with d'Alembert's equation. Similarly, we have from (E.2a) that $-J_k{}^2D = A_k{}^2D$, and by summing over k

$$-\mathbf{J}^2D = (A_x{}^2+A_y{}^2+A_z{}^2)D. \tag{E.21}$$

Introducing in (E.21) the explicit form (E.11) or (E.12a) of the A_k and specializing to irreducible r-transformations of degree j, one obtains the second order equation

$$\left[\frac{\partial^2}{\partial\theta^2} + \operatorname{cotg}\theta\,\frac{\partial}{\partial\theta} + \frac{1}{\sin^2\theta}\left(\frac{\partial^2}{\partial\psi^2} + \frac{\partial^2}{\partial\varphi^2} - 2\cos\theta\,\frac{\partial^2}{\partial\psi\partial\varphi}\right)\right]D^{(j)} = -j(j+1)D^{(j)}. \tag{E.22}$$

This equation is known as the Schroedinger equation for the symmetrical top. It is obeyed by each matrix element of any irreducible r-transformation of degree j.

The classical procedure of separation of variables, to solve (E.22), may be introduced here by seeking simultaneous solutions of the eigenvalue equations (E.22) and (E.13). The solutions must then have the form (E.14), where $\mathfrak{d}^{(j)}{}_{m'm}(\theta)$ is a solution of

$$\frac{d^2\mathfrak{d}^{(j)}{}_{m'm}}{d\theta^2}+\operatorname{cotg}\theta\,\frac{d\mathfrak{d}^{(j)}{}_{m'm}}{d\theta}+\frac{m'^2+m^2-2mm'\cos\theta}{\sin^2\theta}\,\mathfrak{d}^{(j)}{}_{m'm}=-j(j+1)\mathfrak{d}^{(j)}{}_{m'm}. \tag{E.23}$$

This equation belongs to the class whose solutions can be expressed in terms of hypergeometric functions (Whittaker and Watson, 1946, Chapter 14). The solutions have the form

$$\mathfrak{d}^{(j)}{}_{m'm}=C(\sin\tfrac{1}{2}\theta)^p\,(\cos\tfrac{1}{2}\theta)^q\,F[\tfrac{1}{2}(p+q)+j+1,\tfrac{1}{2}(p+q)-j,q+1,\sin^2\tfrac{1}{2}\theta] \tag{E.24}$$

where $p=|m'+m|$, $q=|m'-m|$, and the hypergeometric series F reduces to a polynomial because $\frac{1}{2}(p+q)-j$ is a negative integer. In the special cases $m'=0$ or $m=0$, (E.23) reduces to the equation of the associated Legendre polynomials, and for $m'=m=0$ to the equation of the ordinary Legendre polynomials. Notice that (E.24) has an undetermined constant factor C. This factor has to be normalized properly, in order that the $\mathfrak{d}^{(j)}{}_{m'm}(\theta)$ with different m' and m constitute an r-transformation matrix. The normalization is provided only by the system of equations (E.16), or by equivalent data, but not by the second order equation which does not relate the different matrix elements. Similarly, the d'Alembert equation provides less information about the electromagnetic field than the system of Maxwell equations.

Because the $\mathfrak{D}^{(j)}{}_{m'm}(\psi,\theta,\varphi)$ are eigenfunctions of the three equations (E.22) and (E.13), they constitute an orthogonal system, a result derived by a more abstract proof in Appendix A. To prove that the $\mathfrak{D}^{(j)}{}_{m'm}$ for all j, m', and m constitute a complete system of functions of the Euler angles, one must verify that all eigenfunctions of (E.22) and (E.13) are, if properly normalized, matrix elements of an irreducible r-transformation. Indeed, given any eigenfunction of these equations, other eigenfunctions corresponding to the same eigenvalue of (E.22) and different eigenvalues of (E.13) are obtained by successive application of the operators $A_x\pm iA_y$ and $B_x\pm iB_y$. All these eigenfunctions properly normalized constitute a matrix which is an r-transformation (Casimir 1931).

Any function of the Euler angles can be expanded into standard matrix elements $\mathfrak{D}^{(j)}{}_{\mu m}(\psi,\theta,\varphi)$, because these matrix elements constitute a complete system. In particular the expansion formula of a general

r-transformation matrix element $D_{ik}(\psi, \theta, \varphi)$ may be expressed in the form of a transformation equation (2.11), namely $D' = ADA^{-1}$, with the reduction-standardization matrices $(\alpha jm|i)$ and $(k|\alpha j\mu)$ from (5.8) and (5.9) in the place of A^{-1} and A,

$$D_{ki}(\psi, \theta, \varphi) = \Sigma_{\alpha j\mu m}(k|\alpha j\mu)\, \mathfrak{D}^{(j)}{}_{\mu m}(\psi, \theta, \varphi)\, (\alpha jm|i). \tag{E.25}$$

The coefficients of the expansion are given by the usual method of multiplying the expansion by $\mathfrak{D}^{(j)}{}_{\mu m}{}^*$, integrating over ψ, θ and φ and utilizing the orthogonality of the eigenfunctions and the value of the normalization integral given in (A.32). This yields

$$\sum_\alpha (k|\alpha j\mu)\, (\alpha jm|i) \tag{E.26}$$

$$= \frac{2j+1}{8\pi^2} \int_0^{2\pi} d\psi \int_0^{2\pi} \sin\theta\, d\theta \int_0^{\pi} d\varphi\, \mathfrak{D}^{(j)}{}_{\mu m}{}^*(\psi, \theta, \varphi)\, D_{ki}(\psi, \theta, \varphi).$$

If the reduced form of the r-transformation contains no two irreducible submatrices with the same j, the index α is unnecessary, the Σ_α drops out and the integral in (E.26) may actually be utilized to calculate the reduction-standardization matrix. (See Appendix G for an application of this procedure.) That is, the expansion of the initial r-transformation matrix D is equivalent to all those stages of the reduction-standardization procedure which consist of diagonalizing $\mathbf{J}^2$ and J_z and making J_x real and positive. The additional step of this procedure, namely the diagonalization of other matrices M, if any, is not provided for by expanding D.

That the coefficient on the left of (E.26) is not a general number $c_{kij\mu m}$ but a sum of products of elements of two reciprocal matrices, follows from the fact that the $D_{ki}(\psi, \theta, \varphi)$ are not arbitrary functions but have the group property (A.9).

F

Products of Identical Standard Sets of Degree $\frac{1}{2}$

Consider a standard set $\mathfrak{a}^{(\frac{1}{2})}$ of order two, whose elements will be called $u = \mathfrak{a}^{(\frac{1}{2})}_{\frac{1}{2}}$ and $v = \mathfrak{a}^{(\frac{1}{2})}_{-\frac{1}{2}}$, and consider the direct product of n identical sets $[\mathfrak{a}^{(\frac{1}{2})}]^n$. The direct product of n sets of order 2 has in general 2^n elements, but only $n+1$ of these elements are different from one another if the sets are identical; they are u^n, $u^{n-1}v, \ldots, v^n$. A general r-transformation (D.7) of $\mathfrak{a}^{(\frac{1}{2})}$ replaces u and v with two linear combinations of u and v, and thereby replaces each element of the set u^n, $u^{n-1}v, \ldots, v^n$ with a linear combination of all other elements of this set.

However, the set of elements $u^p v^{n-p}$ has r-transformations which are not unitary. A set has unitary r-transformations if the hermitian product of the set with itself is invariant. To find a set related to the set $u^p v^{n-p}$ but with unitary r-transformations we start from the hermitian product of $\mathfrak{a}^{(\frac{1}{2})}$ with itself, namely

$$\tilde{\mathfrak{a}}^{*[\frac{1}{2}]}\mathfrak{a}^{(\frac{1}{2})} = u^*u + v^*v, \tag{F.1}$$

and take its nth power,

$$[\tilde{\mathfrak{a}}^{*[\frac{1}{2}]}\mathfrak{a}^{(\frac{1}{2})}]^n = \sum_p \binom{n}{p} u^{*p} u^p v^{*n-p} v^{n-p}. \tag{F.2}$$

A regrouping of factors changes (F.2) to the form

$$\sum_p \left[\binom{n}{p}^{\frac{1}{2}} u^p v^{n-p}\right]^* \left[\binom{n}{p}^{\frac{1}{2}} u^p v^{n-p}\right], \tag{F.3}$$

which represents the hermitian product of a set with itself. We conclude that the r-transformations of the set of elements

$$\binom{n}{p}^{\frac{1}{2}} u^p v^{n-p} \tag{F.4}$$

are unitary.

This set is irreducible and standard. A coordinate rotation of φ radians about the z axis multiplies u by $\exp(i\frac{1}{2}\varphi)$ and v by $\exp(-i\frac{1}{2}\varphi)$ because $\mathfrak{a}^{(\frac{1}{2})}$ is standard. Therefore it multiplies $u^p v^{n-p}$ by $\exp[i\varphi(p-\frac{1}{2}n)]$, where $-\frac{1}{2}n \leq p-\frac{1}{2}n \leq \frac{1}{2}n$. It follows from Appendix B that the set is irreducible of degree $j = \frac{1}{2}n$. The set has a diagonal J_z and, since the elements of the matrix J_x pertaining to $\mathfrak{a}^{(\frac{1}{2})}$ are real and positive, so will be the elements of the matrix J_x pertaining to the set (F.4). Introducing then $j = \frac{1}{2}n$ and $m = p-\frac{1}{2}n = p-j$, we can write

$$\mathfrak{A}^{(j)}{}_m = \binom{2j}{j+m}^{\frac{1}{2}} u^{j+m} v^{j-m} \tag{F.5}$$

The r-transformation $\mathfrak{D}^{(j)}$ of the set $\mathfrak{A}^{(j)}$, has been calculated explicitly (Güttinger, 1931; Wigner, 1931) from the expression (D.7) of the r-transformation of the set u, v. This procedure for calculating $\mathfrak{D}^{(j)}$ relies on the construction of the particular set (F.5) but involves a minimum of calculation and is therefore the best known one.

The analysis of invariants constructed with standard sets of degree $\frac{1}{2}$, such as (F.2), has been in the past a main tool, called the "spinor method", for developing the algebra of tensorial sets. The most advanced applications of this method have been made by Kramers (1931) and collaborators and are reviewed by Brinkman (1956). One application is made in Appendix G.

G

Calculation of the Wigner Coefficients

The matrix elements $(jm|m_1m_2)$ were first calculated by Wigner (1931). Various methods of calculation will be outlined here because they illustrate different aspects of the formalism.

Wigner's approach, through group theory, may be regarded as an application of the expansion theorem (E.25). This theorem is adequate to perform the reduction because no index α is required and the Σ_α drops out. In applying (E.26) the indices k and i are to be replaced with pairs of indices $(\mu_1\mu_2)$ and (m_1m_2), and in the place of D_{ik} one enters the r-transformation matrix of the direct product of standard sets, $\mathfrak{D}^{(j_1)}_{\mu_1m_1}$ $\mathfrak{D}^{(j_2)}_{\mu_2m_2}$. Equation (E.26) becomes then

$$(\mu_1\mu_2|j\mu)\,(jm|m_1m_2) \tag{G.1}$$

$$= \frac{2j+1}{8\pi^2}\int_0^{2\pi} d\psi \int_0^{\pi} \sin\theta\, d\theta \int_0^{2\pi} d\varphi\; \mathfrak{D}^{(j)}_{\mu m}{}^*(\psi,\theta,\varphi)\, \mathfrak{D}^{(j_1)}_{\mu_1m_1}(\psi,\theta,\varphi)\, \mathfrak{D}^{(j_2)}_{\mu_2m_2}(\psi,\theta,\varphi).$$

Wigner entered the expressions (5.2) of the $\mathfrak{D}$ in (G.1) and carried out the integration. The results thus obtained for fixed values of μ_1, μ_2, and j and for all values of m_1 and m_2 determine the ratios among the matrix elements $(jm|m_1m_2)$ with different m_1 and m_2. The common proportionality factor of these matrix elements is restricted by the knowledge that the matrix is real, and by the condition that it be unitary, namely

$$\Sigma_{m_1m_2}(jm|m_1m_2)\,(m_1m_2|jm) = \Sigma_{m_1m_2}(jm|m_1m_2)^2 = 1. \tag{G.2}$$

The Wigner coefficients are thereby determined to within a factor ± 1. This factor can be fixed arbitrarily for each block of matrix elements with the same value of j and determines the sign of each irreducible product. Wigner fixed this factor by the condition

$$(j_1j_2j\; j_1{-}j_2|j_1j_1, j_2{-}j_2) \geq 0. \tag{G.3}$$

The calculation given by Racah (1942) starts from the requirement that the reducing matrix transforms according to (2.11) the r-transformation $D = \mathfrak{D}^{(j_1)} \times \mathfrak{D}^{(j_2)}$ into a matrix D' which is an aggregate of $\mathfrak{D}^{(j)}$. This requirement is completely fulfilled, provided it is obeyed for the infinitesimal rotation matrices. Since (2.11) can be expressed as $D'A = AD$, one is led to the equation

$$\Sigma_{m'}(J_x \pm iJ_y)_{mm'}(jm'|m_1m_2) \tag{G.4}$$
$$= \Sigma_{m_1'm_2'}(jm|m_1'm_2')\,[(J_{1x} \pm iJ_{1y})_{m_1'm_1}\,\delta_{m_2'm_2} + (J_{2x} \pm iJ_{2y})_{m_2'm_2}\,\delta_{m_1'm_1}].$$

The corresponding equation for J_z is trivial as discussed in Section 7. The standard matrix elements of J_x and J_y are given by (5.1), and we have here a system of linear equations which determines the Wigner coefficients to within a normalization factor common to all coefficients with the same j. Racah determined this factor by requiring that the matrix of J_{1z} operating on the irreducible product sets has a standard form described by Condon and Shortley (1935). More conveniently, the magnitude of this factor may be fixed by the unitary condition (G.2) and its sign by the condition (G.3). This condition is equivalent to

$$(j_1 j_2 j j | j_1 j_1,\, j_2 j{-}j_1) \geq 0, \tag{G.5}$$

which includes explicitly the customary requirement that the element with $m = j$ of the irreducible product of highest degree $j = j_1+j_2$ be simply $\mathfrak{a}^{(j_1)}{}_{j_1}\,\mathfrak{b}^{(j_2)}{}_{j_2}$. No rational basis for the conventions (G.3) or (G.5), which fix the sign of irreducible products seems to have been given.

The expressions for $(jm|m_1m_2)$ derived by the methods indicated above are quite asymmetric, but may be symmetrized to the form (7.5) by algebraic manipulations. This form can also be obtained directly by the following procedure (Van der Waerden, 1932).

Consider three sets of degree $\frac{1}{2}$ two of them standard, $\mathfrak{a}^{(\frac{1}{2})}$ and $\mathfrak{b}^{(\frac{1}{2})}$, and one contrastandard, $\mathfrak{c}^{[\frac{1}{2}]}$, and the expression

$$(\mathfrak{b}^{(\frac{1}{2})}\cdot\mathfrak{a}^{(\frac{1}{2})})^{j_1+j_2-j}\,(\widetilde{\mathfrak{c}}^{[\frac{1}{2}]}\,\mathfrak{a}^{(\frac{1}{2})})^{j+j_1-j_2}\,(\widetilde{\mathfrak{c}}^{[\frac{1}{2}]}\,\mathfrak{b}^{(\frac{1}{2})})^{j+j_2-j_1} \tag{G.6}$$

constructed with invariant products. This expression is of degree $2j_1$ in $\mathfrak{a}^{(\frac{1}{2})}$, of degree $2j_2$ in $\mathfrak{b}^{(\frac{1}{2})}$, and of degree $2j$ in $\mathfrak{c}^{[\frac{1}{2}]}$. According to Appendix F, it must then be a linear function of the elements of the standard set $\mathfrak{A}^{(j_1)}$ with elements

$$\mathfrak{A}^{(j_1)}{}_{m_1} = \binom{2j_1}{j_1+m_1}^{\frac{1}{2}} \mathfrak{a}^{(\frac{1}{2})}{}_{\frac{1}{2}}{}^{j_1+m_1}\,\mathfrak{a}^{(\frac{1}{2})}{}_{-\frac{1}{2}}{}^{j_1-m_1}$$

constructed according to (F.5) and of the similarly constructed sets $\mathfrak{B}^{(j_2)}$ and $\mathfrak{C}^{[j]}$. Because (G.6) is invariant, it must be an invariant product of these three sets. Because $\mathfrak{C}^{[j]}$ is contrastandard any invariant product may be expressed as the inner product of $\mathfrak{C}^{[j]}$ and of an irreducible product of degree j of $\mathfrak{A}^{(j_1)}$ and $\mathfrak{B}^{(j_2)}$. We know that there is only one such irreducible product, to within a proportionality factor, and therefore (G.6) must be proportional to

$$\tilde{\mathfrak{C}}^{[j]}\,[\mathfrak{A}^{(j_1)} \times \mathfrak{B}^{(j_2)}]^{(j)} = \Sigma_{mm_1m_2} \mathfrak{C}^{[j]}{}_{m}(jm|m_1m_2)\, \mathfrak{A}^{(j_1)}{}_{m_1}\, \mathfrak{B}^{(j_2)}{}_{m_2}. \tag{G.7}$$

On the other hand, each of the products in (G.6) contains a sum of two terms and all three binomials can be expanded, so that (G.6) takes the form

$$\sum_{pqr} \binom{j_1+j_2-j}{p}\binom{j+j_1-j_2}{q}\binom{j+j_2-j_1}{r}(-1)^p \times \tag{G.8}$$
$$\mathfrak{a}^{(\frac{1}{2})}{}_{\frac{1}{2}}{}^{2j_1-p-q}\, \mathfrak{a}^{(\frac{1}{2})}{}_{-\frac{1}{2}}{}^{p+q}\, \mathfrak{b}^{(\frac{1}{2})}{}_{\frac{1}{2}}{}^{p+j+j_2-j_1-r}\, \mathfrak{b}^{(\frac{1}{2})}{}_{-\frac{1}{2}}{}^{j_1+j_2-j-p+r}\, \mathfrak{c}^{[\frac{1}{2}]}{}_{\frac{1}{2}}{}^{2j-q-r}\, \mathfrak{c}^{[\frac{1}{2}]}{}_{-\frac{1}{2}}{}^{q+r}.$$

This expression is related to (G.7) by establishing a term-by-term correspondence, setting $q = j_1-m_1-p$, $r = j-j_1-m_2+p$ in (G.8) and $m = m_1+m_2$, as it must be, in (G.7). The powers of the set elements are independent of p and can be identified with those that appear in $\mathfrak{A}^{(j_1)}{}_{m_1}$, $\mathfrak{B}^{(j_2)}{}_{m_2}$, and $\mathfrak{C}^{[j]}{}_{m_1+m_2}$. The Σ_{pqr} becomes $\Sigma_{m_1m_2}\,\Sigma_p$ and the Σ_p of the product of binomial coefficients coincides with the Σ_p in the Wigner coefficient expression (7.5), to within a proportionality constant. The normalization remains to be determined through (G.2) and (G.5).

H

Diagrams of Recoupling Relationships

The symmetry of $\overline{W}$ and X coefficients and the relationships among recoupling transformations can be illustrated by plane diagrams which have a wider range of application than the tetrahedron of Fig. 4.

Each irreducible set and each irreducible product is represented by one point of the diagram. This point may be visualized as the intersection

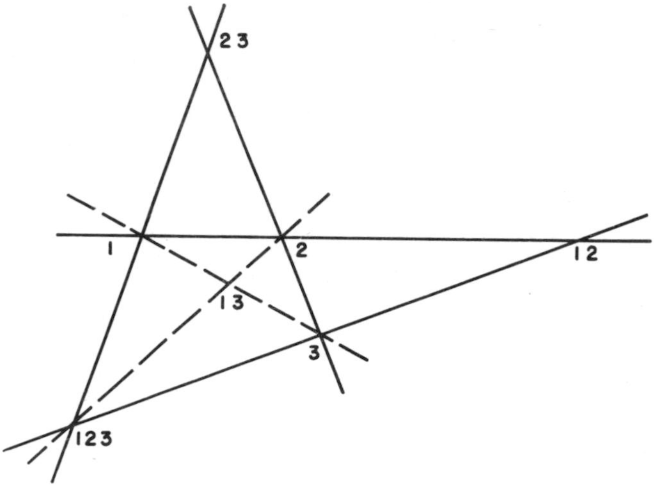

FIG. 7. Diagram of triple product recouplings.

of the plane of the drawing with the vector which represents an angular momentum. Accordingly, the points which represent any two sets and their irreducible product lie *on a straight line*, because the corresponding vectors in a space diagram such as Fig. 4 lie in a plane.

The diagram in Fig. 7 represents the recoupling $(j_{12}j_3|j_1j_{23})^{(j_{123})}$. The point 12 lies on the straight line defined by 1 and 2, and 123 on the straight line through 12 and 3. For the other coupling scheme, 23 lies on the straight line through 2 and 3, and 123 is aligned with 1 and 23. The recoupling involves the six intersections of the four full lines of the diagram. These lines constitute a complete quadrilateral ‡ which has the same topological symmetry as the tetrahedron of Fig. 4. The points corresponding to each of the triads lie on one of the sides of the quadri-

‡ A complete quadrilateral is a geometrical figure consisting of four sides and *six* vertices, which lie at the intersection of each side with the other three.

lateral, and the full symmetry of the function $\overline{W}$ in (11.8) with respect to its variables is displayed quite clearly.

The four vertices 1, 2, 3, and 123 are joined in pairs not only by the four straight lines considered thus far, but also by the broken lines. Figure 7 shows that these vertices are common to *three* different quadrilaterals. One of these quadrilaterals is the one considered above. Each

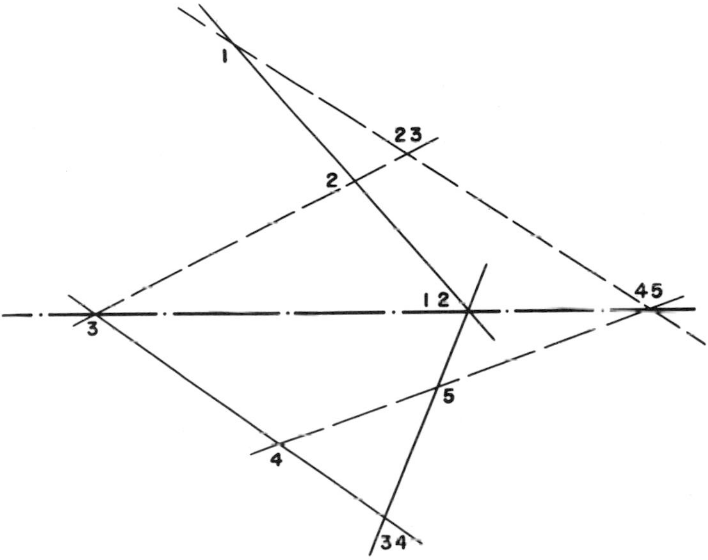

FIG. 8. Two-step recoupling of quintuple products of degree zero.

of the other two contains the two broken lines, and therefore the new vertex 13, and one pair of full lines, and therefore either the vertex 12 or 23. Each triple product is represented by one pair of lines through 1, 2, 3, and 123, and is characterized by one additional vertex at the intersection of the two lines. Each recoupling is represented by *two pairs* of lines, that is, by one quadrilateral, and the pertinent analytical transformation consists, to within a normalization factor, of the $\overline{W}$ function of the j-numbers corresponding to the six vertices. The three quadrilaterals correspond to three possible recouplings and to as many $\overline{W}$. The three $\overline{W}$ are related to one another by the associative property represented by (11.16).

To represent the recoupling of quadruple products of degree zero, one simply relabels the point 123 of Fig. 7 as "4." Similarly the diagrams of quadruple product recouplings and of the recouplings of quintuple products of degree zero differ only in the labeling of one point.

Figure 8 shows in full lines the coupling scheme $(j_{12}j_{34}j_5)$ and in broken lines the scheme $(j_1j_{23}j_{45})$, which are related by the transformation (12.2). This transformation factors out according to (12.4) into two simpler recouplings, through the intermediate coupling scheme $(j_{12}j_3j_{45})$ which is indicated in the diagram by a dot-dashed line together with the full

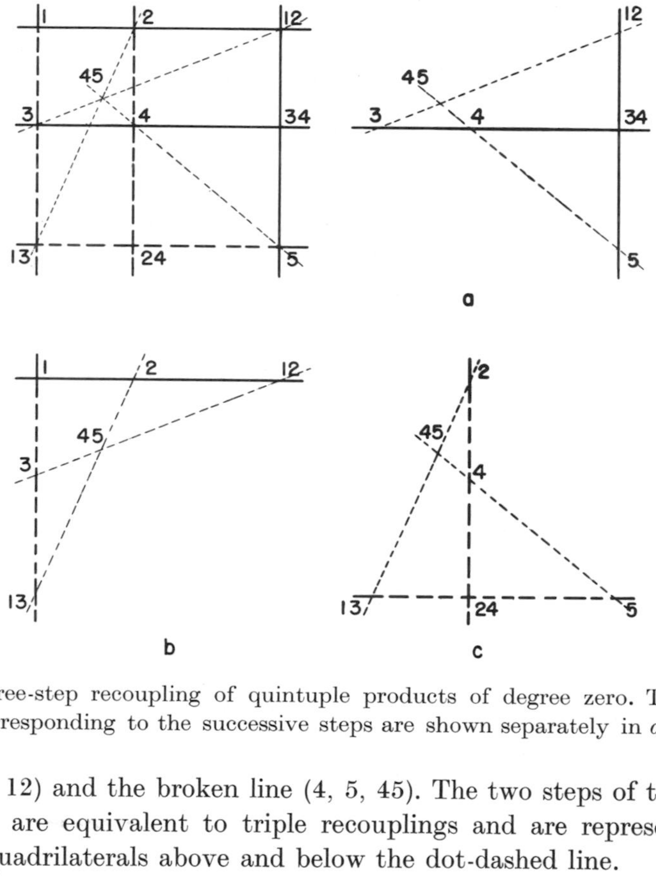

FIG. 9. Three-step recoupling of quintuple products of degree zero. The quadrilaterals corresponding to the successive steps are shown separately in *a*, *b*, and *c*.

line (1, 2, 12) and the broken line (4, 5, 45). The two steps of the transformation are equivalent to triple recouplings and are represented by the two quadrilaterals above and below the dot-dashed line.

Figure 9 shows the coupling scheme $(j_{12}j_{34}j_5)$ in full lines and the coupling $(j_{13}j_{24}j_5)$ in broken lines. These schemes are related by the transformation (12.3). There is no other coupling scheme that has one line in common with each of these two, as there was in Fig. 8. Therefore the two schemes are interconnected by a minimum sequence of three quadrilaterals each of them having one side in common with the next one. The three quadrilaterals are shown separately in the diagrams *a*, *b*, and *c*, and correspond to the three $\overline{W}$ in terms of which the transformation $(j_{12}j_{34}j_5|j_{13}j_{24}j_5)$ is resolved in (12.5).

I

Calculation of $\overline{W}$ by Recursion Formulas

The Biedenharn Identity

The calculation of $\overline{W}$ coefficients need not rely on their definition (11.6) or on their explicit algebraic representation (11.9) but can proceed in terms of orthonormalization and recursion relationships. The normalization is given by (11.15)

$$\sum_c (2c+1)\,\overline{W}\begin{pmatrix} abc \\ def \end{pmatrix} \overline{W}\begin{pmatrix} abc \\ deg \end{pmatrix} = \frac{\delta_{fg}\,\delta(a,e,f)\,\delta(d,b,f)}{2f+1} \tag{I.1}$$

One recursion formula is provided by the associative property (11.16),

$$\sum_c (-1)^{c+f+g}\,(2c+1)\,\overline{W}\begin{pmatrix} abc \\ def \end{pmatrix} \overline{W}\begin{pmatrix} abc \\ edg \end{pmatrix} = \overline{W}\begin{pmatrix} aef \\ bdg \end{pmatrix}. \tag{I.2}$$

Another recursion formula is provided by the identity

$$\begin{aligned} &\overline{W}\begin{pmatrix} abc \\ def \end{pmatrix} \overline{W}\begin{pmatrix} ab\bar{c} \\ \bar{d}\bar{e}\bar{f} \end{pmatrix} \\ &\quad = \sum_g (-1)^{a+b+c+d+e+f+\bar{d}+\bar{e}+\bar{f}+g}(2g+1)\,\overline{W}\begin{pmatrix} ge\bar{e} \\ a\bar{f}f \end{pmatrix} \overline{W}\begin{pmatrix} gf\bar{f} \\ b\bar{d}d \end{pmatrix} \overline{W}\begin{pmatrix} gd\bar{d} \\ c\bar{e}e \end{pmatrix}, \end{aligned} \tag{I.3}$$

which has been established by Biedenharn (1953) and Elliott (1953) and derives from the following consideration.

The transformation (12.2) can be carried out not only in two steps, as indicated in (12.4),

$$\begin{aligned} (j_{12}j_{34}j_5|j_1j_{23}j_{45})^{(0)} &= (j_{12}j_{34}j_5|j_{12}j_3j_{45})^{(0)}\,(j_{12}j_3j_{45}|j_1j_{23}j_{45})^{(0)} \\ &= (j_{34}j_5|j_3j_{45})^{(j_{12})}\,(j_{12}j_3|j_1j_{23})^{(j_{45})}, \end{aligned} \tag{I.4}$$

but also through a more complicated sequence of three steps. For example, we can replace (I.4) with

$$\begin{aligned} &(j_{12}j_{34}j_5|j_1j_{23}j_{45})^{(0)} \\ &\quad = \Sigma_{j_{15}}(j_{12}j_{34}j_5|j_{15}j_2j_{34})^{(0)}\,(j_{15}j_2j_{34}|j_{15}j_{23}j_4)^{(0)}\,(j_{15}j_{23}j_4|j_1j_{23}j_{45})^{(0)} \\ &\quad = \Sigma_{j_{15}}(-1)^{j_{34}+j_5-j_{12}}(j_{12}j_5|j_{15}j_2)^{(j_{34})}\,(j_2j_{34}|j_{23}j_4)^{(j_{15})} \times \\ &\qquad\qquad (-1)^{2j_{23}+j_4-j_{15}-j_1}(j_{15}j_4|j_1j_{45})^{(j_{23})}. \end{aligned} \tag{I.5}$$

If one represents each partial transformation on the right of (I.4) and (I.5) in terms of a $\overline{W}$ coefficient and equates the two expressions thus obtained, one finds the Biedenharn identity (I.3).

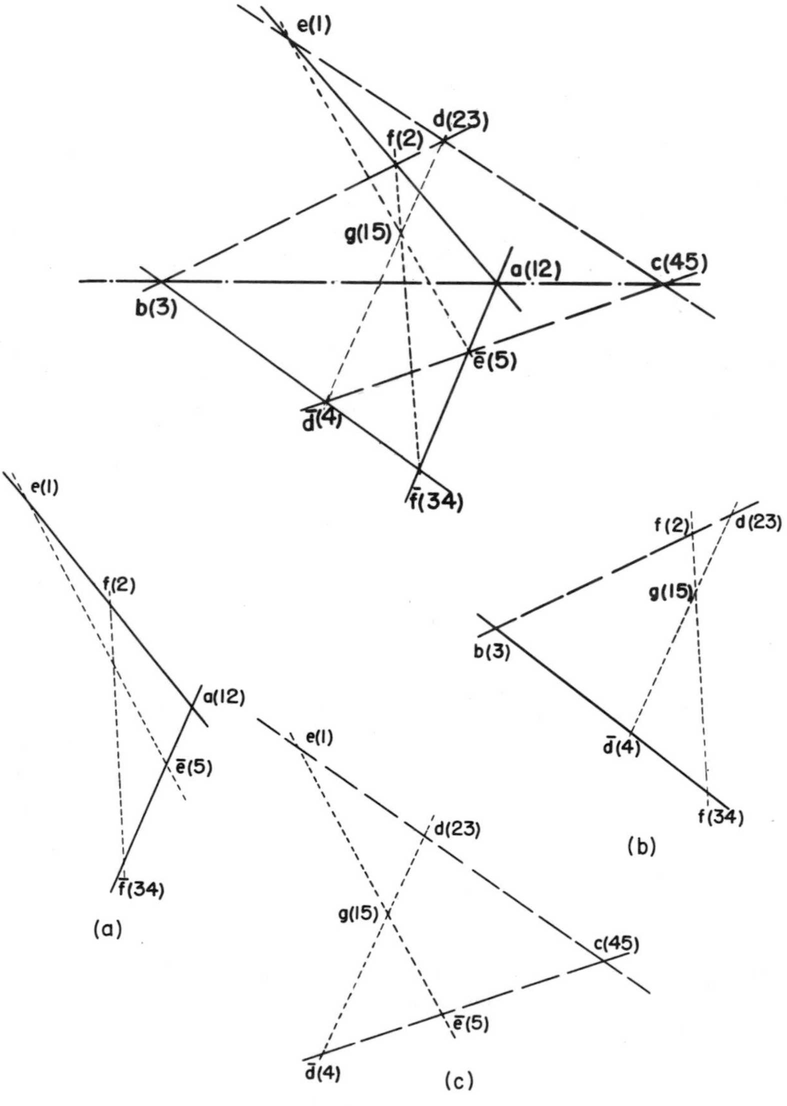

FIG. 10. Diagram of the Biedenharn identity, with alternative two-step and three-step recouplings. Two-step sequence as in Fig. 8, three-step sequence shown separately in *a*, *b*, and *c*.

The three-step transformation (I.5) is indicated in Fig. 10 by a diagram of the type described in Appendix H, for comparison with the two-step recoupling of Fig. 8. The quadrilaterals corresponding to the three steps of recoupling are shown separately in the sub-diagrams. In addition to the lines of Fig. 8, Fig. 10 contains three lines drawn respectively through 1 and 5, 2 and 34, 4 and 23. These lines intersect in the single point 15. The existence of this joint intersection is known as the Desargues theorem (see Coxeter, 1949, p. 12) which expresses a nontrivial relationship between the 10 lines of the diagram and their 10 intersections ‡.

For $a = 0$ the sum in (I.1) with $f = g$ reduces to one term, and is therefore sufficient to fix the absolute value of all $\overline{W}(0bc/def)$. For $a = \frac{1}{2}$ the same sum reduces in general to two terms, but to one term only in the extreme cases $b = d+e+\frac{1}{2}$ and $b = |d-e|-\frac{1}{2}$; (I.1) is then still sufficient to fix the absolute values of all $\overline{W}(\frac{1}{2}bc/def)$ by recursion.

The residual indeterminacy by ± 1 is partially eliminated by (I.1) with $f \neq g$ and by (I.2), but cannot be completely eliminated for the following reason. If there be defined a normalization factor $N(abc)$, function of a triad of parameters, invariant with respect to permutations of a, b, and c, and equal to ± 1 but otherwise arbitrary, the equations (I.1), (I.2), and (I.3) are invariant with respect to multiplication of each $\overline{W}(abc/def)$ by $N(abc)N(aef)N(dbf)N(dec)$. This invariance of the equations determining $\overline{W}$ reflects through (11.6) the fact that the equations determining $\overline{V}$ are invariant with respect to multiplication of $\overline{V}(abc;\alpha\beta\gamma)$ by $N(abc)$. Therefore any indeterminacy of $\overline{W}$ by ± 1 is in fact removed by the conventions (G.3) or (G.5) which normalize the Wigner coefficients and thereby the $\overline{V}$.

We adopt then the value of $\overline{W}(abc/def)$ with the sign as given in (11.12) and the value of $\overline{W}(\frac{1}{2}bc/def)$ as obtained from the general expression (11.9), namely

$$\overline{W}\begin{pmatrix}\frac{1}{2}\,b\,c\\ d\,e\,f\end{pmatrix} = (-1)^{c+d+e}\left[\frac{(d+\frac{1}{2}+b-e)\,(d+\frac{1}{2}-b+e)}{(2b+1)\,(2c+1)\,(2e+1)\,(2f+1)}\right]^{\frac{1}{2}}$$

$$\text{for } c = b\pm\tfrac{1}{2},\; f = e\pm\tfrac{1}{2}, \qquad \text{(I.6)}$$

‡ The Desargues theorem states that, when the diagram of Fig. 10 is constructed beginning from points a, b, c, of a straight line, the lines $d\bar{d}$, $e\bar{e}$, and $f\bar{f}$ will intersect at a single point g. Conversely, if the construction starts from three lines through g, the final points a, b, and c lie on a straight line.

$$\overline{W}\begin{pmatrix}\frac{1}{2}\,b\,c\\ d\,e\,f\end{pmatrix} = (-1)^{\frac{1}{2}+b+d+e}\left[\frac{(b+e+\frac{3}{2}+d)\,(b+e+\frac{1}{2}-d)}{(2b+1)\,(2c+1)\,(2e+1)\,(2f+1)}\right]^{\frac{1}{2}}$$

for $c = b\pm\frac{1}{2},\ f = e\mp\frac{1}{2}$.

We take now (I.3) with $\bar{d} = b+\frac{1}{2}$, $\bar{e} = a+\frac{1}{2}$, $\bar{f} = \frac{1}{2}$ and with the value (I.6) of $\overline{W}(\frac{1}{2}bc/def)$, which gives

$$\overline{W}\begin{pmatrix}a+\frac{1}{2} & b+\frac{1}{2} & c\\ d & e & f+\frac{1}{2}\end{pmatrix}$$

$$= \left[\frac{(a+e-f+1)\,(e+f-a)\,(b+d-f+1)\,(d+f-b)}{(a+e+f+2)\,(a+f-e+1)\,(b+d+f+2)\,(b+f-d+1)}\right]^{\frac{1}{2}}\times$$

$$\overline{W}\begin{pmatrix}a+\frac{1}{2} & b+\frac{1}{2} & c\\ d & e & f-\frac{1}{2}\end{pmatrix} - (2f+1)\times \qquad \text{(I.7)}$$

$$\left[\frac{(a+b+c+2)\,(a+b-c+1)}{(a+c+f+2)\,(a+f-e+1)\,(b+d+f+2)\,(b+f-d+1)}\right]^{\frac{1}{2}}\overline{W}\begin{pmatrix}a\,b\,c\\ d\,e\,f\end{pmatrix}.$$

This equation may be used as a recursion formula for calculating any $\overline{W}(abc/def)$ starting from (11.12) and (I.6). Because all coefficients $\overline{W}$ are determined by this procedure, any further equation among them must follow from (I.1), (I.2), and (I.3), i.e., there cannot exist any further independent property of these functions.

The fact that (I.3) is independent of (I.1) and (I.2), but that there is no further independent equation, relates to the correspondence between the Biedenharn identity (I.3) and the Desargues theorem. In projective geometry restricted to the plane, the Desargues theorem does not follow from preceding postulates of the theory, but must be accepted as a new, and last, postulate (Coxeter, 1949).

J

Tensorial Formulation of the Dipole-Dipole Interaction ("Tensor Force")

Consider two dipoles, electric or magnetic, whose magnitudes and orientations are indicated by vectors $\boldsymbol{\mu}_1$ and $\boldsymbol{\mu}_2$ and whose relative position is indicated in magnitude and direction by

$$\mathbf{r} = r\mathbf{u} = \mathbf{r}_1 - \mathbf{r}_2. \tag{J.1}$$

The potential energy of the dipole interaction is usually expressed in the form

$$V = -\frac{1}{r^3}[\boldsymbol{\mu}_1 \cdot \boldsymbol{\mu}_2 \quad 3(\boldsymbol{\mu}_1 \cdot \mathbf{u})(\boldsymbol{\mu}_2 \cdot \mathbf{u})] \tag{J.2}$$

and is often called a tensor force.

The tensorial character of this interaction is illustrated by the following formulation in terms of irreducible products. Let us start from the definition of the interaction energy

$$V = -(\boldsymbol{\mu}_1 \cdot \boldsymbol{\nabla}_1)(\boldsymbol{\mu}_2 \cdot \boldsymbol{\nabla}_2)\frac{1}{r} = (\boldsymbol{\mu}_1 \cdot \boldsymbol{\nabla}_1)(\boldsymbol{\mu}_2 \cdot \boldsymbol{\nabla}_1)\frac{1}{r} = (\boldsymbol{\mu}_1 \cdot \boldsymbol{\nabla})(\boldsymbol{\mu}_2 \cdot \boldsymbol{\nabla})\frac{1}{r}, \tag{J.3}$$

where $\boldsymbol{\nabla}_i$ is the gradient operator of the variable $\mathbf{r}_i$ and, when applied to a function of $\mathbf{r}$, $-\boldsymbol{\nabla}_2 = \boldsymbol{\nabla}_1 = \boldsymbol{\nabla}$. Since the scalar product of vectors or tensors equals the scalar product of their sets of components, one can recouple the product $(\boldsymbol{\mu}_1 \cdot \boldsymbol{\nabla})(\boldsymbol{\mu}_2 \cdot \boldsymbol{\nabla})$ by the procedure given at the end of Section 9, so as to couple first the operators $\boldsymbol{\nabla}$ with one another. This yields

$$(\boldsymbol{\mu}_1 \cdot \boldsymbol{\nabla})(\boldsymbol{\mu}_2 \cdot \boldsymbol{\nabla}) = [\boldsymbol{\mu}_1 \times \boldsymbol{\mu}_2]^{(0)} \cdot [\boldsymbol{\nabla} \times \boldsymbol{\nabla}]^{(0)} + [\boldsymbol{\mu}_1 \times \boldsymbol{\mu}_2]^{(1)} \cdot [\boldsymbol{\nabla} \times \boldsymbol{\nabla}]^{(1)} + [\boldsymbol{\mu}_1 \times \boldsymbol{\mu}_2]^{(2)} \cdot [\boldsymbol{\nabla} \times \boldsymbol{\nabla}]^{(2)}, \tag{J.4}$$

where the expressions on the right are tensor products, defined as at the end of Section 7.

On the right of (J.4), the product of degree 1, $[\boldsymbol{\nabla} \times \boldsymbol{\nabla}]^{(1)}$, vanishes because it is an antisymmetric product of two identical commutable factors. The product of degree 0, $[\boldsymbol{\nabla} \times \boldsymbol{\nabla}]^{(0)}$, coincides with the Laplace operator Δ, to within normalization, and hence vanishes when applied to $1/r$. Therefore the energy (J.3), expanded according to (J.4), reduces to

$$V = [\boldsymbol{\mu}_1 \times \boldsymbol{\mu}_2]^{(2)} \cdot [\boldsymbol{\nabla} \times \boldsymbol{\nabla}]^{(2)} \frac{1}{r}. \tag{J.5}$$

To calculate $[\boldsymbol{\nabla} \times \boldsymbol{\nabla}]^{(2)}(1/r)$, consider first that $\boldsymbol{\nabla}(1/r) = -\mathbf{r}/r^3 = -\mathbf{u}/r^2$, and therefore

$$[\boldsymbol{\nabla} \times \boldsymbol{\nabla}]^{(2)}(1/r) = -[\boldsymbol{\nabla} \times (\mathbf{r}/r^3)]^{(2)} = -(1/r^3)[\boldsymbol{\nabla} \times \mathbf{r}]^{(2)} - [(\boldsymbol{\nabla}(1/r^3)) \times \mathbf{r}]^{(2)}. \tag{J.6}$$

The first term on the right side vanishes, because the direct product of $\boldsymbol{\nabla}$ and $\mathbf{r}$ has cartesian components $\boldsymbol{\nabla}_i r_k = \delta_{ik}$, such that its only non-vanishing irreducible part is of degree zero. In the second term on the right we have $\boldsymbol{\nabla}(1/r^3) = -3\mathbf{r}/r^5 = -3\mathbf{u}/r^4$. Thus one finds that

$$[\boldsymbol{\nabla} \times \boldsymbol{\nabla}]^{(2)}(1/r) = (3/r^5)[\mathbf{r} \times \mathbf{r}]^{(2)} = (3/r^3)[\mathbf{u} \times \mathbf{u}]^{(2)}. \tag{J.7}$$

The interaction energy becomes now

$$V = (3/r^3)[\boldsymbol{\mu}_1 \times \boldsymbol{\mu}_2]^{(2)} \cdot [\mathbf{u} \times \mathbf{u}]^{(2)}, \tag{J.8}$$

where the dependence on the relative position of the dipoles is represented by an irreducible tensor of second degree. The connection between (J.8) and (J.2) is given by an expansion analogous to (J.4), namely,

$$\begin{aligned}(\boldsymbol{\mu}_1 \cdot \mathbf{u})(\boldsymbol{\mu}_2 \cdot \mathbf{u}) &= [\boldsymbol{\mu}_1 \times \boldsymbol{\mu}_2]^{(0)} \cdot [\mathbf{u} \times \mathbf{u}]^{(0)} + [\boldsymbol{\mu}_1 \times \boldsymbol{\mu}_2]^{(2)} \cdot [\mathbf{u} \times \mathbf{u}]^{(2)} \\ &= \tfrac{1}{3}\boldsymbol{\mu}_1 \cdot \boldsymbol{\mu}_2 + [\boldsymbol{\mu}_1 \times \boldsymbol{\mu}_2]^{(2)} \cdot [\mathbf{u} \times \mathbf{u}]^{(2)}. \end{aligned} \tag{J.9}$$

The set $\mathbf{u}^{[1]}$ of contrastandard components of $\mathbf{u} = \mathbf{r}/r$ coincides with the set of harmonic functions $\mathfrak{C}^{[1]}(\theta, \varphi)$ defined by (5.19). Therefore the tensor $[\mathbf{u} \times \mathbf{u}]^{(2)}$ has the set of contrastandard components $[\mathfrak{C}^{[1]} \times \mathfrak{C}^{[1]}]^{[2]}$. The elements of this set, being functions of the direction $\mathbf{u} = (\theta, \varphi)$, can be expanded into spherical harmonics $\mathfrak{C}^{[l]}_m(\theta, \varphi)$. In this expansion all terms of degree other than 2 must vanish, because they would have r-transformations different from those of $[\mathfrak{C}^{[1]} \times \mathfrak{C}^{[1]}]^{[2]}$. The coefficient of the single term of degree 2 is obtained from the definition of irreducible product and from (14.10), (14.11), and (14.12). One finds the general formula

$$[\mathfrak{C}^{[l_1]} \times \mathfrak{C}^{[l_2]}]^{[l]} = (-1)^{\frac{1}{2}(l_1+l_2+l)} \sqrt{2l+1}\, \overline{V}\begin{pmatrix} l_1 & l_2 & l \\ 0 & 0 & 0 \end{pmatrix} \mathfrak{C}^{[l]}, \tag{J.10}$$

and in particular

$$[\mathfrak{C}^{[1]} \times \mathfrak{C}^{[1]}]^{[2]} = \sqrt{2/3}\, \mathfrak{C}^{[2]}. \tag{J.11}$$

If the sets of contrastandard components of $\boldsymbol{\mu}_1$ and $\boldsymbol{\mu}_2$ are indicated by $\boldsymbol{\mu}_1^{[1]}$ and $\boldsymbol{\mu}_2^{[1]}$, the interaction energy (J.8) becomes

$$V = \frac{\sqrt{6}}{r^3} [\boldsymbol{\mu}_1{}^{[1]} \times \boldsymbol{\mu}_2{}^{[1]}]^{[2]} \cdot \mathfrak{C}^{[2]}(\theta, \varphi). \tag{J.12}$$

We can also couple together the quantities that depend on the orientation and position of the dipole 1, utilizing the connection (7.15) between scalar products and products of degree zero, together with the association and commutation properties of triple products of degree zero considered in Section 10. One finds that

$$V = \frac{\sqrt{30}}{r^3} [\boldsymbol{\mu}_1{}^{[1]} \times \boldsymbol{\mu}_2{}^{[1]} \times \mathfrak{C}^{[2]}]^{[0]} = \frac{\sqrt{30}}{r^3} [\boldsymbol{\mu}_1{}^{[1]} \times \mathfrak{C}^{[2]} \times \boldsymbol{\mu}_2{}^{[1]}]^{[0]}$$

$$= \frac{\sqrt{10}}{r^3} [\boldsymbol{\mu}_1{}^{[1]} \times \mathfrak{C}^{[2]}]^{[1]} \cdot \boldsymbol{\mu}_2{}^{[1]}. \tag{J.13}$$

The first factor of the last scalar product represents, to within a factor -1, the contrastandard set of components of the field generated by dipole 1 at the position of dipole 2.

K

References

Arima, A., Horie, H., and Tanabe, Y. (1954) *Progr. Theoret. Phys.* **11**, 143.
Biedenharn, L. C. (1952) *Oak Ridge Natl. Lab. Rept.* **1098**.
Biedenharn, L. C. (1953) *J. Math. and Phys.* **31**, 287.
Biedenharn, L. C., and Rose, M. E. (1953) *Revs. Mod. Phys.* **25**, 729.
Blatt, J. M., and Biedenharn, L. C. (1953) *Revs. Mod. Phys.* **25**, 258.
Brinkman, H. C. (1956) "Application of Spinor Invariants in Atomic Physics." North Holland Publishing, Co., Amsterdam.
Brouwer, F. (1930) Utrecht Dissertation.
Casimir, H. B. G. (1931) *Proc. Acad. Sci. Amsterdam* **34**, 844; "Rotation of a Rigid Body in Quantum Mechanics." Walters, Groningen, Netherlands.
Casimir, H. B. G. (1935) *Physica* **2**, 719.
Cisotti, U. (1930) *Rend. Accad. Naz. Lincei* **11**, 727.
Cohen, M. H. (1954) *Phys. Rev.* **95**, 674.
Condon, E. U., and Shortley, G. (1935) "The Theory of Atomic Spectra." Cambridge Univ. Press, London.
Coxeter, H. S. M. (1949) "The Real Projective Plane." McGraw-Hill, New York.
Eisner, E., and Sachs, R. G. (1947) *Phys. Rev.* **72**, 680.
Elliott, J. P. (1953) *Proc. Roy. Soc.* **A218**, 345.
Elliott, J. P., and Flowers, B. H. (1955) *Proc. Roy. Soc.* **A229**, 536.
Fano, U. (1948) *J. Research Natl. Bur. Standards* **40**, 215.
Fano, U. (1951) *U. S. Natl. Bur. Standards, Rept.* **1214**, unpublished.
Fano, U. (1953) *Phys. Rev.* **90**, 577.
Fano, U. (1957) *Revs. Mod. Phys.* **29**, 76.
Fano, U. (1957a) *Nuovo Cimento* **5**, 1358.
Frobenius, G., and Schur, I. (1906) *Sitzber. Preuss. Akad. Wiss. Physik. Math. Kl.* **VI**, 186.
Güttinger, P. (1931) *Z. Physik,* **73**, 179.
Hope, J. (1952) Ph. D. Thesis, London University.
Jahn, H. A., and Hope, J. (1954) *Phys. Rev.* **93**, 318;
Kennedy, J. M., Sears, B. J., and Sharp, W. T. (1954) *Report* CRT 569, Chalk River, Ontario.
Kramers, H. A. (1931) *Proc. Acad. Sci. Amsterdam* **34**, 956.
Matsunobu, H., and Takebe, H. (1955) *Progr. Theoret. Phys.* **14**, 589.
Obi, S., Ishidzu, T., Horie, H., Yanagawa, S., Tanabe, Y., and Sato, M. (1953) *Ann. Tokyo Astron. Observatory* [2] **3**, 87.
Obi, S., Ishidzu, T., Horie, H., Yanagawa, S., Tanabe, Y., and Sato, M. (1954) *Ann. Tokyo Astron. Observatory* [2] **4**, 1.
Obi, S., Ishidzu, T., Horie, H., Yanagawa, S., Tanabe, Y., and Sato, M. (1955) *Ann. Tokyo Astron. Observatory* [2] **4**, 75.
Ord-Smith, R. H. (1954) *Phys. Rev.* **94**, 1227.
Peter, F., and Weyl, H. (1927) *Math. Ann.* **97**, 737.

Racah, G. (1933) *Rend. Accad. Naz. Lincei* **17**, 386.

Racah, G. (1942) *Phys. Rev.* **62**, 438.

Racah, G. (1943) *Phys. Rev.* **63**, 367.

Racah, G. (1950) *Physica* **16**, 651.

Redmond, P. J. (1954) *Proc. Roy. Soc.* **A222**, 84.

Schouten, J. A. (1924) "Ricci Kalkül." Springer, Berlin.

Schur. I. (1905) *Sitzber. Preuss. Akad. Wiss. Physik. Math. Kl.* **V**, 406.

Schwinger, J. (1952) *Report* NYO 3071, Nuclear Development Associates, White Plains, New York.

Sharp, W. T., Kennedy, J. M., Sears, B. J. and Hoyle, M. G. (1953) *Report* CRT 556, Chalk River, Ontario.

Simon, A., Van der Sluis, J. H. and Biedenharn, L. C. (1954), *Oak Ridge Natl. Lab. Rept.* **1679.**

Simon, A. (1954) *Oak Ridge Natl. Lab. Rept.* **1718.**

Smith, K., and Stevenson, J. W. (1957) *Argonne Natl. Lab. Rept.* ANL-5776.

Van der Waerden, B. J. (1932) "Die Gruppentheoretische Methode in der Quantenmechanik." Springer, Berlin.

von Neumann, J. (1927) *Nachr. Ges. Wiss. Göttingen* pp. 245, 273.

Weyl, H. (1931) "Theory of Groups and Quantum Mechanics." Dover, New York.

Weyl, H. (1939) "The Classical groups." Princeton Univ. Press, Princeton, New Jersey.

Whittaker, E. T., and Watson, G. N. (1946) "Modern Analysis". Cambridge Univ. Press, London.

Wick, G. C., Wightman, A. S., and Wigner, E. P. (1952) *Phys. Rev.* **88**, 102.

Wigner, E. (1931) "Gruppentheorie und ihre Anwendung auf die Quantenmechanik der Atomspektren." Vieweg, Braunschweig, Germany.

Wigner, E. P. (1932) *Nachr. Ges. Wiss. Göttingen* p. 546.

Wigner, E. P. (1937) unpublished manuscript circulated in 1952.

Wigner, E. P. (1958). "Group Theory and its Application to the Quantum Mechanics of Atomic Spectra." In press. Academic Press, New York.

Yang, C. N. (1948) *Phys. Rev.* **74**, 764.

SUBJECT INDEX